Study Guide with Selected Solutions and Visual Calculus

CALCULUS AND ITS APPLICATIONS
Eighth Edition

BRIEF CALCULUS AND ITS APPLICATIONS
Eighth Edition

LARRY J. GOLDSTEIN · DAVID C. LAY · DAVID I. SCHNEIDER

PRENTICE HALL, Upper Saddle River, NJ 07458

Executive Editor: Sally Simpson
Editorial Assistant: Sara Beth Newell
Special Projects Manager: Barbara A. Murray
Production Editor: Mark Marsden
Supplement Cover Manager: Paul Gourhan
Supplement Cover Designer: PM Workshop Inc.
Manufacturing Buyer: Alan Fischer

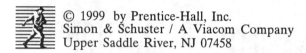

Printed in the United States of America

10 9 8 7 6 5 4 3

ISBN   0-13-096128-0

Prentice-Hall International (UK) Limited, *London*
Prentice-Hall of Australia Pty. Limited, *Sydney*
Prentice-Hall Canada, Inc., *London*
Prentice-Hall Hispanoamericana, S.A., *Mexico*
Prentice-Hall of India Private Limited, *New Delhi*
Prentice-Hall of Japan, Inc., *Tokyo*
Simon & Schuster Asia Pte. Ltd., *Singapore*
Editora Prentice-Hall do Brazil, Ltda., *Rio de Janeiro*

CONTENTS

How To Use This Study Guide

Proper use of this study guide can help to improve your performance in your calculus course. There are detailed explanations here to guide you carefully and patiently through hundreds of exercises. And there are helpful hints and strategies for studying that several thousand of our students have used successfully over the past twenty years. Students who apply the techniques in this guide consistently score from five to fifteen percentage points higher on campus-wide final exams than students who have no systematic strategy for mastering the material in this course.

The study guide is organized by the sections in *Calculus and Its Applications, Eighth Edition*, by Goldstein, Lay, and Schneider. Most sections begin with some remarks about the section, its general purpose and layout, or its relation to other material. Following that, there are complete solutions to every sixth problem. Essentially all of the basic skills are covered in these problems. The solutions are written in the style of the examples in the text, but they tend to contain more warnings and side remarks than in the text. At the end of many chapters you will find a brief review to help you prepare for an exam.

<u>Special</u> <u>note</u> for readers of *Brief Calculus and Its Applications, Eighth Edition:* The material here for Chapters 0 to 5 and Chapters 7 and 8 exactly matches your text. So does the material for Sections 6.1 to 6.5. After Section 6.5, you'll find special sections marked "Brief Edition" that correspond to the rest of your Chapter 6.

The way you use this study guide should be determined by an overall strategy for success in your calculus course. We have listed below five things you can do to improve your performance and make the course an enjoyable experience. Hardly a semester passes without several of our students writing on their (anonymous) course evaluations that they never thought they would enjoy a math course, and yet they found themselves liking this course more than most of the courses in their major. If you have the proper background, there is no reason why you cannot do well in this course, and enjoy it at the same time!

SECRETS FOR SUCCESS IN CALCULUS

1. Work on exercises nearly every day, keeping up with the lectures in your class. You will minimize the time you need to learn calculus if you heed this advice. Concepts in calculus are usually introduced and explained in terms of concepts you have studied earlier. When you fall behind, the class explanations will be harder to understand and you will spend more time on your own trying to catch up. In this sense, studying calculus is like learning a foreign language, where each lesson builds on the previous lessons, and if you miss one lesson you may not understand a thing that is said in class.

2. Read the text and examples carefully before you attempt the exercises. Then try the exercises. If you get "stuck" on a problem, look for a relevant example, but don't reread the whole example. Read just enough to get you started on the exercise. If you studied the example earlier, parts of the explanation may still be floating in your mind, and the quick glance at the example may be all you need. If the problem is complex and you get stuck again, take another peek at the example. This process of trying to recall an example that you have already studied is the key to learning how to work the problem yourself.

Many students read the examples after they have tried (unsuccessfully) to work an exercise. When a problem seems difficult, a student may look for a similar example and "copy" the example with the numbers changed. In this approach very little learning takes place. *Being able to read an explanation and understand each step is entirely different from really knowing how to work the problem by yourself.* We cannot emphasize this too strongly. You must first *attempt* a problem by yourself, with no text or study guide to help you. When you need help, accept only enough assistance to get started on the problem.

3. Treat this study guide as a tutor. One function of a tutor is to point out where you are making mistakes. After you work a problem whose solution is in the study guide, compare your solution to the one printed here. If your final answer is correct, have you included all the important steps? (We have included nearly all algebraic steps. You may feel comfortable with fewer steps, but be careful. Check with your instructor if you're not sure about how much detail is desired.) If your final answer is incorrect, find your first mistake and correct it. If the solution is long, then you may uncover other mistakes by reworking the part that followed your first mistake.

Another function of a tutor is to help you on a problem when you cannot proceed further. If you get stuck on a problem that has a solution in this study guide, and if the examples in the text are not sufficient, then read the first part of the solution. But only read enough to get started. *Don't sit back and watch your "tutor" work the entire problem.* You must have the practice of working it yourself. Return to the solution later for more help, if necessary.

4. Keep a list of places where errors are likely to occur. The text warns of some potential errors. This study guide will point out many more. Identify *your* weaknesses. As you work exercises, make a note of the most common mistakes you make. Do the same with any quizzes you take. Then review the list before each exam.

5. Develop a strategy for taking each test. You should be able to walk into an exam knowing what most of the questions will concern and knowing where your own strengths and weaknesses lie.

a. Read over the entire exam for a few minutes instead of beginning work immediately on the first problem. Then as you work one problem, your subconscious mind can be thinking about related problems that appear elsewhere on the exam. (This strategy works for math exams just as well as it does for essay exams, once you learn how to do it.)

b. Begin the exam by working on the problem in which you have the most confidence. Successful completion of one or two problems will help to calm the "test anxiety" (or panic!) that most people feel to some extent.

c. Move from easier to harder problems. Avoid getting bogged down in a problem where you spend a lot of time and yet have the potential to earn only a few points.

There are other suggestions we could give, but that's probably enough for now. We'll be adding to this list at strategic points in the study guide.

A WARNING

Although this study guide has the potential to help you tremendously, it also has the power to undermine your chances of success. Because the guide contains complete solutions to many homework problems, you will be tempted to read the explanations here instead of working the problems yourself. While this may shorten the time you spend on homework, it will have a *disastrous* effect on your exam performance! In the long run, a proper use of the guide *will* save you time and it *will* make the time you spend more productive, but you must use the guide wisely.

Chapter 0

Functions

0.1 Functions and Their Graphs

You should read Sections 0.1 and 0.2 even if you don't plan to work the exercises. The concept of a function is a fundamental idea and the notation for functions is used in nearly every section of the text.

1. The notation $[-1,4]$ is equivalent to $-1 \le x \le 4$. Both -1 and 4 belong to the interval.

7. The inequalities $2 \le x < 3$ describe the half-open interval $[2,3)$. The right parenthesis indicates that 3 is not in the set.

13. If $f(x) = x^2 - 3x$, then $f(0) = (0)^2 - 3(0) = 0$,

$$f(5) = (5)^2 - 3(5) = 25 - 15 = 10,$$

$$f(3) = (3)^2 - 3(3) = 9 - 9 = 0,$$

$$f(-7) = (-7)^2 - 3(-7) = 49 + 21 = 70.$$

19. If $f(x) = x^2 - 2x$, then

$$f(a+1) = (a+1)^2 - 2(a+1) = (a+1)(a+1) - 2a - 2$$
$$= (a^2+2a+1) - 2a - 2 = a^2 - 1.$$

$$f(a+2) = (a+2)^2 - 2(a+2) = (a+2)(a+2) - 2a - 4$$
$$= (a^2+4a+4) - 2a - 4 = a^2 + 2a.$$

25. The domain of $g(x) = \dfrac{1}{\sqrt{3-x}}$ consists of those x for which $x < 3$, since division by zero is not permissible and since square roots of negative numbers are not defined.

31. This is not the graph of a function by the "vertical line test".

37. By referring to the graph, we find that f(4) is positive since the graph of the function is above the x-axis when x = 4.

43. The concentration of the drug when t = 1 is .03 units because the graph tells us that f(1) = .03.

49. If the point $\left(\frac{1}{2}, \frac{2}{5}\right)$ is on the graph of the function

$g(x) = \dfrac{3x - 1}{x^2 + 1}$, then we must have $g\left(\frac{1}{2}\right) = \frac{2}{5}$. This is the case since

$$g\left(\frac{1}{2}\right) = \frac{3\left(\frac{1}{2}\right) - 1}{\left(\frac{1}{2}\right)^2 + 1} = \frac{\frac{3}{2} - 1}{\frac{1}{4} + 1} = \frac{\frac{1}{2}}{\frac{5}{4}} = \frac{1}{2} \cdot \frac{4}{5} = \frac{2}{5}$$

so $\left(\frac{1}{2}, \frac{2}{5}\right)$ is on the graph.

55. Since f(x) = πx^2 for x < 2, f(1) = $\pi(1)^2$ = π.
    Since f(x) = 1 + x for 2 ≤ x ≤ 2.5, f(2) = 1 + 2 = 3.
    Since f(x) = 4x for 2.5 < x, f(3) = 4(3) = 12.

Help for Technology Exercises: Appendices A through D in your text contain practically all the information you need to use a TI-82, TI-83, TI-85, or TI-86 graphing calculator. For other calculators or computer software, you will need some sort of user's manual. The information in the Appendices more or less parallels the order of calculus topics in the text. When we refer to "the Appendix", we mean the appendix corresponding to your TI-calculator. You might wish to place a paper or plastic "Tab" in your text, on the first page of the appropriate appendix.

   For the technology exercises in Section 0.1, read parts A, B, and C in the Appendix section entitled **Functions**. Also, read part A in the second section, **Specify Window Settings**.

61. The formula X^3/4 gives the same results as (X^3)/4.
    The correct formula for $x^{3/4}$ is X^(3/4). Test each formula with X = 16, noting that $16^{3/4} = (16^{1/4})^3 = 2^3 = 8$.

67. For a TI-82, 83, or 86 choose table settings to make the table appear as shown in the text. For help with tables, see the Appendix section, **Tables**. Then press the down-arrow key until the value 7 is displayed for X. If you are interested, the Appendix tells how to to display function values in a table for arbitrary values of x.

The TI-85 does not have a table function, but you can evaluate a function at any specified value of x. The commands evalF(and EVAL are discussed in part C of the Appendix section, **Special Points on the Graph of y1**.

0.2   Some Important Functions

The most important functions here are the linear functions, the quadratic functions, and the power functions. Absolute values appear only briefly in Sections 4.5, 6.1, and then more frequently in Chapters 9 and 10.

1.   The function $f(x) = 2x - 1$ is linear. Since a line is determined by any two of its points, we may choose any two points on the graph of $f(x)$ and draw the line through them. For instance, we find $f(0) = 2(0) - 1 = 0 - 1 = -1$ and $f(1) = 2(1) - 1 = 2 - 1 = 1$. So $(0,-1)$ and $(1,1)$ are two points on the graph of $f(x)$. See the sketch in the answer section of the text.

7.   To find the y-intercept evaluate $f(x)$ at $x = 0$.

$$f(0) = 9(0) + 3 = 0 + 3 = 3.$$

So the y-intercept is $(0,3)$. To find the x-intercept set $f(x) = 0$ and solve for x.

$$9x + 3 = 0,$$
$$9x = -3,$$
$$x = \frac{-3}{9} = \frac{-1}{3}.$$

So the x-intercept is $\left(\frac{-1}{3}, 0\right)$.

13. a.   We wish to write $f(x) = .2x + 50$ in the form

$$f(x) = \left(\frac{K}{V}\right)x + \frac{1}{V}, \text{ so we set}$$

$$\frac{K}{V} = .2 \text{ and } \frac{1}{V} = 50.$$

If $\frac{1}{V} = 50$, then $V = \frac{1}{50}$. Substituting $\frac{1}{50}$ for V in $\frac{K}{V} = .2$, we get

$$\frac{K}{\left(\frac{1}{50}\right)} = .2, \text{ and hence } K = .2\left(\frac{1}{50}\right) = \frac{2}{500} = \frac{1}{250}.$$

b. To find the y-intercept evaluate the function at $x = 0$.

$$y = \left(\frac{K}{V}\right)(0) + \frac{1}{V} = \frac{1}{V}.$$

The y-intercept is $\left(0, \frac{1}{V}\right)$. To find the x-intercept set $y = 0$ and solve for x:

$$\left(\frac{K}{V}\right)x + \frac{1}{V} = 0, \quad \left(\frac{K}{V}\right)x = -\frac{1}{V}, \quad \text{and} \quad x = \left(\frac{V}{K}\right)\left(-\frac{1}{V}\right) = -\frac{1}{K}.$$

The x-intercept is $\left(-\frac{1}{K}, 0\right)$.

19. $f(x) = \frac{50x}{105-x}$, $0 \leq x \leq 100$,

   $f(70) = 100$ (million dollars) from Example 5,

   $f(75) = \frac{50(75)}{105-75} = \frac{50(75)}{30} = 125$ (million dollars).

   Thus the added cost to remove another 5% is:

   f(75) - f(70) = 125 - 100 (million dollars)
   = 25 million dollars.

   From Example 5 the cost of removing the final 5% of the pollutant is 525 million dollars. This is twenty-one times the cost of removing an extra 5% of pollutant after 70% has been removed.

25. If we write $y = 1 - x^2$ in the form $y = ax^2 + bx + c$, we have $y = (-1)x^2 + (0)x + 1$, so $a = -1$, $b = 0$, and $c = 1$.

31. This function is defined by three distinct linear functions. For $0 \leq x < 2$ we have $f(x) = 4 - x$. This graph is determined by two points, say at $x = 0$ and $x = 2$.

   $$f(0) = 4 - 0 = 4, \quad f(2) = 4 - 2 = 2$$

   So (0,4) and (2,2) determine this part of the graph. Draw a line segment between these points. ((0,4) is part of the graph but (2,2) cannot yet be counted as part of the graph since x < 2.)

For 2 ≤ x < 3 we have f(x) = 2x - 2.

This graph is also determined by two points, say at x = 2 and x = 3.

$$f(2) = 2(2) - 2 = 2, \quad f(3) = 2(3) - 2 = 4.$$

So (2,2) and (3,4) determine this part of the graph. Draw a line segment between these points. Now (2,2) is part of the graph but (3,4) cannot yet be counted as part of the graph since x < 3.

For x ≥ 3 we have f(x) = x + 1.

This graph is also determined by two points say at x = 3 and x = 4:

$$f(3) = 3 + 1 = 4, \quad f(4) = 4 + 1 = 5.$$

So (3,4) and (4,5) determine this part of the graph.

Draw a line segment through these points and extend it to the right as x tends to infinity.

37. $f(x) = |x|$, where

$$|x| = \begin{cases} x \text{ if } x \text{ is positive or zero,} \\ -x \text{ if } x \text{ is negative.} \end{cases}$$

Here x = -2.5, which is a negative number so $|x| = -(-2.5)$ = 2.5. This gives f(x) = 2.5 when x = -2.5.

43. Experiment with various windows, perhaps of the form [0, N] by [-40, 40], where N is a positive integer. For the TI-82 and TI-83, the only small integer that works is N = 4. For other integers from 3 to 11, the undesirable vertical line appears. For the TI-85 and 86, good values of N include 3, 4, 6, 7, and 9.

0.3   The Algebra of Functions

The algebraic skills in this section will be used frequently throughout the course. You should review the material here on composition of functions before you read Section 3.2.

1. $f(x) + g(x) = (x^2 + 1) + 9x = x^2 + 9x + 1.$

7. $f(x) + g(x) = \dfrac{2}{x - 3} + \dfrac{1}{x + 2}.$ In order to add two fractions, the denominators must be the same. A common denominator for $\dfrac{2}{x - 3}$ and $\dfrac{1}{x + 2}$ is $(x-3)(x+2)$. If we multiply $\dfrac{2}{x - 3}$ by $\dfrac{x + 2}{x + 2}$ we obtain an equivalent expression whose denominator is $(x-3)(x+2)$. Similarly, if we multiply $\dfrac{1}{x + 2}$ by $\dfrac{x - 3}{x - 3}$ we obtain an equivalent expression whose denominator is $(x-3)(x+2)$. Thus

$$f(x) + g(x) = \frac{2}{x - 3} + \frac{1}{x + 2}$$

$$= \frac{2}{x - 3} \cdot \frac{x + 2}{x + 2} + \frac{1}{x + 2} \cdot \frac{x - 3}{x - 3}$$

$$= \frac{2(x + 2)}{(x - 3)(x + 2)} + \frac{x - 3}{(x - 3)(x + 2)}$$

$$= \frac{2x + 4 + x - 3}{(x - 3)(x + 2)} = \frac{3x + 1}{(x - 3)(x + 2)} = \frac{3x + 1}{x^2 - x - 6}.$$

13. $f(x) - g(x) = \dfrac{x}{x - 2} - \dfrac{5 - x}{5 + x}.$ A common denominator for $\dfrac{x}{x - 2}$ and $\dfrac{5 - x}{5 + x}$ is $(x-2)(5+x)$. Proceeding as in exercise 7, we have

$$f(x) - g(x) = \frac{x}{x - 2} \cdot \frac{5 + x}{5 + x} - \frac{5 - x}{5 + x} \cdot \frac{x - 2}{x - 2}$$

$$= \frac{x(5 + x)}{(x - 2)(5 + x)} - \frac{(5 - x)(x - 2)}{(x - 2)(5 + x)}$$

$$= \frac{5x + x^2 - (-x^2 + 7x - 10)}{(x - 2)(5 + x)}$$

$$= \frac{2x^2 - 2x + 10}{x^2 + 3x - 10}.$$

19. $f(x+1)g(x+1) = \left[\dfrac{x + 1}{(x + 1) - 2}\right]\left[\dfrac{5 - (x + 1)}{5 + (x + 1)}\right]$

$$= \left[\frac{x + 1}{x - 1}\right]\left[\frac{4 - x}{6 + x}\right] = \frac{(x + 1)(4 - x)}{(x - 1)(6 + x)}$$

$$= \frac{-x^2 + 3x + 4}{x^2 + 5x - 6}.$$

25. To find $f(g(x))$ we substitute $g(x)$ in place of each x in $f(x) = x^6$. Thus $f(x) = \left[g(x)\right]^6 = \left(\dfrac{x}{1-x}\right)^6$.

31. If $f(x) = x$ then

$$f(x+h) - f(x) = (x+h)^2 - x^2$$
$$= x^2 + 2hx + h^2 - x^2$$
$$= 2hx + h^2.$$

37. $f(x) = \frac{1}{8}x$, $g(x) = 8x + 1$. Substitute $g(x)$ in place of each x in $f(x)$. Thus

$$h(x) = f(g(x)) = \frac{1}{8}g(x)$$
$$= \frac{1}{8}[8x + 1]$$
$$= x + \frac{1}{8}.$$

$g(x)$ converts British sizes to French sizes.
$f(x)$ converts French sizes to American sizes.
So $h(x) = f(g(x))$ converts British sizes to American sizes. For example, consider the British hat size of $6\frac{3}{4}$. Since $h(x) = x + \frac{1}{8}$, the American size is $h(6\frac{3}{4}) = 6\frac{3}{4} + \frac{1}{8} = 6\frac{7}{8}$, which agrees with the table.

43. For function composition on a TI-calculator, see part E of the first Appendix section, **Functions**. On a TI-83, for example, if $Y_1 = X/(X - 1)$, set

$$Y_2 = Y_1(Y_1).$$

Before graphing Y_2, you should "deselect" Y_1, so its graph will not appear also. See part B of **Functions**, in the Appendix. Use the TRACE feature to get an impression of what the formula for Y_2 might be.
  To actually determine the formula for $f(f(x))$, substitute $x/(x - 1)$ for each occurrence of x in the formula for $f(x)$. (Note that $f(x)$ is not defined for $x = 1$.)

$$f(f(x)) = \frac{x/(x - 1)}{x/(x - 1) - 1}, \quad x \neq 1.$$

The denominator can be simplified:

$$\frac{x}{x-1} - 1 = \frac{x}{x-1} - \frac{x-1}{x-1} = \frac{x-(x-1)}{x-1} = \frac{1}{x-1}.$$

Multiplying numerator and denominator of the formula for $f(f(x))$ by $x-1$, we obtain

$$f(f(x)) = \frac{x/(x-1)}{1/(x-1)} = \frac{x}{1} = x, \quad x \neq 1.$$

0.4 Zeros of Functions — The Quadratic Formula and Factoring

The material in this section will be used routinely through-out the text, beginning in Section 2.3. (Factoring skill is also needed for a few exercises in Section 1.4.) By Section 2.3 you must have *mastered* the ability to factor quadratic polynomials and to solve problems such as Exercises 33-38 (in Section 0.4). You should also be able to factor cubic poly-nomials where every term contains a power of x. (See (b) and (c) of Example 6.) Problems such as those in Exercises 25-32 will appear in Section 6.4 and in later sections. The quadra-tic formula should be memorized although you will not need to use it as often as factoring skills.

1. In the equation $2x^2 - 7x + 6 = 0$, we have $a = 2$, $b = -7$, and $c = 6$. Substituting these values into the quadratic formula, we find that

$$x = \frac{-(-7) \pm \sqrt{(-7)^2 - 4(2)(6)}}{2(2)} = \frac{7 \pm \sqrt{49 - 48}}{4} = \frac{7 \pm 1}{4}.$$

Thus $x = \frac{7+1}{4} = 2$ or $x = \frac{7-1}{4} = \frac{3}{2}$. So the zeros of the function $2x^2 - 7x + 6$ are 2 and $\frac{3}{2}$.

7. In the equation $5x^2 - 4x - 1 = 0$, we have $a = 5$, $b = -4$, and $c = -1$. By the quadratic formula,

$$x = \frac{-(-4) \pm \sqrt{(-4)^2 - 4(5)(-1)}}{2(5)} = \frac{4 \pm \sqrt{16 + 20}}{10}$$

$$= \frac{4 \pm \sqrt{36}}{10} = \frac{4 \pm 6}{10}.$$

So the solutions of the equation $5x^2 - 4x - 1 = 0$ are

$$x = \frac{4+6}{10} = \frac{10}{10} = 1, \text{ and } x = \frac{4-6}{10} = \frac{-2}{10} = -\frac{1}{5}.$$

13. To factor $x^2 + 8x + 15$, find values for c and d such that $cd = 15$ and $c + d = 8$. The solution is c = 3, d = 5, and

$$x^2 + 8x + 15 = (x+3)(x+5).$$

19. To factor $30 - 4x - 2x^2$, first factor out the coefficient -2 in front of x^2. That is,

$$30 - 4x - 2x^2 = -2(x^2 + 2x - 15).$$

Then to factor $x^2 + 2x - 15$, find values for c and d such that $cd = -15$ and $c + d = 2$. The solution is c = 5, d = -3, and $x^2 + 2x - 15 = (x+5)(x-3)$. Thus

$$30 - 4x - 2x^2 = -2(x+5)(x-3).$$

25. If a point (x,y) is on both graphs, then its coordinates must satisfy both equations. That is, x and y must satisfy $y = 2x^2 - 5x - 6$ and $y = 3x + 4$. Equating the two expressions for y, we have

$$2x^2 - 5x - 6 = 3x + 4.$$

To use the quadratic formula, rewrite the equation in the form

$$2x^2 - 8x - 10 = 0,$$

and divide both sides by 2:

$$x^2 - 4x - 5 = 0.$$

By the quadratic formula

$$x = \frac{-(-4) \pm \sqrt{(-4)^2 - 4(1)(-5)}}{2(1)} = \frac{4 \pm \sqrt{16 + 20}}{2}$$

$$= \frac{4 \pm \sqrt{36}}{2} = \frac{4 \pm 6}{2}.$$

So $x = \frac{4 + 6}{2} = 5$ or $x = \frac{4 - 6}{2} = -1$. Thus the x-coordinates of the points of intersection are 5 and -1. To find the y-coordinates, we substitute these values of x into either equation, $y = 2x^2 - 5x - 6$, or $y = 3x + 4$. Since $y = 3x + 4$ is simpler we use this equation to find that at $x = 5$, $y = 3(5) + 4 = 15 + 4 = 19$. Also, at $x = -1$, $y = 3(-1) + 4 = -3 + 4 = 1$. Thus the points of intersection are $(5,19)$ and $(-1,1)$.

31. As in Exercise 5, equate the two expressions for y to get

$$\tfrac{1}{2}x^3 + x^2 + 5 = 3x^2 - \tfrac{1}{2}x + 5.$$

Then rewrite this as

$$\tfrac{1}{2}x^3 - 2x^2 + \tfrac{1}{2}x = 0,$$

and factor out a common factor of x to get

$$x\left(\tfrac{1}{2}x^2 - 2x + \tfrac{1}{2}\right) = 0.$$

This tells us that one of the points of intersection has x-coordinate 0. To find the x-coordinate of the remaining points of intersection, apply the quadratic formula to $\tfrac{1}{2}x^2 - 2x + \tfrac{1}{2} = 0$:

$$x = \frac{-(-2) \pm \sqrt{(-2)^2 - 4\left(\tfrac{1}{2}\right)\left(\tfrac{1}{2}\right)}}{2\left(\tfrac{1}{2}\right)} = \frac{2 \pm \sqrt{4 - 1}}{1} = 2 \pm \sqrt{3}.$$

Substituting these values into $y = 3x^2 - \tfrac{1}{2}x + 5$, we find at $x = 0$, $y = 3(0)^2 - \tfrac{1}{2}(0) + 5 = 5$; at $x = 2 + \sqrt{3}$,

$$y = 3(2+\sqrt{3})^2 - \tfrac{1}{2}(2+\sqrt{3}) + 5$$

$$= 3(7+4\sqrt{3}) - \tfrac{1}{2}(2+\sqrt{3}) + 5$$

$$= 21 + 12\sqrt{3} - 1 - \tfrac{1}{2}\sqrt{3} + 5 = 25 + \tfrac{23}{2}\sqrt{3};$$

and at $x = 2 - \sqrt{3}$,

$$y = 3(2-\sqrt{3})^2 - \tfrac{1}{2}(2-\sqrt{3}) + 5$$

$$= 3(7-4\sqrt{3}) - 1 + \tfrac{1}{2}\sqrt{3} + 5$$

$$= 21 - 12\sqrt{3} + 4 + \tfrac{1}{2}\sqrt{3} = 25 - \tfrac{23}{2}\sqrt{3}.$$

Thus the points of intersection are:

$$(0,5), \quad (2+\sqrt{3}, 25+\tfrac{23}{2}\sqrt{3}), \quad \text{and} \quad (2-\sqrt{3}, 25-\tfrac{23}{2}\sqrt{3}).$$

37. A rational function will be zero only if the numerator is zero. Thus we solve

$$x^2 + 14x + 49 = 0,$$
$$(x + 7)^2 = 0,$$
$$x + 7 = 0.$$

That is, $x = -7$. Since the denominator is not 0 at $x = -7$, we conclude that $x = -7$ is the solution.

43. You can graph the function and use TRACE to estimate the zero as approximately 4.6. (Your estimate is influenced by your choice of viewing window.) Another procedure, which is usually more accurate, is described in the Appendix section on **Special Points on the Graph of Y_1**. Part E of the section explains how to find an x-intercept. The exact answer is $x = 32/7$.

Note: For the TI-85, when TRACE is used in the window specified, the cursor happens to land exactly on the zero of $f(x)$, so the displayed value of is accurate to 10 decimal places.

Helpful Hint: Exercises 49—52 are somewhat difficult because you do not yet have the tools of calculus available. To find an interval that contains the zeros of $f(x)$, use the comment that follows Figs. 7 and 8 in the text. In Exercise 51, for example, write $f(x) = 3\left(x^3 + \frac{52}{3}x^2 - 4x - 4\right)$ and let M be the number that is one more than the largest magnitude of the coefficients 52/3, −4, and −4. That is, let $M = 55/3$. Then the zeros of $f(x)$ lie between $-M$ and M. For a first graphing attempt, use x values in the interval $-55/3 \le x \le 55/3$, or perhaps $-19 \le x \le 19$.

49. Since $f(x) = x^3 - 22x^2 + 17x + 19$, and the coefficient of the highest power of x is 1, you can let M be the number that is one more that the largest magnitude of the coefficients −22, 17, and 19. That is, let M = 23. Then the zeros of the polynomial lie between −M and M, in the interval $-23 \le x \le 23$.

Sketch the graph in the window $[-23, 23]$ *by* $[-10, 10]$ (If necessary, refer to the Appendix section, **Specify Window Settings.**)

In this first window, you should see three nearly vertical lines. The "lines" connect somewhere off the screen. So enlarge the range of y-values, say, $-100 \le y \le 100$. Also, since two of the "lines" in the graph are close to x = 0 and one is close to x = 23, you can chop off most of the negative x-axis. Try the window $[-5, 25]$ *by* $[-100, 100]$.

This time, you should observe that the *y*-values seem to get very negative. The TRACE command might be helpful now, to find out about how negative the *y*-values become. Move the cursor along the curve until it disappears at the bottom of the screen. The coordinates of points on the graph will continue to appear on the screen even when the cursor is not visible. Watching the *y*-coordinates, you should see them go down to about -1300. So, try the window [-5, 25] *by* [-1500, 100]. (When you use such a large *y*-range, set the *y*-scale to, say, 100.)

0.5 Exponents and Power Functions

We have found that operations with exponents cause our students more difficulty than any other algebraic skill, so we have included lots of drill exercises. Try some of each group of problems. If you cannot work them accurately with relative ease and confidence, keep working more problems. If you need more practice, get a college algebra text or Schaum's *Outline of College Algebra*. Do this immediately, because operations with exponents are used in Section 1.3 and in most sections thereafter.

Helpful Hint: We are all so accustomed to reading formulas from left to right that it is more difficult to use a formula such as $b^r b^s = b^{r+s}$ in "reverse," that is, in the form $b^{r+s} = b^r b^s$. Yet the laws of exponents are sometimes needed in reverse from the way they are written in the text. So *memorize* the following list, as well as the list on page 41 of the text.

Laws of Exponents (continued)	
1'. $b^{r+s} = b^r \cdot b^s$	4'. $b^{rs} = (b^r)^s$
2'. $\dfrac{1}{b^r} = b^{-r}$	5'. $a^r b^r = (ab)^r$
3'. $b^{r-s} = b^r \cdot b^{-s} = \dfrac{b^r}{b^s}$	6'. $\dfrac{a^r}{b^r} = \left(\dfrac{a}{b}\right)^r$

A common use of Law 4' is in the form $b^{m/n} = (b^{1/n})^m$. For instance, $9^{3/2} = (9^{1/2})^3 = (3)^3 = 27$, and $27^{4/3} = (27^{1/3})^4 = (3)^4 = 81$. Most instructors will assume that you can compute the square roots of the following numbers without using a calculator:

$$4, \ 9, \ 16, \ 25, \ 36, \ 49, \ 64, \ 81, \ 100.$$

You should also know the following cube roots:

$$8^{1/3} = 2, \ 27^{1/3} = 3, \ 64^{1/3} = 4, \text{ and possibly } 125^{1/3} = 5.$$

It wouldn't hurt also to learn the following fourth roots:

$$16^{1/4} = 2, \ 81^{1/4} = 3.$$

Solutions for Section 0.5:

1. $3^3 = 3 \cdot (3 \cdot 3) = 3 \cdot 9 = 27.$

7. $-4^2 = -16.$ Note that the exponent 2 does not act on the negative sign. That is, -4^2 is not the same as $(-4)^2 = (-4) \cdot (-4) = +16.$

13. $6^{-1} = \frac{1}{6}$ \qquad (Law 2).

19. $(25)^{3/2} = (25^{1/2})^3$ \qquad (Law 4')

$$= 5^3 = 125.$$

25. $4^{-1/2} = \dfrac{1}{4^{1/2}}$ \qquad (Law 2)

$$= \frac{1}{2}.$$

31. $6^{1/3} \cdot 6^{2/3} = 6^{1/3 + 2/3}$ \qquad (Law 1)

$$= 6^1 = 6.$$

37. $\left(\dfrac{8}{27}\right)^{2/3} = \dfrac{8^{2/3}}{27^{2/3}}$ \qquad (Law 6)

$$= \frac{(8^{1/3})^2}{(27^{1/3})^2} \qquad \text{(Law 4')}$$

$$= \frac{2^2}{3^2} = \frac{4}{9}.$$

43. $\dfrac{x^4 \cdot y^5}{xy^2} = \left(\dfrac{x^4}{x}\right)\left(\dfrac{y^5}{y^2}\right)$

$$= (x^{4-1})(y^{5-2}) \quad \text{(Law 3)}$$

$$= x^3 y^3.$$

49. $(x^3 y^5)^4 = (x^3)^4 (y^5)^4 \quad \text{(Law 5)}$

$$= x^{12} y^{20} \quad \text{(Law 4).}$$

55. $\dfrac{-x^3 y}{-xy} = \dfrac{x^3 y}{xy} = \dfrac{x^3}{x} \cdot \dfrac{y}{y}$

$$= x^{3-1} y^{1-1} \quad \text{(Law 3)}$$

$$= x^2 y^0 = x^2.$$

61. $\left(\dfrac{3x^2}{2y}\right)^3 = \dfrac{(3x^2)^3}{(2y)^3} \quad \text{(Law 6)}$ $\qquad \begin{bmatrix}\text{Don't forget} \\ \text{parentheses.}\end{bmatrix}$

$$= \dfrac{3^3 (x^2)^3}{2^3 y^3} \quad \text{(Law 5)} \qquad \begin{bmatrix}\text{Careful: This step} \\ \text{is where mistakes} \\ \text{usually happen.}\end{bmatrix}$$

$$= \dfrac{27 (x^2)^3}{8y^3} = \dfrac{27x^6}{8y^3} \quad \text{(Law 4).}$$

67. $\sqrt{x}\left(\dfrac{1}{4x}\right)^{5/2} = x^{1/2}\left(\dfrac{1}{4x}\right)^{5/2}$

$$= x^{1/2} \cdot \dfrac{1^{5/2}}{(4x)^{5/2}} \quad \text{(Law 6)} \qquad \begin{bmatrix}\text{Careful: Don't} \\ \text{forget parenthe-} \\ \text{ses around 4x.}\end{bmatrix}$$

$$= x^{1/2} \cdot \dfrac{1}{4^{5/2} x^{5/2}} \quad \text{(Law 5)}$$

$$= \dfrac{x^{1/2}}{(4^{1/2})^5 x^{5/2}} \quad \text{(Law 4)}$$

$$= \dfrac{x^{1/2}}{2^5 x^{5/2}} = \dfrac{1}{32} \cdot x^{1/2 - 5/2} \quad \text{(Law 3)}$$

$$= \frac{1}{32} \cdot x^{-2} = \frac{1}{32x^2}.$$

73. $x^{-1/4} + 6x^{1/4} = x^{-1/4}(1 + 6x^{1/2}) = x^{-1/4}(1 + 6\sqrt{x})$.

79. $f(4) = (4)^{-1} = \frac{1}{4}$.

85. $A = P(1 + \frac{r}{m})^{mt}$, where $P = 100$, $r = .06$, $m = 1$, $t = 6$

$$= 500(1 + \frac{.06}{1})^{1 \cdot 6}$$

$$= 500(1.06)^6 = \$709.26.$$

91. $A = P(1 + \frac{r}{m})^{mt}$, where $P = 1500$, $r = .06$, $m = 360$, $t = 1$

$$= 1500(1 + \frac{.06}{360})^{360 \cdot 1}$$

$$= 1500(1.0001667)^{360} = \$1592.75.$$

97. [new stopping distance] $= \frac{1}{20}(2x)^2 = \frac{1}{20} \cdot 4x^2 = 4(\frac{1}{20}x^2)$

$$= 4 \cdot [\text{old stopping distance}]$$

0.6   Functions and Graphs in Applications

The crucial step in many of these problems is to express the function in one variable using the information given. Exercise 7 is a typical example. Both the height and width are expressed in terms of x. The function, here perimeter, is now in terms of x.

1.   If x = width, then the height is 3(width) = 3x.

7.   Perimeter = 2·height + 2·width
           = 2(3x) + 2(x) = 6x + 2x = 8x.

     Area = height × width
           = (3x)(x) = $3x^2$.

But   Area = 25 square feet, so
           $3x^2 = 25$.

13.   Volume = $\pi r^2 h$, where r is the radius of the circular ends and h is the height of the cylinder. Since the

volume is supposed to be 100 cubic inches,
$$\pi r^2 h = 100.$$

Using the solution to Practice Problems 0.6,

Area of the left end: πr^2,

Area of the right end: πr^2,

Area of the side (a "rolled-up rectangle"): $2\pi rh$.

Cost for the left end: $5(\pi r^2) = 5\pi r^2$,

Cost for the right end: $6(\pi r^2) = 6\pi r^2$,

Cost for the side: $7(2\pi rh) = 14\pi rh$.

So the total cost is $11\pi r^2 + 14\pi rh$ (dollars).

19. From Exercise 7, perimeter = 8x (for rectangle of Exercise 1), hence
$$8x = 40,$$
$$x = 5.$$

Also from Exercise 7 the area is $3x^2$ (for the rectangle of Exercise 1). Therefore, since x = 5,

$$\text{Area} = 3(5)^2 = 75 \text{ cm}^2.$$

25. a. $P(x) = R(x) - C(x)$
$$= 21x - (9x + 800) = (12x - 800) \text{ dollars.}$$

b. x = number of sales,
here x = 120, so P(x) = P(120) = 12(120) - 800
$$= 640 \text{ dollars in profit.}$$

c. Weekly profit function is P(x) = 12x - 800 (from (a)), and we are given a weekly profit of $1000, so
$$12x - 800 = 1000,$$
$$12x = 1800,$$
$$x = 150.$$

Weekly revenue is R(x) = 21x,
$$\Rightarrow \text{revenue} = 21(150) = \$3150.$$

31. (3,162), (6,270) are points on the graph y = f(r). The cost of constructing a cylinder of radius 3 inches is 162 cents, and similarly, for a radius of 6 inches it is 270 cents. Thus the additional cost of increasing the radius from 3 inches to 6 inches is 270 - 162 = 108 cents.

37. C(1000) = 4000.

43. Use Table 1.
Find the x-coordinates of the points on the graph whose y-coordinate is 30,000.

49. h(t) = height of the ball (in feet) after t seconds. Given that the height = h(t) = 100 feet, we want to find the value of the time t. (Example 7 gives an example of a height function.)

So our task is to find the t-coordinates of the points on the graph whose y-coordinate is 100.

Chapter 0: Supplementary Exercises

Study the Review of Fundamental Concepts. Write out your own answers. Can you handle the algebra of functions as in Section 0.3? Can you factor quadratic (and simple cubic) polynomials? Have you memorized the quadratic formula? Have you thoroughly (and successfully) practiced using the laws of exponents? If you cannot answer "yes" to all these questions by the time you finish Chapter 1, you are not seriously interested in succeeding in this calculus course, or you need to take a refresher course in college algebra before you study calculus.

The supplementary exercises provide a brief review of the main skills of the chapter.

1. If $f(x) = x^3 + \frac{1}{x}$, then

$$f(1) = 1^3 + \frac{1}{1} = 1 + 1 = 2,$$

$$f(3) = 3^3 + \frac{1}{3} = 27 + \frac{1}{3} = 27\frac{1}{3},$$

$$f(-1) = (-1)^3 + \frac{1}{-1} = -1 - 1 = -2,$$

$$f\left(-\frac{1}{2}\right) = \left(-\frac{1}{2}\right)^3 + \frac{1}{-\frac{1}{2}} = -\frac{1}{8} - 2 = -2\frac{1}{8},$$

$$f(\sqrt{2}) = (\sqrt{2})^3 + \frac{1}{\sqrt{2}} = 2\sqrt{2} + \frac{1}{\sqrt{2}} = 2\sqrt{2} + \frac{\sqrt{2}}{2} = \frac{5\sqrt{2}}{2}.$$

7. The domain of $f(x) = \sqrt{x^2 + 1}$ consists of all values of x since $x^2 + 1$ is never negative.

13. To factor $18 + 3x - x^2$ we first factor out the coefficient -1 of x^2 to get $-1(x^2 - 3x - 18)$. Now, to factor $x^2 - 3x - 18$ we must find c and d such that cd = -18 and c + d = -3. The solution is c = -6 and d = 3 and

0-17

$$x^2 - 3x - 18 = (x-6)(x+3).$$

Thus

$$18 + 3x - x^2 = -1(x^2-3x-18) = -1(x-6)(x+3).$$

19. $f(x) + g(x) = (x^2 - 2x) + (3x - 1) = x^2 + x - 1.$

25. $f(x) - g(x) = \dfrac{x}{(x^2 - 1)} - \dfrac{(1 - x)}{(1 + x)}$. In order to add two fractions, their denominators must be the same. Observe that $x^2 - 1 = (x+1)(x-1)$. Thus a common denominator for $\dfrac{x}{x^2 - 1}$ and $\dfrac{1 - x}{1 + x}$ is $x^2 - 1$. If we multiply $\dfrac{1 - x}{1 + x}$ by $\dfrac{x - 1}{x - 1}$, we get an equivalent expression whose denominator is $x^2 - 1$. Thus

$$\frac{x}{x^2 - 1} - \frac{1 - x}{1 + x} = \frac{x}{x^2 - 1} - \frac{1 - x}{1 + x}\cdot\frac{x - 1}{x - 1}$$

$$= \frac{x}{x^2 - 1} - \frac{(1 - x)(x - 1)}{x^2 - 1}$$

$$= \frac{x - (-x^2 + 2x - 1)}{x^2 - 1}$$

$$= \frac{x^2 - x + 1}{x^2 - 1}.$$

31. If we substitute $g(x)$ for each occurrence of x in $f(x)$ we obtain $f(g(x))$. Thus

$$f(g(x)) = \left(\frac{1}{x^2}\right)^2 - 2\left(\frac{1}{x^2}\right) + 4 = \frac{1}{x^4} - \frac{2}{x^2} + 4.$$

37. $(81)^{3/4} = (81^{1/4})^3 = 3^3 = 27,$ \qquad (Law 4′)

$8^{5/3} = (8^{1/3})^5 = 2^5 = 32,$ \qquad (Law 4′)

$(.25)^{-1} = \left(\frac{1}{4}\right)^{-1} = 4.$

43. $\dfrac{x^{3/2}}{\sqrt{x}} = \dfrac{x^{3/2}}{x^{1/2}} = x^{(3/2-1/2)} = x^1 = x.$ \qquad (Law 3)

Chapter 1

The Derivative

1.1 The Slope of a Straight Line

Slope Property 1 will help you understand the concept of the slope of a line. Property 2 is needed when you have to find the slope of a line between two points. Property 3 is the most useful. You must memorize the *point-slope* form of the equation of a line. Exercises 11-16 are simple but very important. Check with your instructor to see how much attention you should give to Slope Properties 4 and 5. They are seldom needed later in the text.

1. If we put the equation

$$y = 2 - 5x,$$

in the form $y = mx + b$, we have

$$y = -5x + 2.$$

Hence the slope is -5.

7. To write the equation

$$2x + 3y = 6,$$

in the form $y = mx + b$, solve for y:

$$3y = -2x + 6,$$

$$y = -\frac{2}{3}x + 2.$$

The slope is $-\frac{2}{3}$.

13. Let $(x_1, y_1) = (5, 0)$ and $m = -7$, and use Slope Property 3. The equation of the line is

$$y - 0 = -7(x - 5),$$

or

$$y = 35 - 7x.$$

19. By Slope Property 2, the slope of the line is

$$\frac{-2 - 0}{1 - 0} = \frac{-2}{1} = -2.$$

Since $(0,0)$ is on the line, we can use Slope Property 3 to get the equation of the line:

$$y - 0 = -2(x - 0),$$

or

$$y = -2x.$$

25. (a) is matched with (C). To see this we look at the intercepts. The x-intercept is the value of x when $y = 0$. Thus for $x + y = 1$, we see that:

$$y = 0 \Rightarrow x = 1.$$

The y-intercept is the value of y when $x = 0$, so again

$$x = 0 \Rightarrow y = 1.$$

Graph (C) is the only graph which has both intercepts positive.

(b) is matched with (B). Repeating the above process we find that the x-intercept is $x = 1$, and the y-intercept is $y = -1$. The only graph which has a positive x-intercept and a negative y-intercept is (B). By similar reasoning:

(c) is matched with (D).

(d) is matched with (A).

31. Since the slope of this line is 2, if we start at a point on the line and move 1 unit to the right and then 2 units up (in the positive y-direction) we will reach another point on the line. If we start at $(1,3)$ and move 1 unit to the right and 2 units up, we arrive at $(2,5)$. So $(2,5)$ is on the line. A similar move from $(2,5)$ takes us to $(3,7)$, so $(3,7)$ is on the line.

Finally, suppose that $(0,y)$ is on the line. This point is one unit to the left of $(1,3)$ in the x-direction. Starting at $(0,y)$ and moving one unit to the right and 2 units up, we arrive at $(1,y+2)$. This point is on the line and so is $(1,3)$. Hence we must have $y + 2 = 3$, and $y = 1$. Thus $(0,1)$ is on the line.

37. By Slope Property 3,

$$y - (-1) = -2(x - 0)$$

or,
$$y = -2x - 1.$$

To graph this line, first plot the y-intercept $(0,-1)$. Then since the slope is -2, we start at $(0,-1)$ and move one unit right, and then two units in the negative y-direction. The new point $(1,-3)$ is on the line. Draw the straight line through these two points.

43. Parallel lines by definition always have the same slope. So we need to find the slope of $4x + 5y = 6$. Thus
$$5y = -4x + 6,$$
$$y = \frac{-4}{5}x + \frac{6}{5}.$$

Now since $y = mx + b$ is the equation of a line we have that the slope m is $-\frac{4}{5}$.

Using Slope Property 3, we see that the equation of a line through a general point (x_1, y_1) with slope $-\frac{4}{5}$ is, using Slope Property 3:
$$y - y_1 = -\frac{4}{5}(x - x_1),$$
$$y - y_1 = -\frac{4}{5}x + \frac{4}{5}x_1.$$
So,
$$\frac{4}{5}x + y = y + \frac{4}{5}x,$$
$$4x + 5y = 5y_1 + 4x_1.$$

Since $5y_1 + 4x_1$ is any constant C, the possible lines are $4x + 5y = C$.

49. At a point (x,y) the tangent line to the parabola has slope $2x$. The point $\left(-\frac{1}{2}, \frac{1}{4}\right)$ corresponds to $x = -\frac{1}{2}$, so the slope of the tangent line at this point is $2\left(-\frac{1}{2}\right) = -1$. Now, let $(x_1, y_1) = \left(-\frac{1}{2}, \frac{1}{4}\right)$ and $m = -1$, and use Slope Property 3. The equation of the tangent line through $\left(-\frac{1}{2}, \frac{1}{4}\right)$ is
$$y - \frac{1}{4} = -1\left(x - \left(-\frac{1}{2}\right)\right),$$
or,

$$y - \frac{1}{4} = -\left(x + \frac{1}{2}\right).$$

55. By Slope Property 1: m_1 is positive; m_2 is negative.

Slope of ℓ_1 is $\frac{m_1}{1}$; slope of ℓ_2 is $\frac{m_2}{1}$.

We have two right-angled triangles. The first has sides of length a, 1, and m, which by Pythagorus produces

$$a^2 = m_1{}^2 + 1^2 = m_1{}^2 + 1 \ (a = \text{hypotenuse}).$$

The other right-angled triangle has sides of length b, 1, and $(-m_2)$. (Note: $-m_2$, since m_2 is negative and we can't have a negative length, we make it positive.) So similarly: $b^2 = m_1{}^2 + 1$. Combining these results we obtain:

$$a^2 + b^2 = m_1{}^2 + m_2{}^2 + 2 \quad (*).$$

Since $\ell_1 \perp \ell_2$, we have yet another right-angled triangle with sides of length:

$$a, \ b, \ \text{and} \ (m_1 + (-m_2)),$$
$$\text{i.e., } a, \ b, \ \text{and} \ m_1 - m_2 \ (\text{hypotenuse}).$$

Hence, as before

$$a^2 + b^2 = (m_1 - m_2)^2 = m_1{}^2 + m_2{}^2 - 2m_1m_2.$$

From (*) we know that $m_1{}^2 + m_2{}^2 + 2 = m_1{}^2 + m_2{}^2 - 2m_1m_2$. This leads to

$$2 = -2m_1m_2,$$
$$m_1m_2 = -1.$$

Help for Technology Exercises: If your course starts with Chapter 1, please read pages 11-12 in your text, and note that Appendices A through D in the text contain practically all the information you need to use a TI-82, TI-83, TI-85, or TI-86 graphing calculator. (For other calculators or computer software, you will need some sort of user's manual.) When we refer to "the Appendix", we mean the appropriate appendix for your TI-calculator.

For the technology exercises in Section 1.1, you should refer to the first two Appendix sections entitled **Functions** and **Specify Window Settings**. A good window for Exercise 56 is [0, 75,000] *by* [0, 2000]. For Exercise 57, use the window [0, 40] *by* [0, 100].

1.2 The Slope of a Curve at a Point

This brief section should be read carefully. Example 2 and Exercises 23, 24, and 33 are very important, and so we have included a solution of Exercise 23. Of the students who do *not* use this study guide, at least 20% will miss an exam problem on the equation of a tangent line. If you carefully study the solution of Exercise 23 here and the solution of Exercise 43 in Section 1.6, you should have no difficulty on an exam.

1. See the sketch in the answer section of the text.

7. The slope of the curve at the point P is, by definition, the slope of the tangent line at P. If we move one unit in the positive x-direction from P, we can return to the line by moving one unit in the positive y-direction. Therefore the slope is 1.

13. Small positive slope.

19. The slope of the graph of $y = x^2$ at the point (x,y) is 2x. The point (-2,4) corresponds to x = -2, so the slope at this point is 2x = 2(-2) = -4. Now, let $(x_1,y_1) = (-2,4)$ and m = -4 and use Slope Property 3. The equation of the tangent line through (-2,4) is:

$$y - 4 = -4(x - (-2)),$$

or,

$$y - 4 = -4(x + 2).$$

23. We will use the point-slope equation of the tangent line to the graph of $y = x^2$ at x = 1.5. We need a point (x_1,y_1) and a slope m. There are two basic principles to keep in mind.

   (i) Use the *original equation* $y = x^2$ to find a *point* on the graph. When x = 1.5, we have $y = (1.5)^2 = 2.25$. Thus (1.5,2.25) is on the graph of $y = x^2$.

   (ii) Use the *slope formula* 2x to find the *slope* of the graph at a point. When x = 1.5, the slope of the graph is 2(1.5) = 3. By definition, this slope is the slope of the tangent line to the graph at the point where x = 1.5.

The desired tangent line equation has the form $y - y_1 = m(x - x_1)$, where $x_1 = 1.5$, $y_1 = 2.25$, and m = 3. That is,

$$y - 2.25 = 3(x - 1.5).$$

Leave the answer in this form unless you are specifically asked to rewrite the answer in some equivalent form such as the slope intercept form.

Warning: A common mistake in Exercise 23 is to replace m in the equation $y - y_1 = m(x - x_1)$ by the slope formula 2x instead of a specific *value* of m. But the equation $y - 2.25 = 2x(x - 1.5)$ is *not* the equation of a line. (In fact, this equation simplifies to $y - 2.25 = 2x^2 - 3x$, or $y = 2x^2 - 3x + 2.25$, which is a quadratic equation.) The equation of a tangent *line* must involve a specific *number* m that gives the slope of the desired tangent line.

25. The slope of the graph of $y = x^2$ at the point (x, y) is 2x. Hence, if the slope is $\frac{5}{3}$, then

$$2x = \frac{5}{3},$$

$$x = \frac{5}{3} \cdot \frac{1}{2} = \frac{5}{6}.$$

To find the y-coordinate of the point where $x = \frac{5}{6}$, use the original equation $y = x^2$.

$$y = \left(\frac{5}{6}\right)^2 = \frac{25}{36}.$$

Hence, $\left(\frac{5}{6}, \frac{25}{36}\right)$ is the desired point on the graph.

31. The slope formula for the curve $y = x^3$ is given by the formula $3x^2$. The point $\left(-\frac{1}{2}, -\frac{1}{8}\right)$ corresponds to $x = -\frac{1}{2}$, so the slope at $\left(-\frac{1}{2}, -\frac{1}{8}\right)$ is $3x^2 = 3\left(-\frac{1}{2}\right)^2 = 3\left(\frac{1}{4}\right) = \frac{3}{4}$.

37. See the Appendix section, **Derivatives, Slopes, and Tangent Lines.** Refer to part D, "Draw a tangent line to a graph." For the TI-82, you will also need to use part C, "Compute the slope of a graph at a point." When the TI-83 adds the tangent line to the graph, it also displays the equation of the tangent line, but in slope-intercept form.

In any case, you should obtain the slope .204 (to three decimal places) at x = 4. Next, obtain the value of 2.449 (to three decimal places) for f(4). You'll find help in part C of the Appendix section, **Special Points on the Graph of Y₁.** [For a TI-83, select TRACE and enter 4 on the graphing screen. When you press ENTER, the value of Y_1 at 4 will appear.]

Finally, use the point-slope form for the equation of the tangent line:

$$y - 2.449 = .204(x - 4) \quad \text{or} \quad y - 2.45 = .2(x - 4).$$

1.3 The Derivative

Your short-term goal for this section should be to learn the derivative formulas that appear in boxes and to become familiar with the notation introduced on pages 81—82. This will enable you to do the homework for this section. Your longterm goal should be to have some understanding of the secant-line calculation of the derivative, as described on page 82. This material is not grasped easily. Reading it *out loud* will help you to go over the ideas slowly and carefully. Plan to review this section before your first exam and again when you reach Chapter 3.

1. If $f(x) = mx + b$, then $f'(x) = m$. Hence if $f(x) = 2x - 5$, then $f'(x) = 2$.

7. Since $\sqrt[3]{x} = x^{1/3}$, we may apply the power rule with $r = \frac{1}{3}$:

$$f(x) = x^{1/3},$$

$$f'(x) = \frac{1}{3}x^{(1/3)-1} = \frac{1}{3}x^{-2/3}.$$

13. The derivative of a constant function $f(x) = b$ is the zero function. Hence if $f(x) = \frac{3}{4}$, then $f'(x) = 0$.

19. If $f(x) = \frac{1}{x}$, then $f'(x) = -\frac{1}{x^2}$ $(x \neq 0)$, by formula (5) on page 81. Hence at $x = 3$, $f'(3) = -\frac{1}{3^2} = -\frac{1}{9}$.

Helpful Hint: Formula (5) for the derivative of $\frac{1}{x}$ is used so frequently that you should memorize it even though it is only a special case of the power rule.

25. Use the power rule with $r = 4$:

$$\frac{d}{dx}(x^4) = 4x^{4-1} = 4x^3.$$

Setting x = 3 in this derivative, we find that the slope of the curve $y = x^4$ at x = 3 is $4(3)^3 = 4 \cdot 27 = 108$.

31. If $f(x) = \dfrac{1}{x^5}$, then $f(2) = \dfrac{1}{2^5} = \dfrac{1}{32}$. To compute $f'(2)$, we first determine $f'(x)$ and *then* substitute 2 for x in the expression for $f'(x)$. Since $\dfrac{1}{x^5} = x^{-5}$, we may apply the power rule with r = -5.

$$f(x) = x^{-5},$$

$$f'(x) = -5x^{-5-1} = -5x^{-6} = -\frac{5}{x^6}.$$

$$f'(2) = -\frac{5}{2^6} = -\frac{5}{64}.$$

37. Using the power rule with r = 8, we find

$$\frac{d}{dx}(x^8) = 8x^{8-1} = 8x^7.$$

43. Apply the power rule with $r = \frac{1}{5}$:

$$y = x^{1/5},$$

$$\frac{dy}{dx} = \frac{1}{5}x^{(1/5)-1} = \frac{1}{5}x^{-4/5}.$$

49. The three lines and y = f(x) intersect at the point (a,f(a)). Take the line y = 2.01x - .51 at this point. Then:

$$f(a) = 2.01a - .51,$$

similarly using y = 2.02x - .52,

$$f(a) = 2.02a - .52.$$

So,

$$2.01a - .51 = 2.02a - .52,$$

$$0.01 = 0.01 \, a,$$

$$a = 1,$$

$$f(a) = 2.02a - .52 = 2.02 - .52 = 1.5.$$

To estimate f'(a) use the secant line calculation.

The secant line y = 2.01x - .51 is "nearly" a tangent line, therefore the slope of this line is nearly f'(a).

The slope of the tangent line is slightly less than the secant lines slope of 2.01. Hence,

$$f'(a) \approx 2.$$

55. $f'(x) = \lim\limits_{h \to 0} \dfrac{f(x + h) - f(x)}{h}, \qquad (h \neq 0)$

Taking $f(x) = x^3$, and substituting into the above equation

we have: $f'(x) = \lim\limits_{h \to 0} \dfrac{(x + h)^3 - (x)^3}{h}$

$\qquad\qquad = \lim\limits_{h \to 0} \dfrac{x^3 + 3x^2h + 3xh^2 + h^3 - x^3}{h}$

$\qquad\qquad = \lim\limits_{h \to 0} 3x^2 + 3xh + h^2 = 3x^2.$

61. See the Appendix section, **Derivatives, Slopes, and Tangent Lines.** Part A shows how to compute $f'(a)$ from the Home screen. For Exercise 61, use 1 as *a*.

TI-82: nDeriv(Y_1,X,1) = .7071066928   (a numerical deriv.)
TI-83: nDeriv(Y_1,X,1) = .7071066928   "
TI-85: der1(y1,x,1) = .707106781187   (a symbolic deriv.)
TI-86: der1(y1,x,1) = .707106781187   "

67. $f(x) = \sqrt{x} = x^{1/2}, \quad f(9) = 3$

$f'(x) = (1/2)x^{-1/2}, \quad f'(9) = (1/2)(9)^{-1/2} = \dfrac{1}{2} \cdot \dfrac{1}{3} = \dfrac{1}{6}.$

Equation of tangent line at (9,3): $y - 3 = \dfrac{1}{6}(x - 9).$

On your calculator, define

$\qquad Y_1 = \sqrt{x}$ and $Y_2 = 3 + (x - 9)/6.$

Make sure that both functions are "selected" for graphing. Use the window [0,25] *by* [-2,6]. (See the discussion above for Exercise 37 in Section 1.2.)

69. Use the window [0,2] *by* [-2,10].

73. Use the Z-std window to graph the functions

$\qquad Y_1 = x^3 - 12x^2 + 46x - 50$

$\qquad Y_2 = 14 - 2x.$

Using TRACE in the TI-83 Z-std window, for example, it seems that the curves are closest at approximately (4.043, 5.915). Perhaps *a* = 4. How could you check this?

1.4 Limits and the Derivative

Instructors differ widely about how much theoretical material to include in a course using our text. We recommend that
at a minimum, you read page 88, even if no exercises are
assigned. The skills practiced in this section are not needed
for later work, but the exercises will give you valuable
experience with simple limits and will improve your understanding of derivatives.

1. $\lim\limits_{x \to 3} g(x)$ does not exist. As x approaches 3 from the
    right, g(x) approaches 2, but as x approaches 3 from the
    left, the values for g(x) do not approach 2. In order for
    a limit to exist, the values of the function must approach
    the same number as x approaches 2 from each direction.

7. Since 1 - 6x is a polynomial, the limit exists and

$$\lim_{x \to 1} (1 - 6x) = 1 - 6(1) = 1 - 6 = -5.$$

13. Using the Limit Theorems, we have

$$\lim_{x \to 7} (x + \sqrt{x - 6})(x^2 - 2x + 1)$$

$$= \left[\lim_{x \to 7} (x + \sqrt{x - 6})\right]\left[\lim_{x \to 7} (x^2 - 2x + 1)\right] \qquad \text{(Thm. V)}$$

$$= \left[\lim_{x \to 7} x + \lim_{x \to 7} (x - 6)^{1/2}\right]\left[\lim_{x \to 7} (x^2 - 2x + 1)\right] \qquad \text{(Thm. III)}$$

$$= \left[\lim_{x \to 7} x + \left(\lim_{x \to 7} (x - 6)\right)^{1/2}\right]\left[\lim_{x \to 7}(x^2 - 2x + 1)\right] \qquad \text{(Thm. II)}$$

$$= [7 + (1)^{1/2}][49 - 14 + 1] \qquad \begin{bmatrix}\text{Limits of poly-} \\ \text{nomial functions}\end{bmatrix}$$

$$= (8)(36) = 288.$$

19. Since $\dfrac{-2x^2 + 4x}{x - 2} = \dfrac{-2x(x - 2)}{x - 2} = -2x$ for $x \neq 2$,

$$\lim_{x \to 2} \frac{-2x^2 + 4x}{x - 2} = \lim_{x \to 2} -2x = -2(2) = -4.$$

25. No limit exists. Observe that $\lim\limits_{x \to 8} x^2 + 64 = 128$ and
    $\lim\limits_{x \to 8} x - 8 = 0$, as x approaches 8. So the denominator gets

very small and the numerator approaches 128. For example, if x = 8.00001, then the numerator is 128.00016 and the denominator is .00001. The quotient is 12,800,016. As x approaches 8 even more closely, the quotient gets arbitrarily large and cannot possibly approach a limit.

31. Since $f'(a) = \lim\limits_{h \to 0} \dfrac{f(a + h) - f(a)}{h}$, we must calculate

$$\lim\limits_{h \to 0} \dfrac{f(0 + h) - f(0)}{h}.$$

If $f(x) = x^3 + 3x + 1$, then

$$\dfrac{f(0+h) - f(0)}{h} = \dfrac{[(0+h)^3 + 3(0+h) + 1] - [0^3 + 3(0) + 1]}{h}$$

$$= \dfrac{h^3 + 3h + 1 - 1}{h} = \dfrac{h^3 + 3h}{h} = h^2 + 3.$$

Therefore, $f'(0) = \lim\limits_{h \to 0} (h^2 + 3) = 0^2 + 3 = 3.$

37. We must calculate $f'(0) = \lim\limits_{h \to 0} \dfrac{f(0 + h) - f(0)}{h}.$

If $f(x) = \sqrt{1 - x^2}$, then

$$\dfrac{f(0 + h) - f(0)}{h} = \dfrac{\sqrt{1 - (0 + h)^2} - \sqrt{1 - 0^2}}{h}$$

$$= \dfrac{\sqrt{1 - h^2} - 1}{h}.$$

In order to find $\lim\limits_{h \to 0} \dfrac{\sqrt{1 - h^2} - 1}{h}$, we must apply an algebraic trick since the denominator of this expression approaches zero. We multiply numerator and denominator by $\sqrt{1 - h^2} + 1$ and use the fact that $(a - 1)(a + 1) = a^2 - 1$, where $a = \sqrt{1 - h^2}$.

$$\dfrac{\sqrt{1 - h^2} - 1}{h} \cdot \dfrac{\sqrt{1 - h^2} + 1}{\sqrt{1 - h^2} + 1} = \dfrac{(1 - h^2) - 1}{h\left(\sqrt{1 - h^2} + 1\right)}$$

$$= \frac{-h^2}{h\left(\sqrt{1 - h^2} + 1\right)}$$

$$= \frac{-h}{\sqrt{1 - h^2} + 1}.$$

Now $f'(0) = \lim_{h \to 0} \dfrac{-h}{\sqrt{1 - h^2} + 1} = \dfrac{-0}{\sqrt{1 - 0^2} + 1} = \dfrac{0}{2} = 0.$

43. We want to find $f(x)$ so that $\displaystyle\lim_{h \to 0} \frac{\frac{1}{10 + h} - .1}{h}$ has the

same form as

$$f'(a) = \lim_{h \to 0} \frac{f(a + h) - f(a)}{h}.$$

So we want $f(a+h) = \dfrac{1}{10 + h}$; and $f(a) = 0.1 = \dfrac{1}{10}$. From

this we see that $f(x) = \dfrac{1}{x}$ and $a = 10$. Note that $f(a + h)$ $= f(10 + h) = 1/(10 + h)$.

49. As x increases without bound so does x - 8. Therefore, $\dfrac{1}{x - 8}$ approaches zero as x approaches ∞. That is,

$$\lim_{x \to \infty} \frac{1}{x - 8} = 0.$$

55. Set $Y_1 = (X^2 - 2X + 3)/(2x^2 + 1)$, and graph in the window $[0, 50]$ *by* $[0, 2]$. TRACE to $(50, .48050)$ and observe that the limit might be a little more than .48. [For the TI-83, with TRACE on, just type 50 [ENTER] to get the value .48050 immediately.]

For a second window, try $[0, 500]$ *by* $[0, 2]$. The limit should seem to be slightly more than .498.

For a third window, try $[0, 5000]$ *by* $[0, 2]$. The graph should look perfectly flat, but TRACE will show that the y-values continue to grow as x increases beyond 2500; however, the values are very close to .5.

These calculations suggest that the limit is .5, but they do not actually prove this.

1.5 Differentiability and Continuity

We want you to be aware that real applications sometimes involve functions that may not be differentiable at one or more
points in their domains. So this section gives you a rare opportunity to see functions whose graphs are not as "nice" as
the ones we usually consider.

1. No, the graph in Fig. 6 is not continuous at x = 0 since
    the limit as x approaches zero does not exist.

7. No, the graph in Fig. 6 is not differentiable at x = 0 be-
    cause the function is not even *defined* at x = 0. Even if
    the function were given some value at x = 0, say f(0) = 1,
    the graph would have a vertical tangent line at x = 0.

13. Since f(x) = x^2, the power rule gives a slope-formula,
    namely, 2x, that is valid for all x.   This slope-formula
    was verified in Section 1.3 using the limit of the slopes
    of secant lines. Thus f(x) has a derivative (in the for-
    mal sense of Section 1.4) for all x.   In particular, f(x)
    is differentiable at x = 1. By Theorem 1 on page 100, f(x)
    is necessarily continuous at x = 1.

19. At x = 1 the function f(x) is defined, namely f(1) = 0.
    When computing $\lim\limits_{x\to1} f(x)$, we exclude consideration of the
    value x = 1; therefore,

    $$\lim_{x\to1} f(x) = \lim_{x\to1} \frac{1}{x-1} \quad \text{which does not exist.}$$

    Hence $\lim\limits_{x\to1} f(x) \neq f(1)$, so f(x) is not continuous at x = 1.

    By Theorem 1, since f(x) is not continuous at x = 1, it
    cannot be differentiable at x = 1.

25. f(x) is continuous at x = a, if

    $$\lim_{x\to a} f(x) = f(a), \text{ here } f(x) = \frac{(6 + x)^2 - 36}{x}, \quad x \neq 0.$$

    Where a = 0, we have:

    $$\lim_{x\to0} \frac{(6 + x)^2 - 36}{x}$$
    $$= \lim_{x\to0} \frac{36 + 12x + x^2 - 36}{x}$$

$$= \lim_{x \to 0} (12 + x) = 12.$$

so define $f(0) = 12$, and this definition will make $f(x)$ continuous for all x.

1.6 Some Rules for Differentiation

The rules in this section are mastered by working lots of problems. Make sure you learn to distinguish between a constant that is *added* to a function and a constant that *multiplies* a function. For instance, $x^3 + 5$ is the sum of the cube function $f(x) = x^3$ and the constant function $g(x) = 5$. Thus

$$\frac{d}{dx}(x^3 + 5) = \frac{d}{dx}(x^3) + \frac{d}{dx} 5 \qquad \text{(Sum rule)}$$
$$= 3x^2 + 0,$$

because the derivative of a constant function is zero. However, the constant 5 in the formula $5x^3$ *multiplies* the function x^3. Hence, by the constant-multiple rule,

$$\frac{d}{dx} 5x^3 = 5 \cdot \frac{d}{dx}(x^3) = 5 \cdot 3x^2 = 15x^2.$$

Exercise 43 is very important. But before you look at the solution here, go back and read the solution to Exercise 23 in Section 1.2. Then try Exercise 43 in Section 1.6 by yourself. Peek at the solution only if you get stuck.

1. To differentiate $y = x^3 + x^2$, let $f(x) = x^3$ and $g(x) = x^2$ and apply the sum rule.

$$\frac{dy}{dx} = \frac{d}{dx}(x^3 + x^2) = \frac{d}{dx}(x^3) + \frac{d}{dx}(x^2) = 3x^2 + 2x.$$

7. $\frac{d}{dx}(x^4 + x^3 + x) = \frac{d}{dx}(x^4) + \frac{d}{dx}(x^3 + x)$ (Sum rule)

$$= \frac{d}{dx}(x^4) + \frac{d}{dx}(x^3) + \frac{d}{dx}(x) \qquad \text{(Sum rule)}$$

$$= 4x^3 + 3x^2 + 1.$$

13. Write $\dfrac{4}{x^2}$ in the form $4 \cdot x^{-2}$. Then

$$\frac{dy}{dx} = \frac{d}{dx}(4 \cdot x^{-2})$$

$$= 4 \cdot \frac{d}{dx}(x^{-2}) \qquad \text{(Constant-multiple rule)}$$

$$= 4(-2)x^{-3} \qquad \text{(Power rule)}$$

$$= -8x^{-3}, \text{ or } -\frac{8}{x^3}.$$

19. Since $-\dfrac{1}{5x^5} = -\dfrac{1}{5} \cdot \dfrac{1}{x^5} = \left(-\dfrac{1}{5}\right) \cdot x^{-5}$, we use the constant-multiple rule and the power rule.

$$\frac{dy}{dx} = \frac{d}{dx}\left(-\frac{1}{5} \cdot x^{-5}\right) = -\frac{1}{5} \cdot \frac{d}{dx}(x^{-5}) = -\frac{1}{5}(-5)x^{-6} = x^{-6}, \text{ or } \frac{1}{x^6}.$$

Warning: Problems like those in Exercises 13, 19, and 29 tend to be missed on exams by many students. The difficulty lies in the first step—recognizing how to write the function as a constant times a power of x. Be sure to review this before the exam.

25. $\dfrac{d}{dx} 5\sqrt{3x^3 + x} = \dfrac{d}{dx} 5(3x^3 + x)^{1/2}$

$$= \frac{5}{2}(3x^3 + x)^{-1/2} \cdot \frac{d}{dx}(3x^3 + x) \quad \text{(Gen power rule)}$$

$$= \frac{5}{2}(3x^3 + x)^{-1/2}\left[\frac{d}{dx}(3x^3) + \frac{d}{dx}(x)\right] \quad \text{(Sum rule)}$$

$$= \frac{5}{2}(3x^3 + x)^{-1/2}\left[3 \cdot \frac{d}{dx}(x^3) + \frac{d}{dx}(x)\right]$$

$$\text{(Constant-multiple rule)}$$

$$= \frac{5}{2}(3x^3 + x)^{-1/2}[3(3x^2) + 1] = \frac{45x^2 + 5}{2\sqrt{3x^3 + x}}.$$

Warning: Don't forget to use parentheses (or brackets) when appropriate in the general power rule. The next-to-last line in the solution above is incorrect if written in the form:

$$= \frac{5}{2}(3x^3 + x)^{-1/2} \cdot 3(3x^2) + 1.$$

$$\underbrace{\qquad\qquad\qquad\qquad}$$

missing brackets

31. Note that $y = \dfrac{2}{1 - 5x} = 2 \cdot \dfrac{1}{1 - 5x} = 2 \cdot (1 - 5x)^{-1}$. Hence

$$\frac{dy}{dx} = \frac{d}{dx}(2 \cdot (1 - 5x)^{-1})$$

$$= 2 \cdot \frac{d}{dx}(1 - 5x)^{-1} \qquad \text{(Constant-multiple rule)}$$

$$= 2(-1)(1 - 5x)^{-2} \cdot \frac{d}{dx}(1 - 5x) \quad \text{(General power rule)}$$

$$= -2(1 - 5x)^{-2}(-5) = 10(1 - 5x)^{-2}.$$

Warning: Forgetting the -5 in the next-to-last line above is a common mistake. Another common error is to carelessly forget the parentheses and write the derivative as

$$-2(1 - 5x)^{-2}-5.$$

This is definitely incorrect, and many instructors will give no part credit for such an answer. Your ability to find a derivative is of no value to anyone if your algebra is careless and incorrect.

In this *Study Guide*, we'll point where algebra errors are likely to occur so you can guard against them. One key to avoiding such errors on exams is to practice working carefully on your homework.

37. If $f(x) = \left(\dfrac{\sqrt{x}}{2} + 1\right)^{3/2}$ then

$$f'(x) = \frac{d}{dx}\left(\frac{\sqrt{x}}{2} + 1\right)^{3/2}$$

$$= \frac{3}{2}\left(\frac{\sqrt{x}}{2} + 1\right)^{1/2} \cdot \frac{d}{dx}\left(\frac{\sqrt{x}}{2} + 1\right) \qquad \text{(General power rule)}$$

$$= \frac{3}{2}\left(\frac{\sqrt{x}}{2} + 1\right)^{1/2}\left[\frac{d}{dx}\left(\frac{\sqrt{x}}{2}\right) + \frac{d}{dx}(1)\right] \qquad \text{(Sum rule)}$$

$$= \frac{3}{2}\left(\frac{\sqrt{x}}{2} + 1\right)^{1/2}\left[\frac{1}{2} \cdot \frac{d}{dx}(x^{1/2}) + \frac{d}{dx}(1)\right]$$
$$\text{(Constant-multiple rule)}$$

$$= \frac{3}{2}\left(\frac{\sqrt{x}}{2} + 1\right)^{1/2}\left[\frac{1}{2}\left(\frac{1}{2}\right)x^{-1/2} + 0\right]$$

$$= \frac{3}{2}\left(\frac{\sqrt{x}}{2} + 1\right)^{1/2}\left(\frac{1}{4}x^{-1/2}\right).$$

43. The general slope-formula for the curve $y = (x^2 - 15)^6$ is given by the derivative.

$$\frac{dy}{dx} = 6(x^2 - 15)^5 \cdot \frac{d}{dx}(x^2 - 15) \qquad \text{(General power rule)}$$

$$= 6(x^2 - 15)^5 (2x)$$

$$= 12x(x^2 - 15)^5.$$

To find the *slope* m of the tangent line at the particular point where x = 4, substitute 4 for x in the *derivative* formula to get

$$m = 12(4)[(4)^2 - 15]^5 = 48(1)^5 = 48.$$

For the equation of the tangent line at x = 4, use the point-slope form. We already have the slope m = 48. To find a *point* (x_1, y_1) on the curve when x_1 = 4, substitute 4 for x in the *original* equation to get

$$y_1 = [(4)^2 - 15]^6 = (1)^6 = 1.$$

The equation of the tangent line is

$$y - 1 = 48(x - 4).$$

Warning: Exercise 43 helped you to get the equation of the tangent line by asking you first for the slope of the line. Exam questions tend to be more like Exercise 44. You are expected to know that you need to find the slope of the line and a point on the line. [Try Exercise 44; the answer is $y - 1 = -\frac{5}{8}(x - 2)$.] Also, see the solution to Exercise 23 in Section 1.2.

49. $f(5) = 2$, $g(5) = 4$, and $f'(5) = 3$, $g'(5) = 1$. We are given that,

$$h(x) = 3f(x) + 2g(x),$$

$$h(5) = 3f(5) + 2g(5) = 3(2) + 2(4) = 14,$$

$$h'(x) = 3f'(x) + 2g'(x),$$

$$h'(5) = 3f'(5) + 2g'(5) = 3(3) + 2(1) = 11.$$

55. The point of intersection of the tangent line and $f(x)$ is (4,5), which alternatively can be stated as $f(4) = 5$. The tangent line goes through (0,3) and (4,5), which means its slope is $m = \frac{5 - 3}{4 - 0} = \frac{2}{4} = \frac{1}{2}$. That is, $f'(4) = \frac{1}{2}$.

1.7 More About Derivatives

Your ability to differentiate functions easily and correctly depends upon how much you practice. Use the exercises in this section to gain the experience you need. Don't be annoyed that you have to learn so much notation. We want you to be able to read technical articles in your field and be familiar with some of the notation you will find there.

1. $f(t) = (t^2 + 1)^5$

$f'(t) = 5(t^2 + 1)^4 \cdot \frac{d}{dt}(t^2 + 1)$

$= 5(t^2 + 1)^4 2t = 10t(t^2 + 1)^4.$

7. $\frac{d}{dP}(3P^2 - \frac{1}{2}P + 1) = \frac{d}{dP}(3P^2) + \frac{d}{dP}\left(-\frac{1}{2}P\right) + \frac{d}{dP}(1)$

$= 3 \cdot \frac{d}{dP}(P^2) + -\frac{1}{2} \cdot \frac{d}{dP}(P) + \frac{d}{dP}(1)$

$= 3(2P) - \frac{1}{2}(1) + 0$

$= 6P - \frac{1}{2}.$

Helpful Hint: The notation $\frac{d}{dt}$ in Exercise 9 indicates that t is the independent variable when you differentiate. Any other letters appearing in the function represent constants, even though the values of these constants are not specified.

13. $y = \sqrt{x} = x^{1/2},$

$\frac{dy}{dx} = \frac{1}{2}x^{-1/2},$

$\frac{d^2y}{dx^2} = \frac{d}{dx}\left(\frac{dy}{dx}\right) = \frac{d}{dx}\left(\frac{1}{2}x^{-1/2}\right) = \frac{1}{2}\left(-\frac{1}{2}\right)x^{-3/2} = -\frac{1}{4}x^{-3/2}.$

Helpful Hint: Problems involving radical signs (mainly square roots) are handled more easily when you switch to exponential notation, as in the solution to Exercise 13, above. Your instructor will probably permit you to write your answers in this form, too.

19. $f(P) = (3P + 1)^5,$

$$f'(P) = 5(3P + 1)^4 \cdot \frac{d}{dP}(3P + 1) = 5(3P + 1)^4 \cdot 3$$

$$= 15(3P + 1)^4. \quad \text{[Don't forget this.]}$$

$$f''(P) = \frac{d}{dP}f'(P) = \frac{d}{dP}\left[15(3P + 1)^4\right] = 15 \cdot \frac{d}{dP}(3P + 1)^4$$

$$= 15 \cdot 4(3P + 1)^3 \cdot \frac{d}{dP}(3P + 1) = 60(3P + 1)^3(3)$$

$$= 180(3P + 1)^3.$$

25. $\frac{d}{dx}(3x^3 - x^2 + 7x - 1)$

$$= \frac{d}{dx}(3x^3) + \frac{d}{dx}(-x^2) + \frac{d}{dx}(7x) + \frac{d}{dx}(-1)$$

$$= 9x^2 - 2x + 7 + 0$$

$$= 9x^2 - 2x + 7.$$

$$\frac{d^2}{dx^2}(3x^2 - x^2 + 7x - 1) = \frac{d}{dx}(9x^2 - 2x + 7)$$

$$= 18x - 2 + 0$$

$$= 18x - 2.$$

$$\frac{d^2}{dx^2}(3x^2 - x^2 + 7x - 1)\Big|_{x=2} = 18(2) - 2 = 36 - 2 = 34.$$

31. $\frac{dR}{dx} = \frac{d}{dx}(1000 + 80x - .02x^2)$

$$= 0 + 80 - (.02)(2x)$$

$$= 80 - .04x.$$

$$\frac{dR}{dx}\Big|_{x=1500} = 80 - .04(1500) = 80 - 60 = 20.$$

37. Enter the function in Y_1. Then, using the calculator's derivative command, assign the derivative of Y_1 to Y_4 and assign the derivative of Y_4 to Y_5. (You could use Y_2 and Y_3 instead of Y_4 and Y_5, but we recommend keeping Y_2 and Y_3 available for other activities. You will need them later.) See the Appendix section, **Derivatives, Slopes,**

and Tangent Lines.   On the TI-82 and TI-83, use

Y_4 = nDeriv(Y_1,X,X)

Y_5 = nDeriv(Y_2,X,X)

The TI-85 and TI-86 have the more accurate symbolic derivative operations available, so use

Y_4 = der1(y1,x,x)

Y_5 = der1(y4,x,x)

To evaluate Y_5 at X = 3, see part C of the Appendix section **Functions** and see part C of **Special Points on the Graph of Y_1** (and apply the steps to Y_5 in place of Y_1). On the TI-83 home screen, you can enter $Y_5(3)$ on the screen and press ENTER.   You should obtain

$Y_5(3) \approx 127.9129348$.

Helpful Hint: Keep the definitions of Y_4 and Y_5 permanently in your calculator as the first and second derivatives of Y_1 (as in Exercise 37 above).   Then, whenever you need a function and its first two derivatives, all you have to do is assign the function Y_1.   Deselect the derivatives until they are needed. [You may reserve other variables for the derivatives, but in this *Study Guide* we'll assume they are stored in Y_4 and Y_5.]

   On the TI-85 and 86, to define y4 and y5, you need first to (temporarily) assign formulas to y2 and y3.   (Setting them equal to 1 will do.)   You can clear the formulas after y4 and y5 are defined.

1.8   The Derivative as a Rate of Change

This section is crucial for later work.   There are three main categories of problems: (1) the rate of change of some function—either an abstract function or a function in an application where some quantity is changing with respect to time; (2) the rate of change of one economic quantity with respect to another—problems involving the adjective "marginal"; and (3) velocity and acceleration problems.

   Problems in one category may seem quite different from those in another category.   But this difference is superficial and is due to the terminology involved.   Try to discover similarities in the problems.   The key to this lies in the Practice Problems.   Remember to use the practice problems correctly.   Try to answer all four problems yourself before you look at the solutions.

1. **a.** For $f(x) = 4x^2$, the average rate of change of $f(x)$ over the interval 1 to 2 is

$$\frac{f(2) - f(1)}{2 - 1} = \frac{4(2)^2 - 4(1)^2}{2 - 1} = \frac{16 - 4}{1} = 12.$$

On the interval 1 to 1.5, the average rate of change is

$$\frac{f(1.5) - f(1)}{1.5 - 1} = \frac{4(1.5)^2 - 4(1)^2}{1.5 - 1} = \frac{9 - 4}{.5} = 10.$$

On the interval 1 to 1.1:

$$\frac{f(1.1) - f(1)}{1.1 - 1} = \frac{4(1.1)^2 - 4(1)^2}{1.1 - 1} = \frac{4.84 - 4}{.1} = 8.4.$$

b. The (instantaneous) rate of change of $4x^2$ at $x = 1$ is

$$\frac{d}{dx} 4x^2 \Big|_{x=1} = 8x \Big|_{x=1} = 8(1) = 8.$$

7. The average rate of growth of $W(t) = .1t^2$ over the interval 4 to 5 is

$$\frac{W(5) - W(4)}{5 - 4} = \frac{.1(5)^2 - .1(4)^2}{5 - 4} = \frac{2.5 - 1.6}{1} = .9 \text{ g/wk.}$$

Since $W'(t) = .2t$, the instantaneous rate of growth at $t = 4$ is $W'(4) = .2(4) = .8$ grams per week.

13. This exercise, along with Exercise 17, is a key problem. It is essential that you try all five parts without looking at the text or the solutions below. If you must have help, look again at the practice problems. After you have tried Exercise 31, compare your answers with those below. Also look again at the practice problems.

a. Since velocity is the rate of change in position, the initial velocity of the rocket when $t = 0$ is $s'(0)$.

$$s(t) = 160t - 16t^2,$$

$$s'(t) = 160 - 32t,$$

$$s'(0) = 160 - 32(0) = 160.$$

So the velocity at $t = 6$ is 10 km/hr.

b. "Velocity after 2 seconds" means velocity when $t = 2$.

$$v(2) = s'(2) = 160 - 32(2) = 96 \text{ ft/sec.}$$

c. Acceleration involves the rate of change of velocity, that is, the derivative of $v(t) = 160 - 32t$.

$$a(t) = v'(t) = -32.$$

Since the distance is in feet and time is in seconds, the acceleration is -32 feet per second per second. If the units were kilometers and hours, for example, the acceleration would be measured in kilometers per hour per hour.

d. In this part the time is unknown. The rocket hits the ground when the distance above the ground is zero. So set $s'(t) = 0$ and solve for t:

$$160t - 16t^2 = 0,$$

$$16t(10 - t) = 0,$$

$$t = 0, \text{ and } t = 10.$$

The rocket slams into the ground when $t = 10$ seconds.

e. We know the time from (d). The velocity at $t = 10$ seconds is

$$v(t) = 160 - 32(10) = -160 \text{ ft/sec}.$$

A negative sign on the velocity indicates that the distance function is decreasing, that is, the rocket is falling down.

Helpful Hint: Exercise 13(e) is a good exam question. If 13(d) is not on the exam, too, here is how to analyze the problem:

1. "At what velocity" means you must find some value of the velocity. To do this you need the velocity function and some specific time t.

2. You can get the velocity function by computing $s'(t)$.

3. Since you aren't given the time, you must determine the time from the fact that the rocket has just smashed into the ground. That is, you must solve a question like #13(d), even though it may not be listed specifically on the exam.

Helpful Hint: Check with your instructor about whether your test answers for velocity and acceleration problems must include the correct units.

19. Suppose f(100) = 5000 and f'(100) = 10. Then when x is close to 100, the values of f(x) change at the rate of approximately 10 units for each unit change in x. A change in x of h units produces a change of about f'(100)h = 10h units in the values of f(x).

a. For f(101), x changes by 1 unit, so the values change by about 10 units. Thus f(101) ≈ f(100) + 10 = 5010.

b. For f(100.5), x increases by h = .5, so the values of f(x) change by about .5(10) units. Thus f(100.5) ≈ f(100) + 5 = 5005.

c. For f(99), x changes by h = -1 unit, so the values of f(x) change by about -1(10) units. That is, f(99) ≈ f(100) + (-10) = 4990.

d. For f(98), h = -2 unit and

   f(98) ≈ f(100) + (-2)(10) = 5000 - 20 = 4090.

e. For f(99.75), h = -.25 unit and
   f(99.75) ≈ f(100) + (-.25)(10) = 5000 - 2.5 = 4997.5.

25. The equation C(50) = 5000 says that the cost of manufacturing 50 bicycles per day is $5000.

The equation C'(50) = 45 says that the *marginal* cost of manufacturing 50 bicycles per day is $45 per bicycle. That is, at a production level of 50 bicycles per day, the cost of production will increase by about 45 dollars when production is raised to 51 bicycles per day.

The cost of producing 52 bicycles per day is about 5000 + 2(45) = $5090.

31. a. 1987 corresponds to t = 7 years after 1980. The y-coordinate of the point on the graph where t = 7 is 500, so about 500 billion dollars were spent in 1987.

b. The *rate* of expenditures is given by the graph of f'(t). The y-coordinate of the point on this graph where t = 7 is about 40. So expenditures were rising at the rate of about 40 billion dollars per year.

c. A question that asks "when" requires us to find an appropriate value of t. Since the question involves expenditures, we look at the graph of f(t). An expenditure of one trillion (which is one thousand billion) dollars corresponds to the point on the graph of f(t) whose y-coordinate is 1000. This appears to be (14, 1000). That is, the expenditures reached one thousand billion in 1994, about 14 years after 1980.

d. This question involves the *rate* of expenditures, so we look at the graph of f'(t). Rates of expenditures are the *y*-coordinates on the graph. The rate of $100 billion per year occurs at the point on the graph of f(t) whose *y*-coordinate is 100, which seems to be the point (15, 100). Thus, the rate of 100 billion per year occured in 1995, 15 years after 1980.

Review of Chapter 1

The derivative is presented in three different ways. The derivative is defined *geometrically* in Section 1.3.

> The derivative of f(x) is a function f'(x) whose value at x = a gives the slope of the graph of f(x) at x = a.

The secant-line approximation describes how derivative formulas are obtained. This is made more precise in Section 1.4 when the derivative is defined *analytically* as the limit of difference quotients.

$$f'(a) = \lim_{h \to 0} \frac{f(a + h) - f(a)}{h}$$

Finally, in Section 1.8 the derivative is described *operationally* as the rate of change of a function. Your review of Chapter 1 should include an attempt to see how these three aspects of the derivative concept are related. At the same time, of course, you should review the basic techniques for *calculating* derivatives (Sections 1.6 and 1.7). The supplementary exercises will help here. Some instructors tend to look at them when they prepare exams. Finally, don't forget to review Section 1.1.

Chapter 1: Supplementary Exercises

1. Use the point-slope equation $y - y_1 = m(x - x_1)$, with $(x_1, y_1) = (0,3)$ and $m = -2$. That is,

$$y - 3 = -2(x - 0),$$

or

$$y = -2x + 3.$$

To graph this line, first plot the y-intercept (0,3). Then move one unit to the right and then two units in the negative y-direction. The new point (1,1) will also be on the line. Draw the straight line through these two points. (See sketch in the answer section of the text.)

7. Apply Slope Property 2 with $(x_1, y_1) = (-1, 4)$ and $(x_2, y_2) = (3, 7)$. The slope of the line is

$$\frac{y_2 - y_1}{x_2 - x_1} = \frac{7 - 4}{3 - (-1)} = \frac{3}{4}.$$

Now setting $(x_1, y_1) = (-1, 4)$ and $m = \frac{3}{4}$ in the point-slope equation of a line, we have

$$y - 4 = \frac{3}{4}(x - (-1)),$$

or

$$y = \frac{3}{4}x + \frac{19}{4}.$$

To graph this line plot the points $(-1, 4)$ and $(3, 7)$ and then draw the straight line through these two points. (See sketch in the answer section of the text.)

13. The y-axis has the equation $x = 0$. (See the graph in the text.)

19. $\frac{d}{dx}\left(\frac{3}{x}\right) = \frac{d}{dx}(3 \cdot x^{-1}) = 3 \cdot \frac{d}{dx}(x^{-1})$ (Constant-multiple rule)

$$= 3(-1)x^{-2} = -3x^{-2}, \text{ or } -\frac{3}{x^2}.$$

25. $\frac{d}{dx}\sqrt{x^2 + 1} = \frac{d}{dx}(x^2 + 1)^{1/2}$

$$= \frac{1}{2}(x^2 + 1)^{-1/2} \cdot \frac{d}{dx}(x^2 + 1)$$ (Gen. power rule)

$$= \frac{1}{2}(x^2 + 1)^{-1/2}(2x) = x(x^2 + 1)^{-1/2}$$

$$= \frac{x}{\sqrt{x^2 + 1}}.$$

31. If $f(x) = [x^5 - (x - 1)^5]^{10}$, then

$$f'(x) = 10[x^5 - (x - 1)^5]^9 \cdot \frac{d}{dx}[x^5 - (x - 1)^5]$$
                                    (Gen. power rule)

$$= 10[x^5 - (x - 1)^5]^9 \left[\frac{d}{dx}(x^5) - \frac{d}{dx}(x - 1)^5\right]$$
                                    (Sum rule)

1-25

$$= 10[x^5 - (x - 1)^5]^9[5x^4 - 5(x - 1)^4 \cdot \frac{d}{dx}(x - 1)]$$

(Gen. power rule)

$$= 10[x^5 - (x - 1)^5]^9[5x^4 - 5(x - 1)^4].$$

37. If $h(x) = \frac{3}{2}x^{3/2} - 6x^{2/3}$, then

$$h'(x) = \frac{3}{2} \cdot \frac{d}{dx}(x^{3/2}) - 6 \cdot \frac{d}{dx}(x^{2/3})$$

$$= \frac{3}{2}\left(\frac{3}{2}\right)x^{1/2} - 6\left(\frac{2}{3}\right)x^{-1/3}$$

$$= \frac{9}{4}x^{1/2} - 4x^{-1/3}.$$

43. If $f(x) = x^{5/2}$, then

$$f'(x) = \frac{5}{2}x^{3/2}$$

and

$$f''(x) = \left(\frac{5}{2}\right)\left(\frac{3}{2}\right)x^{1/2} = \frac{15}{4}\sqrt{x}.$$

Hence $f''(4) = \frac{15}{4}\sqrt{4} = \frac{15}{4}(2) = \frac{15}{2}.$

49. $\frac{d}{dP}(\sqrt{1 - 3P}) = \frac{d}{dP}(1 - 3P)^{1/2}$

$$= \frac{1}{2}(1 - 3P)^{-1/2} \cdot \frac{d}{dP}(1 - 3P) \quad \text{(Gen. power rule)}$$

$$= \frac{1}{2}(1 - 3P)^{-1/2}(-3)$$

$$= -\frac{3}{2}(1 - 3P)^{-1/2}.$$

55. $\frac{d}{dt}(t^3 + 2t^2 - t) = \frac{d}{dt}(t^3) + 2 \cdot \frac{d}{dt}(t^2) - \frac{d}{dt}(t)$

$$= 3t^2 + 4t - 1.$$

$$\frac{d^2}{dt^2}(t^3 + 2t - t) = \frac{d}{dt}(3t^2 + 4t - 1) = 6t + 4.$$

$$\left.\frac{d^2}{dt^2}(t^3 + 2t - t)\right|_{t=-1} = 6(-1) + 4 = -2.$$

61. The slope of the graph of $y = x^2$ at the point (x,y) is $2x$, hence the slope of the tangent line at $\left(\frac{3}{2}, \frac{9}{4}\right)$ is $2\left(\frac{3}{2}\right) = 3$. Let $(x_1, y_1) = \left(\frac{3}{2}, \frac{9}{4}\right)$ and $m = 3$ and use the point-slope equation for the tangent line to get

$$y - \frac{9}{4} = 3\left(x - \frac{3}{2}\right),$$

or

$$y = 3x - \frac{9}{4}.$$

Now sketch the curve $y = x^2$ by plotting a few points, including the point $\left(\frac{3}{2}, \frac{9}{4}\right)$. Move one unit to the right of $\left(\frac{3}{2}, \frac{9}{4}\right)$ and then 3 units in the positive y-direction to reach another point on the tangent line. Draw the straight line through these two points. (See the answer section of the text.)

Helpful Hint: Make sure you can work Exercises 61 and 63 without any help. Make a note to work 63 later when you have not just finished reading this study guide. If you need help, see the solutions of Exercise 23 in Section 1.2 and Exercise 43 in Section 1.6.

67. $s(t) = -16t^2 + 32t + 128,$ (height of binoculars)

  $s'(t) = -32t + 32.$ (velocity of binoculars)

To answer the question "How fast ..." we must give the value of the velocity, $s'(t)$. But at what time? The time is identified only by the phrase, "when they hit the ground." Can we describe this time using $s(t)$ or $s'(t)$? Yes, since $s(t) = 0$ when the binoculars are on the ground. So we set $s(t)$ equal to zero and solve to find the time when this happens.

$$-16t^2 + 32t + 128 = 0,$$
$$-16(t^2 - 2t - 8) = 0,$$
$$-16(t - 4)(t + 2) = 0.$$

Thus $t - 4 = 0$ or $t + 2 = 0$, so that $t = 4$ or $t = -2$. We discard the possibility $t = -2$ because the appropriate domain for the function $s(t)$ is $t \geq 0$. The binoculars hit the ground when $t = 4$ seconds, and their velocity at that time is $s'(4) = -32(4) + 32 = -128 + 32 = -96$ feet per second.   The negative sign indicates that the distance above the ground is decreasing.   So the binoculars are *falling* at the rate of 96 feet per second.

Helpful Hint: Exercise 67 is a typical exam question.   The solution require two steps—finding t = 4 and computing s'(4). Students who miss this problem usually try to work the problem in one step and don't know where to begin.

73. a. $C(x) = .1x^3 - 6x^2 + 136x + 200,$

$C(21) = .1(21)^3 - 6(21)^2 + 136(21) + 200 = 1336.1,$

$C(20) = .1(20)^3 - 6(20)^2 + 136(20) + 200 = 1320.0,$

$C(21) - C(20) = 1336.1 - 1320.0 = 16.1$ dollars.

This is the extra cost of raising the production from 20 to 21 units.

b. The true marginal cost involves the derivative:

$$C'(x) = .3x^2 - 12x + 136,$$
$$C'(20) = .3(20)^2 - 12(20) + 136$$
$$= 16.0 \text{ dollars per unit.}$$

79. $x^2 - 8x + 16 = (x - 4)^2,$ so

$$\lim_{x \to 4} \frac{x - 4}{x^2 - 8x + 16} = \lim_{x \to 4} \frac{x - 4}{(x - 4)^2} = \lim_{x \to 4} \frac{1}{x - 4},$$

which does not exist since the denominator is 0 at x = 4 and $\frac{1}{0}$ is not defined.

Chapter 2

Applications of the Derivative

This chapter culminates with one of the most powerful applications of the derivative—the solution of optimization problems. Although graphs play a key role in these problems, graphs are important in their own right. Sections 2.1 and 2.2 provide the background for the key topics covered in the remaining sections of the chapter.

2.1 Describing Graphs of Functions

The terms defined in this section are used throughout the text. The words *maximum* and *minimum* are used to refer to both points and values of a function. When referring to a point, they are usually preceded with the word "relative." When referring to values, "maximum value" means the largest value that the function assumes on its domain, and "minimum value" means the smallest value the function assumes on its domain.

1. Functions a, e, and f are increasing for all x since the graphs rise as we move along them from left to right.

7. Since the graph is superimposed on graph paper, we see that $(0,2)$ is a relative minimum point, $(1,3)$ is an inflection point, and $(2,4)$ is a relative maximum point. Therefore, the key features of the graph are as follows:

   (a) Decreasing for $x < 0$.
   (b) Relative minimum point at $x = 0$.
   (c) Increasing for $0 < x < 2$.
   (d) Relative maximum point at $x = 2$.
   (e) Decreasing for $x > 2$.
   (f) Concave up for $x < 1$, concave down for $x > 1$.
   (g) Inflection point at $(1,3)$.
   (h) y-intercept $(0,2)$, x-intercept at about $(3.6,0)$.

13. Take an arbitrary point on the left-hand side of the graph, say x = -5, and gradually increase its value. We see initially that the slope to the graph is negative. As x increases from -5 to x = -2 this slope becomes less negative; i.e., it increases until finally at the point (-2,-2) the slope is zero. This point is the relative minimum. Continuing, as x goes from -2 to x = 2, the slope is positive and increases. So in conclusion, the graph is concave up for all x ≠ -2, hence there are no inflection points.

19.

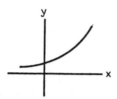

It is clear that both f(x) and its slope increase as x increases, because the curve is rising and it lies above the tangent line at each point.

25.

31. The graph is concave down from t = 1920 to t = 1960 and concave up from t = 1960 to t = 1990. The term "decreasing most rapidly" means, graphically, the place of maximum negative slope, and this occurs at the inflection point; i.e., when t = 1960. Translating, the number of farms was decreasing most rapidly when t = 1960.

37.

$$y = \tfrac{3}{7}x + 5$$

43. Set $Y_1 = 1/(X^3 - 2X^2 + X - 2)$, specify the window [0,4] by [-15,15], and graph the function. Use TRACE to determine the value of x at which the vertical asymptote occurs. You should obtain x = 2.

2.2 The First and Second Derivative Rules

The exercises in this section provide a warm-up to the problem of sketching the graphs of functions. Here we gain insights into the types of questions to ask in order to determine the main features of the graph of a given function.

Examples 3, 4, and 5 discuss important relations between the graphs of f(x) and f'(x). Study the examples carefully. The discussion in Example 5(e) shows that if the graph of f'(x) is decreasing and crosses the x-axis at, say, x = 4, then f(x) has a relative maximum at x = 4. Similarly, if the graph of f'(x) is increasing and crosses the x-axis at, say, x = a, then f(x) has a relative minimum at x = a (because the values of f'(x) change from negative to positive at x = a and so the graph of f(x) changes from decreasing to increasing at x = a).

1. If a function has a positive first derivative for all x, the First Derivative Rule tells us that the function is increasing for all values of x. This is true of graphs b, c, and f.

7. The only specific point on the graph is (2,1). We plot this point and then use the fact that f'(2) = 0 to sketch the tangent line at x = 2. Since the graph is concave up, the point (2,1) must be a minimum point. Since it is con-cave up for all x, there are no other relative extreme points or inflection points.

13. f(3) = 4 ⇒ (3,4) on the graph.
    f'(3) = -1/2, so the slope of the graph at (3,4) is -1/2.
    f"(3) = 5 > 0 ⇒ the graph is concave up at x = 3.

19.

	f	f′	f″
A	POS	POS	NEG
B	0	NEG	0
C	NEG	0	POS

25. Look at the point (6,2) on the graph of f′(x). Since the the y-coordinate of that point is positive, the *slope* of the graph of f(x) is positive at x = 6. So f(x) is increasing at x = 6, by the first derivative rule.

31. At *x* = 1, the graph of f′(x) appears to have a relative maximum. That is, the graph of f′(x) changes from increasing to decreasing at *x* = 1. An increasing derivative means that the graph of the original function f(x) is concave up; a decreasing derivative means that the graph of f(x) is concave down. So the graph of f(x) changes at x = 1 from concave up to concave down, which means that f(x) has an inflection point at x = 1.

Helpful Hint: To find values of x at which f(x) has a relative extreme point, look for places at which the graph of f′(x) *crosses* the x-axis. To find values of x at which f(x) has an inflection point, look for places at which the graph of f′(x) has a relative extreme point. If you are asked to do this on an exam, be sure that you can justify your answers, as in the discussions of Exercises 25 and 31 (above).

37. a. If *h*′(100) = 1/3, then at time t = 100, the water level is rising at the rate of 1/3 inch per hour. In a half-hour, the water will rise about half that much, namely, 1/6 inch.

   b. The conditions *h*′(100) = 2 and *h*″(100) = -5 say that the water is rising, but the *rate* of rise is declining since the derivative of the rate function is negative. That's good news, because the river may not rise much higher. However, condition (ii), *h*′(100) = -2, says that the water level is falling, which is even better news.

Helpful Hint: Exercises 43 and 44 will help you learn how to extract information from graphs of a function and its derivatives. When you look at the graph of f(t), you see how it increases or decreases and how the graph "bends." When you look at a graph of f′(t) or f″(t), focus mainly on the y-coordinates of various points, not on the shapes of the graph.

43. **a.** The number of farms is described by the graph of f(t). The year 1990 corresponds to t = 65 (years after 1925), and the point (65,2) appears to be on the graph of f(t). So there were about 2 million farms in 1995.

b. The *rate* of change in the number of farms is described by f′(t). When t = 65, f′(65) is slightly lower than -.02. Thus in 1990, the number of farms is decreasing (because f′(65) is negative) at the rate of about .02 million per year, that is, at the rate of about 20,000 farms per year.

c. 6 million farms corresponds to the point on the graph of f(t) whose y-coordinate is 6. This point is approximately (5,6), which means that there were about 6 million farms in 1930.

d. Here a rate is given and the question is "when?" The answer is found from the graph of f′(t), by looking for the value of t that corresponds to the given rate of -60,000 farms per year, that is, -.06 million farms per year. The rate is negative because the number of farms is declining. There are two such values of t, namely, 20 and about 52, which correspond to 1945 and 1977.

e. The number of farms is declining the fastest when the rate is the most negative. This corresponds to the inflection point on the graph of f(t), but that point is hard to find. Looking at the graph of f′(t), you might guess that the minimum rate occurs at about t = 35. To be certain, look at f″(t), because the minimum of f′(t) occurs where *its* derivative crosses the t-axis. This happens at t = 35 (that is, 35 years after 1925). Thus the number of farms was declining the fastest in 1960.

2.3 Curve Sketching (Introduction)

The curves sketched in this section will look like one of the curves shown on the right or one of these curves turned upside down. The first type of curve is called a *parabola* and is the graph of a quadratic function. The second curve is called a *cubic* and is the graph of a certain type of cubic polynomial. The purpose of this section is to apply the first and second derivative rules to find the graphs of functions. Therefore, you should not automatically assume that the graph will be one of those on the right, but should reason its shape from the two derivative rules. For instance, every time that you claim that a point is an extreme point, you should determine the value of the second derivative at that point and draw your conclusion from the second derivative test. Later in the text, we will graph functions about which we have no prior information.

1. $f(x) = 2x^2 - 8$,

   $f'(x) = 4x$,

   $f''(x) = 4$.

   Set $f'(x) = 0$ and solve for x.   If $4x = 0$ then $x = 0$. Substitute this value for x back into $f(x)$ to find the y value for this extreme point.

$$f(0) = 2(0)^2 - 8 = -8.$$

   The extreme point is $(0,-8)$.   Since $f''(0) = 4$, which is positive, the graph of $f(x)$ is concave up at $x = 0$.   A graph of this function is shown in the answer section of the text.

7. $f(x) = -x^2 - 8x - 10$,

   $f'(x) = -2x - 8$,

   $f''(x) = -2$.

   Set $f'(x) = 0$ and solve for x:

$$-2x - 8 = 0,$$

$$-2x = 8,$$

$$x = -4.$$

   Substitute this value for x back into $f(x)$ to find the y value for this extreme point.

$$f(-4) = -(-4)^2 - 8(-4) - 10$$
$$= -16 + 32 - 10 = 6.$$

The extreme point is $(-4,6)$. Since $f''(-4) = -2$, which is negative, the graph of $f(x)$ is concave down at $x = -4$. See the text's answer section for the graph of $f(x)$.

13. $f(x) = -\frac{1}{9}x^3 + x^2 + 9x,$

$f'(x) = -\frac{1}{3}x^2 + 2x + 9,$

$f''(x) = -\frac{2}{3}x + 2.$

Set $f'(x) = 0$ and solve for x:

$$-\frac{1}{3}x^2 + 2x + 9 = 0.$$

Multiplying both sides of the equation by -3, we obtain

$$x^2 - 6x - 27 = 0,$$
$$(x + 3)(x - 9) = 0,$$
$$x = -3, \text{ or } x = 9.$$

Substitute these values of x back into $f(x)$ to find the y values for these possible relative extreme points:

$$f(-3) = -\frac{1}{9}(-3)^3 + (-3)^2 + 9(-3) = 3 + 9 - 27 = -15.$$
$$f(9) = -\frac{1}{9}(9)^3 + (9)^2 + 9(9) = -81 + 81 + 81 = 81.$$

The possible extreme points are $(-3,-15)$ and $(9,81)$. Now

$$f''(-3) = -\frac{2}{3}(-3) + 2 = 2 + 2 = 4 > 0.$$
$$f''(9) = -\frac{2}{3}(9) + 2 = -6 + 2 = -4 < 0.$$

The graph of $f(x)$ is concave up at $x = -3$ and concave down at $x = 9$, hence $(-3,-15)$ is a relative minimum point and $(9,81)$ is a relative maximum point. See the graph in the answer section of the text.

19. $y = 1 + 3x^2 - x^3,$

$y' = 6x - 3x^2,$

$y'' = 6 - 6x.$

Set $y' = 0$ and solve for x:

$$6x - 3x^2 = 0, \quad x(6 - 3x) = 0,$$
$$x = 0, \text{ or } x = 2.$$

Use these values for x to find the y values of the possible relative extreme points:

At $x = 0$, $y = 1 + 3(0)^2 - (0)^3 = 1$.

At $x = 2$, $y = 1 + 3(2)^2 - (2)^3 = 1 + 12 - 8 = 5$.

The possible relative extreme points are $(0,1)$ and $(2,5)$. Next, check the second derivative.

At $x = 0$, $y'' = 6 - 6(0) = 6$ (graph concave up).

At $x = 2$, $y'' = 6 - 6(2) = -6$ (graph concave down).

So the function has a relative minimum at $x = 0$ and a relative maximum at $x = 2$. Since the concavity reverses somewhere between $x = 0$ and $x = 2$, there must be at least one inflection point. To find this point set $y'' = 0$:

$$6 - 6x = 0,$$

$$x = 1.$$

Substitute $x = 1$ into the function to find the y value for this inflection point.

$$y = 1 + 3(1)^2 - (1)^3 = 1 + 3 - 1 = 3.$$

The inflection point is $(1,3)$. See the graph in the answer section of the text.

25. $f(x) = ax^2 + bx + c$, $a \neq 0$,
      $f'(x) = 2ax + b$,
      $f''(x) = 2a$.

Since $a \neq 0$, $f''(x)$ is never zero. Since the second derivative of a function must be zero at an inflection point, $f(x)$ has no inflection points.

31. $f(x) = 5x^2 + x - 3$,
      $f'(x) = 10x + 1$,
      $f''(x) = 10$.

Set $f'(x) = 0$ and solve for x:

$$10x + 1 = 0,$$

$$10x = -1,$$

$$x = -.1.$$

Substitute this value for x back into $f(x)$ to find the y value for this relative extreme point.

$$f(-.1) = 5(-.1)^2 + (-.1) - 3 = .05 - .10 - 3.00 = -3.05$$

Since $f''(-.1) = 10$, which is positive, the graph is concave up at $x = -.1$ and hence $(-.1, -3.05)$ is a relative minimum point.

37. a. Solve f(t) = 10 for t. Start at 10 on the y-axis, move
to the right to the graph of y = f(t), and move down to
reach 4 on the t-axis. Therefore, f(4) = 10. So 10% of
the homes had a VCR in 1984.

b. Since 1990 is 10 years after 1980, the answer is f(10),
which is 70. Therefore, 70% of homes had a VRC in 1990.

c. The percentage of VCRs are growing at the greatest rate
where f'(t) has a maximum, at the inflection point on
the graph of f(t). The inflection point occurs where
f"(t) = 0. From the graph, f"(7) = 0, so the maximum
rate of growth occurs in 1987.
   To answer the question about the percentage of
homes that had VCRs, look at the graph of f(t). Since
f(7) = 40, 40% of the homes had VCRs in 1987.

2.4 Curve Sketching (Conclusion)

The two most important types of curves
that are graphed in this section are the
cubics without relative extreme points
(such as the first curve or the upside
down version of this curve) and the
curves with asymptotes. These curves are
stressed since, along with the curves
considered in Section 2.3, they occur
frequently in applications. However,
there are a few other types of curves
that occur in the exercises. As previously, all reasoning should be based on
the first and second derivative tests.

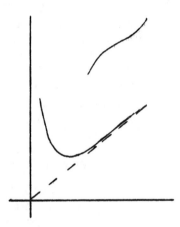

1. To find the x-intercepts of the function $y = x^2 - 3x + 1$,
use the quadratic formula to find the values of x for
which f(x) = 0:

$$y = x^2 - 3x + 1 \quad (a = 1, \ b = -3, \ c = 1),$$

$$b^2 - 4ac = (-3)^2 - 4 \cdot 1 \cdot 1 = 5,$$

$$x = \frac{-(-3) \pm \sqrt{5}}{2 \cdot 1} = \frac{3 \pm \sqrt{5}}{2}.$$

Therefore, the x-intercepts are $\left(\frac{3+\sqrt{5}}{2}, 0\right)$ and $\left(\frac{3-\sqrt{5}}{2}, 0\right)$.

7. If $f(x) = \frac{1}{3}x^3 - 2x^2 + 5x$, then

$$f'(x) = x^2 - 4x + 5.$$

If we apply the quadratic formula to $f'(x)$ with $a = 1$, $b = -4$, and $c = 5$, we find that $b^2 - 4ac = (-4)^2 - 4 \cdot 1 \cdot 5 = -4$, a negative number. Since we cannot take the square root of a negative number, there are no values of x for which $f'(x) = 0$. Hence $f(x)$ has no relative extreme points.

13. $f(x) = 5 - 13x + 6x^2 - x^3$,

$f'(x) = -13 + 12x - 3x^2$,

$f''(x) = 12 - 6x$.

If we apply the quadratic formula to $f'(x)$, we find that

$$b^2 - 4ac = (12)^2 - 4(-3)(-13) = 144 - 156 = -12,$$

which is negative. Since we cannot take the square root of a negative number, there are no values of x for which $f'(x) = 0$. So $f(x)$ has no relative extreme points. If we evaluate $f'(x)$ at some x, say $x = 0$, we see that the first derivative is negative, and so $f(x)$ is decreasing there. Since the graph of $f(x)$ is a smooth curve with no relative extreme points and no breaks, $f(x)$ must be decreasing for all x. Now, to check the concavity of $f(x)$, we must find where $f''(x)$ is negative, positive, or zero.

$$f''(x) = 12 - 6x = 6(2 - x) \quad \text{is:}$$

$\qquad$ positive if $x < 2$, $\qquad$ (graph is concave up)
$\qquad$ negative if $x > 2$, $\qquad$ (graph is concave down)
$\qquad$ zero if $x = 2$. $\qquad$ (concavity reverses)

The inflection point is $(2, f(2)) = (2, -5)$. The y-intercept is $(0, f(0)) = (0, 5)$. To further improve the sketch of the graph, first sketch the tangent line at the inflection point. To do this compute the slope of the graph at $(2, -5)$.

$$f'(2) = -13 + 12(2) - 3(2)^2 = -1.$$

To sketch the graph, plot the inflection point and the y-intercept, draw the tangent line at $(2, -5)$, and then draw a curve that has this tangent line and is decreasing for all x, is concave down for $x > 2$, and concave up for $x < 2$. See the graph in the answer section of the text.

19. $f(x) = x^4 - 6x^2,$

$f'(x) = 4x^3 - 12x,$

$f''(x) = 12x^2 - 12.$

To find possible relative extreme points, set $f'(x) = 0$ and solve for x:

$$4x^3 - 12x = 0,$$
$$4x(x^2 - 3) = 0,$$
$$4x(x - \sqrt{3})(x + \sqrt{3}) = 0,$$
$$x = 0, \text{ or } x = \pm\sqrt{3}.$$

Substitute these values into f(x) to find the y values for these possible relative extreme points:

$$f(0) = (0)^4 - 6(0)^2 = 0,$$
$$f(\sqrt{3}) = (\sqrt{3})^4 - 6(\sqrt{3})^2 = -9,$$
$$f(-\sqrt{3}) = (-\sqrt{3})^4 - 6(-\sqrt{3})^2 = -9.$$

The points are $(0,0)$, $(\sqrt{3},-9)$, and $(-\sqrt{3},-9)$.

Now $f''(0) = 12(0)^2 - 12 = -12$. Therefore, $f(x)$ is concave down at $x = 0$ and $(0,0)$ is a relative maximum point. For the other two points, we compute

$$f''(-\sqrt{3}) = 12(-\sqrt{3})^2 - 12 = 12(3) - 12 = 24,$$
$$f''(\sqrt{3}) = 12(\sqrt{3})^2 - 12 = 12(3) - 12 = 24.$$

Hence $f(x)$ is concave up at $x = -\sqrt{3}$ and $x = \sqrt{3}$, and so $(\sqrt{3},-9)$ and $(-\sqrt{3},-9)$ are relative minimum points. The concavity of this function reverses twice, so there must be at least two inflection points. To find these set $f''(x) = 0$ and solve for x:

$$12x^2 - 12 = 0,$$
$$x^2 - 1 = 0,$$
$$(x - 1)(x + 1) = 0, \text{ or } x = \pm1.$$

The corresponding y-values are given by

$$f(1) = (1)^4 - 6(1)^2 = -5,$$
$$f(-1) = (-1)^4 - 6(-1)^2 = -5.$$

The inflection points are $(1,-5)$ and $(-1,-5)$. See the graph in the answer section of the text.

25. $y = \dfrac{9}{x} + x + 1, \quad x > 0$

$y' = -\dfrac{9}{x^2} + 1,$

$y'' = \dfrac{18}{x^3}.$

Set $y' = 0$ and solve for x:

$$-\dfrac{9}{x^2} + 1 = 0,$$

$$1 = \dfrac{9}{x^2} \quad \text{(Multiply both sides by } x^2\text{.)}$$

$$x^2 = 9,$$

$$x = 3. \quad \text{(Note: We are only considering } x > 0.\text{)}$$

When $x = 3$, $y = \dfrac{9}{3} + 3 + 1 = 7$, and

$$y'' = \dfrac{18}{3^3} > 0 \quad \text{(concave up).}$$

Therefore, $(3,7)$ is a relative minimum point. Since y'' can never be 0, there are no inflection points. The term $\dfrac{9}{x}$ in the function y tells us that the y-axis is an asymptote. Also, as x gets large, the graph of y gets arbitrarily close to the straight line $y = x + 1$. Therefore, $y = x + 1$ is an asymptote of the graph. See the graph in the answer section of the text.

Helpful Hint: In general, $f'(a) = 0$ does not necessarily mean that $f(x)$ has an extreme point at $x = a$. Also, $f''(a) = 0$ does not necessarily mean that $f(x)$ has an inflection point at $x = a$. However, if $f(x)$ is quadratic or of the form $kx + \dfrac{k}{x} + c$, then $f'(a) = 0$ guarantees an extreme point at $x = a$. (Neither of these two types of functions has inflection points.) If $f(x)$ is a cubic polynomial, then there is one inflection point and it occurs where the second derivative is zero. (*Note:* These observations will help you in checking your work. On exams, you must still show that extreme and inflection points have the properties you claim.)

31. $g(x) = f'(x)$,
because $f(x)$ has 2 relative minima and a relative maximum and $g(x) = 0$ for these values of x.

$f(x) \neq g'(x)$.
To see this, look at the relative maximum of $g(x)$. Since $f(x)$ is not zero for this value of x, $f(x) \neq g'(x)$.

2.5 Optimization Problems

The procedure for solving an optimization problem can be thought of as consisting of the following two primary parts.

    (a) Find the function to be minimized.
    (b) Make a rough sketch of the graph of the function.

Part (a) is new to this section and requires careful reading of the problem. Part (b) relies on techniques presented in Sections 2.3 and 2.4. However, certain shortcuts can be taken when sketching curves in this section. For instance, if we only want to find the x-coordinate of a relative extreme point, we can make a very rough estimate of the y-coordinate when sketching the curve.

    One of the common mistakes that students make when working optimization problems on exams is to just set the first derivative equal to 0 and solve for x. They forget to apply the second derivative test at the value of x found.

1. $g(x) = 10 + 40x - x^2$,
      $g'(x) = 40 - 2x$,
      $g''(x) = -2$.

    The graph is obtained by the curve-sketching technique of Section 2.3.

    Therefore, the maximum value of $g(x)$ occurs at $x = 20$.

7.   **a.** See drawing in answer section of the text.

    b. The girth of the box is given by $x + x + x + x = 4x$. The equation for the length plus the girth is

$$h + 4x.$$

    c. The equation for volume, which we wish to maximize, is the objective equation,

$$V = x^2 h.$$

    The constraint equation is

$$h + 4x = 84,$$

    or

$$h = 84 - 4x.$$

    d. Substituting $h = 84 - 4x$ into the objective equation, we have

$$V = x^2(84 - 4x) = -4x^3 + 84x^2.$$

e. By making a rough sketch of the graph of $V = -4x^3 + 84x^2$, we can find the value of x corresponding to the greatest volume.

$$V' = -12x^2 + 168x,$$

$$V'' = -24x + 168.$$

Solve $V' = 0$:

$$-12x^2 + 168x = 0,$$

$$x^2 - 14x = 0,$$

$$x(x - 14) = 0,$$

$$x = 0, \text{ or } x = 14.$$

V'' is positive at $x = 0$ and negative at $x = 14$. Therefore V has a relative minimum at $x = 0$ and a relative maximum at $x = 14$. When $x = 0$, $V = 0$. When $x = 14$, $V = -4(14)^3 + 84(14)^2 = 5488$. The sketch of the graph shows that the maximum value of V occurs when $x = 14$. From the constraint equation, $h = 84 - 4(14) = 28$.

13. The problem asks that total area be maximized. Let A be the area, let x be the length of the fence parallel to the river, and let y the length of each section perpendicular to the river. The objective equation gives an expression for A in terms of the other variables:

$$A = xy \qquad \text{(Objective equation)}.$$

The cost of the fence parallel to the river is $6x$ dollars (x feet at $6 per foot) and the cost of the three sections perpendicular to the river is $3 \cdot 5y$ or $15y$ dollars. Since $1500 is available to build the fence, we must have

$$6x + 15y = 1500 \qquad \text{(Constraint equation)}.$$

Solving for y,

$$15y = -6x + 1500,$$

$$y = -\frac{2}{5}x + 100.$$

Substituting this expression for y into the objective equation, we obtain

$$A = x\left(-\frac{2}{5}x + 100\right) = -\frac{2}{5}x^2 + 100x.$$

(125, 6250)

The graph of $A = -\frac{2}{5}x^2 + 100x$ is easily obtained by our curve sketching techniques. The maximum value occurs when $x = 125$. Substituting into $y = -\frac{2}{5}x + 100$, this gives us $y = -\frac{2}{5}(125) + 100 = 50$. Therefore, the optimum dimensions are $x = 125$, $y = 50$.

19. $x = 20 - \frac{w}{2}$ (from the constraint equation).

$A = wx$ (the objective function).

Therefore:

$$A = w\left(20 - \frac{w}{2}\right) = -\frac{w^2}{2} + 20w \text{ (has a parabola shape)},$$

$$\frac{dA}{dw} = -\frac{2w}{2} + 20 = -w + 20.$$

A relative minimum or maximum occurs when $\frac{dA}{dw} = 0$. Hence $-w + 20 = 0 \Rightarrow w = 20$. (Since $x = 20 - \frac{w}{2}$, $x = 10$.) The next question is whether this is a relative maximum. Thus, looking at the second derivative:

$$\frac{d^2A}{dw^2} = -1 < 0,$$

this means that $w = 20$ is a relative max. To sketch the graph of A we see that $A = 0$ when $w = 0$ and when $x = 0$: $20 - \frac{w}{2} = 0 \Rightarrow \frac{w}{2} = 20$, or $w = 40$. At $w = 20$,

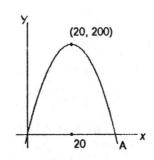

(20, 200)

$$A = 20\left(20 - \frac{20}{2}\right)$$
$$= 200.$$

2.6 Further Optimization Problems

The exercises in this section are of four types.

(a) Variations of the types of exercises considered in Section 2.5.

(b) Inventory problems. These problems have the same constraint equation, $r \cdot x$ = [number of items used or manufactured during the year], and similar objective equations, [costs] = ...

(c) Orchard problems (that is, problems similar to the first practice problem or to Example 1). These problems have the same type of objective equation, [profit or revenue] = [amount of money] · [quantity]. The constraint equations are found by reading the problem to see if [amount of money] depends on [quantity] or vice versa, and expressing the dependent variable in terms of the other.

(d) Original problems. Situations that use the same type of machinery as the examples worked in the text but require a fresh approach.

1. The quantity to be maximized is revenue, call it R. Since the problem asks for the optimum number of prints, let x be the number of prints to be offered for sale. The other quantity that varies is price per print, p. The objective equation is

[revenue] = [price per print] · [number of prints],

$$R = p \cdot x.$$

Since the price per print depends on the number of prints offered for sale, the constraint equation can be obtained by expressing p in terms of x.

[price per print] = $\begin{bmatrix} \text{original price} \\ \text{per print} \end{bmatrix}$ − $\begin{bmatrix} \text{decrease in price} \\ \text{(per print) due} \\ \text{to increase} \end{bmatrix}$.

Thus

[price per print] = 400 − (x − 50)·5

= 400 − 5x + 250

= 650 − 5x.

The decrease in price (per print) due to the increase in the number of prints was obtained by multiplying x − 50, the number of prints in excess of 50, by the price reduction for each excess print. Therefore,

$$R = px = (650 - 5x)x = 650x - 5x^2.$$

The graph of R is found by curve sketching. Its maximum value occurs when x = 65. Therefore, 65 prints should be offered for sale.

7. We let r represent the number of production runs, and x the number of microscopes manufactured per run. Hence the total number of microscopes manufactured is

$$\left[\begin{array}{c}\text{number of microscopes}\\ \text{per production run}\end{array}\right] \cdot \left[\begin{array}{c}\text{number}\\ \text{of runs}\end{array}\right] = xr.$$

Hence we have as a constraint equation

$$xr = 1600, \text{ or } x = \frac{1600}{r}.$$

We wish to minimize inventory expenses. There are three expenses which make up the total cost. The storage costs (SC), based on the maximum number of microscopes in the warehouse, will be

$$SC = 15x,$$

since the warehouse is the most full just after a run, which will produce x microscopes. Since the insurance costs are based on the average number of microscopes in the warehouse, and the average number of microscopes is given by $\frac{x}{2}$, the insurance costs (IC) are

$$IC = 20\left(\frac{x}{2}\right).$$

Each production run costs $2500, so the total production costs (PC) are given by

$$PC = 2500r.$$

Hence the objective equation is

$$C = \quad SC \quad + \quad IC \quad + \quad PC$$

$$= 2500r + 15x + 20\left(\frac{x}{2}\right)$$

$$= 2500r + 25x.$$

Substituting $x = \dfrac{1600}{r}$ into the objective equation we have,

$$C = 2500r + 25\left(\frac{1600}{r}\right)$$

$$= 2500r + \frac{40,000}{r}.$$

We use our curve sketching techniques to make a rough sketch of this function. Only positive values of r are relevant; that is, r > 0.

$$C' = 2500 - \frac{40,000}{r^2},$$

$$C'' = \frac{80,000}{r^3}.$$

Set C' = 0 and solve for r:

$$2,500 - \frac{40,000}{r^2} = 0,$$

$$2,500 = \frac{40,000}{r^2},$$

$$r^2 = \frac{40,000}{2,500} = 16, \text{ or } r = 4.$$

When r = 4, C″ > 0. There is a relative minimum at r = 4. Therefore, there should be 4 production runs.

Note: The value of C when r = 4 need not be calculated. After establishing the existence of a relative minimum point when r = 4, we can use our familiarity with graphs of functions of the form $y = \dfrac{a}{x} + bx$ to make a rough sketch.

13. Let w and x be the dimensions of the corral as shown in the text. The corral is to have an area of 54 square meters, hence the constraint equation is

$$xw = 54 \text{ or } w = \frac{54}{x} \qquad \text{(Constraint)}.$$

The total amount of fencing needed is two pieces of length x and three pieces of length w. Hence the objective equation is

$$F = 2x + 3w \qquad \text{(Objective)}.$$

Substituting $w = \frac{54}{x}$ into the objective equation we have,

$$F = 2x + 3\left(\frac{54}{x}\right) = 2x + \frac{162}{x}.$$

Using curve sketching techniques, we make a rough sketch of the graph.

$$F = 2x + \frac{162}{x}, \quad x > 0,$$

$$F' = 2 - \frac{162}{x^2},$$

$$F'' = \frac{324}{x^3}.$$

Set $F' = 0$ and solve for x:

$$2 - \frac{162}{x^2} = 0,$$

$$2 = \frac{162}{x^2},$$

$$x^2 = \frac{162}{2} = 81, \text{ or } x = 9.$$

Notice that $F'' > 0$ for all positive x, so the graph of F is concave up, and F has a relative minimum at x = 9. In fact the formula for F has the form $y = \frac{a}{x} + bx$, and so the graph has the basic shape shown at the right.

From the constraint equation we find

$$w = \frac{54}{x} = \frac{54}{9} = 6.$$

Therefore, w = 6, x = 9 are the optimum dimensions.

19. First consider the diagram at the right. Let x be the length of each edge of the square ends and h the other dimension. Since the sum of the three dimensions can be at most 120 centimeters, the constraint equation is

$$2x + h = 120, \text{ or } h = 120 - 2x.$$

Since we wish to maximize the volume of the package, the objective equation is

$$V = x^2h.$$

Substituting h = 120 - 2x into the objective equation, we have

$$V = x^2(120 - 2x) = 120x^2 - 2x^3,$$

$$V' = 240x - 6x^2,$$

$$V'' = 240 - 12x.$$

Set V' = 0 and solve for x:

$$240x - 6x^2 = 0,$$

$$6x(40 - x) = 0,$$

$$x = 0, \text{ and } x = 40.$$

Check concavity: At x = 0,

$$V'' = 420 - 12(0) = 240 > 0 \qquad \text{(graph concave up)}.$$

At x = 40,

$$V'' = 240 - 12(40) = -240 < 0 \quad \text{(graph concave down)}.$$

Therefore, the graph has a relative minimum at x = 0 and a relative maximum at x = 40.
When x = 0, V = 0; at x = 40,

$$V = 120(40)^2 - 2(40)^3 = 64,000.$$

A rough sketch of the graph

$$V = 120x^2 - 2x^3, \quad x \geq 0,$$

reveals a maximum value at x = 40. The value of h corresponding to x = 40 is found from the constraint equation

$$h = 120 - 2x = 120 - 2(40) = 40.$$

Thus to achieve maximum volume, the package should be 40cm × 40cm × 40cm.

25. First, consider the diagram at the right. The base of the window has length 2x. The area of the window is given by

$$A = 2xy = 2x(9 - x^2)$$
$$= 18x - 2x^3.$$

We now make a rough sketch of the graph of $A = 18x - 2x^3$, for $x > 0$:

$$A' = 18 - 6x^2,$$
$$A'' = -12x.$$

Set $A' = 0$:

$$18 - 6x^2 = 0,$$
$$18 = 6x^2,$$
$$3 = x^2, \text{ or } x = \sqrt{3}.$$

When $x = \sqrt{3}$, $A'' = -12(\sqrt{3})$ is negative. Therefore the graph of $A = 18x - 2x^3$ has a relative maximum value at $x = \sqrt{3}$. When $x = \sqrt{3}$,

$$A = 18\sqrt{3} - 2(\sqrt{3})^3$$
$$= 18\sqrt{3} - 2\cdot3\cdot\sqrt{3} \text{ [since } (\sqrt{3})^3$$
$$= (\sqrt{3}\cdot\sqrt{3})\cdot\sqrt{3} = 3\sqrt{3}]$$
$$= 12\sqrt{3}.$$

A rough sketch of the graph reveals a maximum value at $x = \sqrt{3}$. The height y, corresponding to $x = \sqrt{3}$ is found from the equation of the parabola

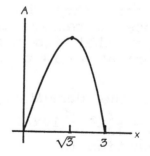

$$y = 9 = x^2$$
$$= 9(\sqrt{3})^2 = 9 - 3 = 6.$$

The window of maximum area should be 6 units high and $2\sqrt{3}$ units wide. (The value of x gives only half the width of the base of the window.)

2.7   Applications of Calculus to Business and Economics

This section, which explores cost, revenue, and profit functions, and applies calculus to the optimization of profits of a firm, is independent of the rest of the text.

1. If the cost function is

$$C(x) = x^3 - 6x^2 + 13x + 15,$$

the marginal cost function is

$$M(x) = C'(x) = 3x^2 - 12x + 13.$$

We find the minimum value of $M(x)$ by making a rough graph, a simple matter since $M(x)$ is a quadratic function.

$$M'(x) = 6x - 12,$$
$$M''(x) = 6.$$

Set $M'(x) = 0$ to locate the x where the marginal cost is minimized.

$$6x - 12 = 0$$
$$6x = 12, \text{ or } x = 2.$$

Now, $M(2) = 3(2)^2 - 12(2) + 13 = 1$ and $M''(2)$ is positive.   Therefore, $M(x)$ has a relative minimum at x = 2.   A sketch of the graph reveals a minimum value of 1.   That is, the minimum marginal cost is \$1.

Note: Sketching the graph is not absolutely necessary. Once we realize that it is a parabola opening upward, we know that its minimum value will occur where the first derivative is zero.

7. If the demand equation for the commodity is given by $p = \frac{1}{12}x^2 - 10x + 300$, $0 \le x \le 60$, then the revenue function is

$$R(x) = x \cdot p = x\left(\frac{1}{12}x^2 - 10x + 300\right) = \frac{1}{12}x^3 - 10x^2 + 300x.$$

To find the maximum value of $R(x)$ we first make a rough sketch of its graph.

$$R(x) = \frac{1}{12}x^3 - 10x^2 + 300x,$$

$$R'(x) = \frac{1}{4}x^2 - 20x + 300,$$

$$R''(x) = \frac{1}{2}x - 20.$$

Set $R'(x) = 0$ and solve for x:

$$\frac{1}{4}x^2 - 20x + 300 = 0,$$

$$x^2 - 80x + 1200 = 0, \quad \text{(multiply by 4)}$$

$$(x - 20)(x - 60) = 0,$$

$$x = 20 \text{ or } x = 60.$$

[Note: To see how to factor $x^2 - 80x + 1200$, first try to factor $x^2 - 8x + 12$.]

Now,

$$R(20) = \frac{1}{12}(20)^3 - 10(20)^2 + 300(20) = 2666 \ 2/3,$$

$$R(60) = \frac{1}{12}(60)^3 - 10(60)^2 + 300(60) = 0,$$

$$R''(20) = \frac{1}{2}(20) - 20 = -10 < 0,$$

$$R''(60) = \frac{1}{2}(60) - 20 = 10 > 0.$$

A rough sketch of the graph reveals that revenue is maximized when $x = 20$. From the demand equation,

$$p = \frac{1}{12}(20)^2 - 10(20) + 300$$

$$= 133 \ 1/3.$$

13. a. Since [profit] = [revenue] - [cost], and since revenue is given by the function

$$R(x) = x \cdot p = 60x - (10^{-5})x^2,$$

the profit function is

$$P(x) = R(x) - C(x) = (60x - (10^{-5})x^2) - (7 \cdot 10^6 + 30x)$$

$$= 30x - (10^{-5})x^2 - 7 \cdot 10^6$$

$$= -(10^{-5})x^2 + 30x - 7 \cdot 10^6.$$

The graph of $P(x)$ is a parabola opening downward [since

the coefficient of x^2 is $-(10^{-5})$, which is negative] and has its maximum value at its unique relative maximum point. Therefore, it is sufficient to solve $P'(x) = 0$ for x.

$$P'(x) = -2(10^{-5})x + 30.$$

Set $P'(x) = 0$:

$$-2(10^{-5})x + 30 = 0,$$

$$-2(10^{-5})x = -30,$$

$$x = \frac{-30}{-2(10^{-5})} = 15 \cdot 10^5.$$

At $x = 15 \cdot 10^5$ the corresponding price for a thousand kilowatt hours is

$$p = 60 - (10^{-5})(15 \cdot 10^5) = \$45.$$

b. The new profit function is given by

$$P_1(x) = R(x) - C_1(x) = 60x - (10^{-5})x^2 - (7 \cdot 10^6 + 40x)$$

$$= 20x - (10^{-5})x^2 - 7 \cdot 10^6.$$

To find the maximum value for this function we find $P_1'(x)$ and then set $P'(x) = 0$ and solve for x:

$$P_1'(x) = 20 - 2 \cdot 10^{-5}x,$$

$$20 - 2 \cdot 10^{-5}x = 0,$$

$$2 \cdot 10^{-5}x = 20, \text{ or } x = 10^6.$$

At $x = 10^6$ the corresponding price for a thousand kilowatt hours is
$$p = 60 - (10^{-5})(10^6) = \$50.$$

So the answer is no, the company should not pass all of the \$10 increase on to the consumer if it wants to maximize profit. With the new cost function the price that maximizes profit is \$50, reflecting a \$5 increase.

Chapter 2: Supplementary Exercises

The most difficult problems in this chapter are the optimization problems. These problems cannot be solved all at once, but require that you break them down into small manageable pieces. Although some of them fit into neat categories, others require patient analysis.

1. a. The graph of f(x) is increasing for values of x at which f'(x) is positive. The graph of f'(x) shows that this happens for -2 < x < 1 and x > 5. The graph of f(x) is decreasing for x < -2 and 1 < x < 5, because the values of f'(x) are negative.

    b. The graph of f(x) is concave up for values of x at which the slopes of the graph are increasing, that is, for values of x at which the graph of f'(x) is *increasing*. Be careful to distinguish between "increasing" and "positive". The graph of f'(x) is increasing for x < -1 and for x > 3, even though the values of f'(x) are not always positive there.
       The graph of f(x) is concave down for values of x at which the slopes of the graph are decreasing, that is, for values of x at which the graph of f'(x) is *decreasing*. This happens for -1 < x < 3.

7. f'(x) is positive at a and c in the sense that it is non-negative f'(x) = 0 at these points.
    f'(x) is positive at d and e and is non-zero at these points.

13. Since f(1) = 2, the graph goes through the point (1,2). Since f'(1) > 0, the graph is increasing at x = 1.

19. Since g(5) = -1, the graph goes through the point (5,-1). Since g'(5) = -2 < 0, the graph is decreasing at x = 5. The fact that g"(5) = 0 is inconclusive since it is possible for g"(x) = 0 without x being an inflection point. For example, if g(x) is a straight line, g"(x) = 0 for all x but g(x) has no inflection points.

25. If $y = x^2 + 3x - 10$, then

    $y' = 2x + 3$,

    $y" = 2$.

    Set y' = 0 and solve for x to find the relative extreme point:

    $$2x + 3 = 0,$$
    $$x = -\frac{3}{2}.$$

If $x = -\frac{3}{2}$, then $y = \left(-\frac{3}{2}\right)^2 + 3\left(-\frac{3}{2}\right) - 10 = \frac{9}{4} - \frac{9}{2} - 10 = -\frac{49}{4}$.
Since $y'' = 2 > 0$, the parabola is concave up and the point $\left(-\frac{3}{2}, -\frac{49}{4}\right)$ is a minimum. When $x = 0$, $y = 0^2 + 3(0) - 10 = -10$. Hence the y-intercept is $(0,-10)$. To find the x-intercepts, set $y = 0$ and solve for x:

$$x^2 + 3x - 10 = 0,$$

$$(x + 5)(x - 2) = 0,$$

$$x = -5 \text{ and } x = 2.$$

So the x-intercepts are $(-5,0)$ and $(2,0)$. See the graph in the answer section of the text.

31. If $y = -x^2 + 20x - 90$, then

$$y' = -2x + 20,$$

$$y'' = -2.$$

Set $y' = 0$ and solve for x to find the relative extreme point:

$$-2x + 20 = 0,$$

$$x = 10.$$

If $x = 10$, $y = -(10)^2 + 20(10) - 90 = -100 + 200 - 90 = 10$. Since $y'' = -2 < 0$, the parabola is concave down and $(10,10)$ is the relative maximum point. When $x = 0$, $y = -0^2 + 20(0) - 90 = -90$. Hence the y-intercept is $(0,-90)$. To find the x-intercept we use the quadratic formula:

$$b^2 - 4ac = (20)^2 - 4(-1)(-90) = 40,$$

$$\sqrt{b^2 - 4ac} = \sqrt{40} = \sqrt{4 \cdot 10} = \sqrt{4} \cdot \sqrt{10} = 2\sqrt{10}.$$

$$x = \frac{-20 \pm 2\sqrt{10}}{-2} = 10 \pm \sqrt{10}.$$

So the x-intercepts are $(10+\sqrt{10}, 0)$ and $(10-\sqrt{10}, 0)$. See the graph in the answer section of the text.

37. $y = \frac{11}{3} + 3x - x^2 - \frac{1}{3}x^3$,

$y' = 3 - 2x - x^2$,

$y'' = -2 - 2x$.

Set $y' = 0$ and solve for x to find the possible relative extreme points:

$$3 - 2x - x^2 = 0.$$

Multiply by -1 and rearrange terms.

$$x^2 + 2x - 3 = 0,$$

$$(x - 1)(x + 3) = 0,$$

$$x = 1, \text{ or } x = -3.$$

If $x = 1$, $y = \frac{11}{3} + 3(1) - (1)^2 - \frac{1}{3}(1)^3 = \frac{16}{3}$, and

$$y'' = -2 - 2 = -4 < 0.$$

Hence the graph is concave down and has a relative maximum at $\left(1, \frac{16}{3}\right)$. At $x = -3$, $y = \frac{11}{3} + 3(-3) - (-3)^2 - \frac{1}{3}(-3)^3 = -\frac{16}{3}$ and $y'' = -2 - 2(-3) = 4 > 0$. Hence the graph is concave up and has a relative minimum at $\left(-3, -\frac{16}{3}\right)$. To find the inflection point we set $y'' = 0$ and solve for x:

$$-2 - 2x = 0,$$

$$-2x = 2,$$

$$x = -1.$$

If $x = -1$, $y = \frac{11}{3} + 3(-1) - (-1)^2 - \frac{1}{3}(-1)^3 = 0$. Hence the inflection point is $(-1, 0)$. See the graph in the answer section of the text.

43. This function has the form $y = g(x) + mx + b$, where $g(x) = \frac{20}{x}$ and $mx + b = \frac{x}{5} + 3$ ($= \frac{1}{5}x + 3$, a straight line of slope 1/5).

$$y = \frac{x}{5} + \frac{20}{x} + 3, \qquad y' = \frac{1}{5} - \frac{20}{x^2}, \qquad y'' = \frac{40}{x^3}.$$

Set $y' = 0$ and solve for x:

$$\frac{1}{5} - \frac{20}{x^2} = 0, \qquad \frac{1}{5} = \frac{20}{x^2}, \qquad x^2 = 100.$$

(The last equation was obtained by cross multiplication.) Thus $x = 10$ (since only $x > 0$ is being considered). When $x = 10$, $y = \frac{10}{5} + \frac{20}{10} + 3 = 2 + 2 + 3 = 7$, and y'' is obviously positive. Therefore the graph is concave up at $x = 10$, and so $(10, 7)$ is a relative minimum point. Since y'' can never be 0, there are no inflection points. The graph has the y-axis as a vertical asymptote and approaches the straight line $y = x/5 + 3$ as x gets large. The graph is shown in the answer section of the text.

49. A and c, because a constant function corresponds to no change in the position of the car.

B and e, because a positive derivative corresponds to an increase of the distance from the reference point, and the fact that s'(t) is constant means that the velocity is a "steady rate".

C and f, because information about s'(a) gives information about f(t) for t close to t = a, and a positive derivative corresponds to "moving forward".

D and b, for the same reason that C matches f, except that a negative derivative goes with "backing up".

E and a. A positive *first* derivative corresponds to "moving forward" and a positive *second* derivative goes with increasing velocity ("speeding up").

F and d, for the same reason that E matches a, except that a negative *second* derivative corresponds to decreasing velocity.

55. First consider the figure. Let x be the width and h the height of the box. The box is to have a volume of 200 cubic feet, hence the constraint equation is

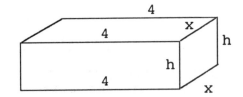

$$4xh = 200 \text{ or } h = \frac{50}{x}.$$

We minimize the amount of material by minimizing the amount of surface area. Our objective equation is

$$A = \underset{\substack{\text{area of} \\ \text{base}}}{4x} + \underset{\substack{\text{area of} \\ \text{2 ends}}}{2xh} + \underset{\substack{\text{area of} \\ \text{2 sides}}}{8h}$$

Substituting the value $h = \frac{50}{x}$ into the objective equation we have,

$$A = 4x + 2x\left(\frac{50}{x}\right) + 8\left(\frac{50}{x}\right)$$

$$= 4x + 100 + \frac{400}{x} \quad (x > 0).$$

To make a rough sketch of the graph of this function, we need the derivatives A:

$$A = 4x + 100 + \frac{400}{x}, \quad x > 0,$$

$$A' = 4 - \frac{400}{x^2},$$

$$A'' = \frac{800}{x^3}.$$

Set $A' = 0$ and solve for x:

$$4 - \frac{400}{x^2} = 0,$$

$$4 = \frac{400}{x^2},$$

$$x^2 = \frac{400}{4} = 100, \quad \text{or } x = 10.$$

When $x = 10$, $A = 4(10) + 100 + \frac{400}{10} = 180$. Since the second derivative $\frac{800}{x^3}$ is positive for all $x > 0$, the graph is concave up for $x > 0$; also, the point $(10, 180)$ is a minimum point.

So the amount of material for the box is minimized when x is 10 feet. The other dimension is $h = \frac{50}{x} = \frac{50}{10} = 5$ feet. The dimensions of the box are $4 \times 5 \times 10$ feet.

61. Since the profit function is

$$P(x) = R(x) - C(x) \qquad \text{(revenue minus cost)},$$

and since

$$R(x) = x \cdot p = x(150 - .02x) = 150x - .02x^2,$$

the profit funtion is

$$P(x) = (150x - .02x^2) - (10x + 300)$$
$$= 140x - .02x^2 - 300$$
$$= -.02x^2 + 140x - 300.$$

This graph of $P(x)$ is a parabola opening downward (since the coefficient of x^2 is negative) and therefore assumes its maximum value where the first derivative is zero.

$$P'(x) = -.04x + 140.$$

Setting $P'(x) = 0$ and solving for x we have

$$-.04x + 140 = 0$$

$$-.04x = -140$$

$$x = \frac{-140}{-.04} = 3500.$$

[Note: One way to evaluate $\frac{140}{.04}$ is to first multiply the numerator and denominator by 100 and then divide. That is, $\frac{140}{.04} = \frac{14,000}{4} = 3500.$] Thus the profit is maximized when the sales level x is 3500 units.

Chapter 3

Techniques of Differentiation

3.1 The Product and Quotient Rules

The first thirty exercises are routine drill. You will be able to tell from the answers if you are mastering the use of the product and quotient rules. In each case, try to obtain the simplified version of the answer shown in the answer section. Most students find this difficult, but now is a good time to practice a skill that may be important for the next exam!

1. To differentiate the product

$$(x+1)(x^3+5x+2)$$

let $f(x) = (x+1)$ and $g(x) = (x^3+5x+2)$ and apply the product rule. Then

$$\frac{d}{dx}[(x+1)(x^3+5x+2)] = (x+1) \cdot \frac{d}{dx}(x^3+5x+2) + (x^3+5x+2) \cdot \frac{d}{dx}(x+1)$$

$$= (x+1)(3x^2+5) + (x^3+5x+2)(1).$$

Carrying out the multiplication in the first product of the derivative and combining like terms we have

$$\frac{d}{dx}[(x+1)(x^3+5x+2)] = (3x^3+3x^2+5x+5) + (x^3+5x+2)$$

$$= 4x^3 + 3x^2 + 10x + 7.$$

7. To differentiate $(x^2+3)(x^2-3)^{10}$, let $f(x) = (x^2+3)$ and $g(x) = (x^2-3)^{10}$ and apply the product rule. When we compute $g'(x)$, we will need the general power rule.

$$\frac{d}{dx}[(x^2+3)(x^2-3)^{10}] = (x^2+3)\frac{d}{dx}(x^2-3)^{10} + (x^2-3)^{10}\cdot\frac{d}{dx}(x^2+3)$$

$$= (x^2+3)10(x^2-3)^9 2x + (x^2-3)^{10}2x.$$

If we factor $2x(x^2-3)^9$ out of each term of the derivative we have

$$\frac{d}{dx}[(x^2+3)(x^2-3)^{10}] = 2x(x^2-3)^9[(x^2+3)10 + (x^2-3)]$$

$$= 2x(x^2-3)^9(11x^2+27).$$

Helpful Hint: Here is a good way to remember the order of the terms in the quotient rule:

1. Draw a long fraction bar and write $[g(x)]^2$ in the denominator:

$$\frac{}{[g(x)]^2}$$

2. While you are still thinking about $g(x)$, write it in the numerator:

$$\frac{g(x)}{[g(x)]^2}$$

3. The rest is easy because each term in the numerator of the derivative involves one function and one derivative. Since $g(x)$ is already written, it must go with $f'(x)$. Next comes the minus sign and then the function and derivative that have not yet been used.

$$\frac{g(x)f'(x) - f(x)g'(x)}{[g(x)]^2}$$

Think of $g(x)$ and $g'(x)$ as being "around the outside" of this formula.

13. To differentiate $\frac{x^2-1}{x^2+1}$, let $f(x) = x^2-1$ and $g(x) = x^2+1$ and apply the quotient rule:

$$\frac{d}{dx}\left(\frac{x^2-1}{x^2+1}\right) = \frac{(x^2+1)\cdot\frac{d}{dx}(x^2-1) - (x^2-1)\cdot\frac{d}{dx}(x^2+1)}{(x^2+1)^2}$$

$$= \frac{(x^2+1)2x - (x^2-1)2x}{(x^2+1)^2}.$$

If we do the multiplication in the numerator, this derivative simplifies.

$$\frac{d}{dx}\left(\frac{x^2-1}{x^2+1}\right) = \frac{2x^3 + 2x - 2x^3 + 2x}{(x^2+1)^2} = \frac{4x}{(x^2+1)^2}.$$

Helpful Hint: A problem such as #15 can be worked with the quotient rule, but since the numerator is a constant, the differentiation is easier if you rewrite the quotient with the notation $(\cdots)^{-1}$. See Practice Problem #2.

19. To differentiate $\dfrac{3x^2 + 5x + 1}{3 - x^2}$, let $f(x) = 3x^2 + 5x + 1$ and $g(x) = 3 - x^2$ and apply the quotient rule.

$$\frac{d}{dx}\left(\frac{3x^2 + 5x + 1}{3 - x^2}\right) = \frac{(3-x^2)\frac{d}{dx}(3x^2+5x+1) - (3x^2+5x+1)\frac{d}{dx}(3-x^2)}{(3-x^2)^2}$$

$$= \frac{(3-x^2)(6x+5) - (3x^2+5x+1)(-2x)}{(3-x^2)^2}.$$

If we do the multiplication in the numerator, we have

$$\frac{d}{dx}\left(\frac{3x^2 + 5x + 1}{3 - x^2}\right) = \frac{(18x+15-6x^3-5x^2) + (6x^3+10x^2+2x)}{(3-x^2)^2}$$

$$= \frac{5x^2 + 20x + 15}{(3-x^2)^2}$$

$$= \frac{5(x+1)(x+3)}{(3-x^2)^2}.$$

Warning: Some students prefer to work #19 using the product rule, but this may cause them more work than they realize. It is possible to write

$$y = \frac{3x^2+5x+1}{3-x^2} = (3x^2+5x+1)(3-x^2)^{-1},$$

and

$$\frac{dy}{dx} = (3x^2+5x+1)\cdot\frac{d}{dx}(3-x^2)^{-1} + (3-x^2)^{-1}\cdot\frac{d}{dx}(3x^2+5x+1)$$

$$= (3x^2+5x+1) \cdot (-1)(3-x^2)^{-2} \cdot (-2x) + (3-x^2)^{-1} \cdot (6x+5).$$

This method is not really shorter, but it does avoid the quotient rule. The main difficulty arises when you try to simplify the derivative, for you must factor out terms that involve negative exponents. However, if you really prefer this method, the next paragraph explains how to handle negative exponents.

How to simplify a sum involving negative exponents: Suppose that various powers of some quantity Q occur in each term of the sum. Find the exponent on Q that lies farthest to the left on the number line and factor out this power of Q from each term in the sum.

In the solution above, notice that $\frac{dy}{dx}$ involves $(3-x^2)^{-2}$ and $(3-x^2)^{-1}$. Since -2 is to the left of -1 on the number line, factor out $(3-x^2)^{-2}$. In the second term below we need $(3-x^2)^1$, because $(3-x^2)^{-1} = (3-x^2)^{-2}(3-x^2)^{+1}$.

$$\frac{dy}{dx} = (3-x^2)^{-2}[(3x^2+5x+1)(-1)(-2x) + (3-x^2)^1(6x+5)]$$

$$= (3-x^2)^{-2}[(6x^3+10x^2+2x) + (18x+15-6x^3-5x^2)]$$

$$= (3-x^2)^{-2}[5x^2+20x+15]$$

$$= 5(3-x^2)^{-2}(x+1)(x+3).$$

Moral of this story: If you have to simplify the derivative of a quotient, use the quotient rule for the differentiation step.

25. Simplify first:

$$\frac{x^4-4x^2+3}{x} = x^3-4x+\frac{3}{x}$$

$$= x^3-4x+3x^{-1}.$$

Then,

$$\frac{d}{dx}(x^3-4x+3x^{-1}) = 3x^2-4-3x^{-2}$$

$$= 3x^2-4-\frac{3}{x^2}$$

$$= \frac{3x^4-4x^2-3}{x^2}.$$

31. The solution to this exercise is a two-step procedure.

   (a) Find the slope at the point where x = 3.

   (b) Use the point-slope formula from Section 1.1 to obtain the equation of the line through the point (3,16) having the slope found in (a).

   Given $y = (x-2)^5(x+1)^2$, we have

   $$\frac{dy}{dx} = (x-2)^5 \cdot \frac{d}{dx}(x+1)^2 + (x+1)^2 \cdot \frac{d}{dx}(x-2)^5 \quad \text{[Product Rule]}$$

   $$= (x-2)^5 2(x+1) + (x+1)^2 5(x-2)^4 \quad \text{[Gen. Power Rule]}$$

   Now, the slope of the curve at x = 3 is

   $$(3-2)^5 2(3+1) + (3+1)^2 5(3-2)^4 = 8 + 5(16) = 88.$$

   Hence, the equation of the tangent line at (3,16) is

   $$y - 16 = 88(x - 3).$$

37. To find the points on the graph of $y = \frac{x^2+3x-1}{x}$ where the slope is 5 we first take the derivative:

   $$\frac{dy}{dx} = \frac{dy}{dx}\left(\frac{x^2+3x-1}{x}\right)$$

   $$= \frac{x \cdot \frac{dy}{dx}(x^2+3x-1) - (x^2+3x-1) \cdot \frac{dy}{dx}(x)}{x^2} \quad \text{[Quotient Rule]}$$

   $$= \frac{x(2x+3) - (x^2+3x-1)}{x^2}$$

   $$= \frac{x^2 + 1}{x^2}.$$

   Now, set the derivative equal to 5 and solve for x:

   $$\frac{x^2 + 1}{x^2} = 5,$$

   $$x^2 + 1 = 5x^2,$$

   $$4x^2 = 1,$$

   $$x^2 = \frac{1}{4}, \text{ or } x = \pm\frac{1}{2}.$$

Substituting $x = \frac{1}{2}$ and $x = -\frac{1}{2}$ into $y = \frac{x^2+3x-1}{x}$ we have

$$y = \frac{\left(\frac{1}{2}\right)^2+3\left(\frac{1}{2}\right)-1}{\frac{1}{2}} = \frac{3}{2},$$

and,

$$y = \frac{\left(-\frac{1}{2}\right)^2+3\left(-\frac{1}{2}\right)-1}{-\frac{1}{2}} = \frac{9}{2}.$$

The points where the slope is 5 are $\left(\frac{1}{2},\frac{3}{2}\right)$ and $\left(-\frac{1}{2},\frac{9}{2}\right)$.

Helpful Hint: Do you try the Practice Problems before starting your homework? You should. If you worked Practice Problem #1 in this section, you may have already learned to think about simplifying a function before starting to differentiate. Often there is no need to simplify first, but in Exercise 37 it really helps. Notice that

$$y = \frac{x^2+3x-1}{x} = x + 3 - \frac{1}{x},$$

so that

$$\frac{dy}{dx} = 1 + \frac{1}{x^2}.$$

43. Recall that the marginal revenue, MR, is defined by

$$MR = R'(x).$$

Now, the average revenue is maximized when

$$\frac{d}{dx}(AR) = 0.$$

To compute this derivative we use the quotient rule.

$$\frac{d}{dx}(AR) = \frac{d}{dx}\left(\frac{R(x)}{x}\right) = \frac{x \cdot R'(x) - R(x) \cdot (1)}{x^2}.$$

Set this derivative equal to zero. If $\frac{xR'(x)-R(x)}{x^2} = 0$

then the numerator must be zero.

$$xR'(x) - R(x) = 0,$$

$$xR'(x) = R(x),$$

$$R'(x) = \frac{R(x)}{x},$$

$$MR = AR.$$

Helpful Hint for Exercises 49 and 50: Remember that when you have to determine when the derivative of a quotient is zero, the algebra is usually easier if you use the quotient rule. Try this before you read the solution to Exercise 49.

49. Apply the quotient rule to the function $y = \dfrac{10x}{1 + .25x^2}$, and set the derivative equal to zero:

$$\frac{dy}{dx} = \frac{(1 + .25x^2) \cdot 10 - 10x \cdot (.50x)}{(1 + .25x^2)^2}.$$

This derivative is zero when its numerator is zero:

$$10 + 2.5x^2 - 5x^2 = 0$$

$$10 = 2.5x^2.$$

Thus $x^2 = 4$, and $x = \pm 2$. Only $+2$ is of interest. The corresponding y-value is

$$y = \frac{10(2)}{1 + .25(2)^2} = \frac{20}{1 + 1} = 10.$$

The maximum point is $(2, 10)$.

55. The value of the derivative at $x = 1$ is found by using the quotient rule and afterwards evaluating all functions at $x = 1$:

$$\frac{d}{dx}\left[\frac{f(x)}{g(x)}\right]\Bigg|_{x=1} = \frac{g(1)f'(1) - f(1)g'(1)}{[g(1)]^2} = \frac{4 \cdot 3 - 2 \cdot 5}{(4)^2} = \frac{1}{8}.$$

61. Set $Y_1 = (160X^{\wedge}(-.4) + 94.8)/(4X^{\wedge}(-.4) + 15.8)$.

a. See the graph in the text's answers.

b. "3 units of light" refers to a value of x. You should find that $Y_1(3) \approx 10.77$. Refer to part C of the Appendix section, **Special Points on the Graph of Y_1**.

c. To find the value of x at which the pupil size is 11 square millimeters, either use the SOLVER for the equation $0 = Y_1 - 11$, or set $Y_2 = 11$, graph both Y_1 and Y_2, and use the Intersect command. Refer to part D or part B of **Special Points** on the **Graph of** Y_1. You should obtain $X \approx 2.61$.

    d. If Y_4 is the derivative of Y_1, compute $Y_4(3) \approx -.547$.

3.2 The Chain Rule and the General Power Rule

The chain rule is used in subsequent chapters to derive formulas for the derivatives of composite functions where the outer function is either a logarithm function, an exponential function, or one of the trigonometric functions. In each case there will be a formula that has the same feel as the general power rule. These formulas will become so automatic that you will sometimes forget that they are special cases of the chain rule.

    Many of the exercises in this section may be solved with the general power rule, but we approach the exercises with the abstract chain rule in mind. The practice you gain here will make it easier to use and remember the later versions of the chain rule.

1. If $f(x) = \frac{x}{x+1}$, $g(x) = x^3$, then $f(g(x)) = \frac{x^3}{x^3+1}$.

7. If $f(g(x)) = \sqrt{4-x^2}$, then $f(x) = \sqrt{x}$ and $g(x) = 4 - x^2$.

13. If $y = 6x^2(x-1)^3$, we have

$$\frac{dy}{dx} = \left[6x^2 \cdot \frac{d}{dx}(x-1)^3\right] + (x-1)^3 \cdot \frac{d}{dx}(6x^2) \qquad \text{[Product Rule]}$$

$$= 6x^2 3(x-1)^2(1) + (x-1)^3 12x \qquad \text{[Gen. Power Rule]}$$

We can factor $6x(x-1)^2$ out of each term to get

$$\frac{dy}{dx} = 6x(x-1)^2[3x+2(x-1)]$$

$$= 6x(x-1)^2(5x-2).$$

19. To differentiate $\left(\frac{4x-1}{3x+1}\right)^3$ let $f(x) = x^3$, $g(x) = \frac{4x-1}{3x+1}$, and use the chain rule. Now $f'(x) = 3x^2$ and

$$g'(x) = \frac{(3x+1)4 - (4x-1)3}{(3x+1)^2} \qquad \text{[Quotient Rule]}$$

Hence

$$\frac{d}{dx}f(g(x)) = f'(g(x))g'(x)$$

$$= 3\left(\frac{4x-1}{3x+1}\right)^2 \cdot \frac{(3x+1)4 - (4x-1)3}{(3x+1)^2}.$$

This simplifies to

$$\frac{d}{dx}f(g(x)) = \frac{3(4x-1)^2(12x+4-12x+3)}{(3x+1)^4} = \frac{21(4x-1)^2}{(3x+1)^4}.$$

25. If $f(x) = x^5$ and $g(x) = 6x-1$, then $f'(x) = 5x^4$ and $g'(x) = 6$. Hence

$$\frac{d}{dx}f(g(x)) = f'(g(x))g'(x) = 5(6x-1)^4 \cdot 6.$$

31. If $f(x) = (x^3+1)^2$ and $g(x) = x^2+5$, then $f'(x) = 2(x^3+1)3x^2$ and $g'(x) = 2x$. Hence

$$\frac{d}{dx}f(g(x)) = f'(g(x))g'(x) = 2((x^2+5)^3+1)3(x^2+5)^2 2x$$

$$= 12x((x^2+5)^3+1)(x^2+5)^2.$$

37. If $y = u(u+1)^5$ and $u = x^2 + x$, then

$$\frac{dy}{du} = u5(u+1)^4 + (u+1)^5 = (u+1)^4[5u+(u+1)]$$

$$= (u+1)^4(6u+1)$$

$$\frac{du}{dx} = 2x + 1.$$

Hence $\frac{dy}{dx} = \frac{dy}{du} \cdot \frac{du}{dx} = (u+1)^4(6u+1)(2x+1)$. To express $\frac{dy}{dx}$ as a function of x alone, we substitute $x^2 + x$ for u to obtain

$$\frac{dy}{dx} = (x^2+x+1)^4(6x^2+6x+1)(2x+1).$$

43. A horizontal tangent line has slope 0; i.e., where $\frac{dy}{dx} = 0$.

$$\frac{dy}{dx} = 3(-x^2+4x-3)^2(-2x+4) \qquad \text{[Gen. Power Rule]}$$

Setting this equation equal to zero produces:

$$-2x+4 = 0, \qquad \text{or} \qquad -x^2+4x-3 = 0,$$
$$x = 2, \qquad\qquad\qquad x^2-4x+3 = 0,$$
$$(x-1)(x-3) = 0,$$
$$x = 1, \ x = 3.$$

Therefore, $x = 2, 1,$ and 3.

49. a. If $P = \dfrac{200x}{100+x^2}$, then the marginal profit is

$$\frac{dP}{dx} = \frac{(100+x^2)200 - 200x(2x)}{(100+x^2)^2} \qquad \text{[Quotient Rule]}$$

$$= \frac{200(100-x^2)}{(100+x^2)^2}.$$

b. If $x = 4 + 2t$, then $\dfrac{dx}{dt} = 2$. By the chain rule

$$\frac{dP}{dt} = \frac{dP}{dx} \cdot \frac{dx}{dt} = \frac{200(100-x^2)}{(100+x^2)^2}(2)$$

$$= \frac{400(100-x^2)}{(100+x^2)^2}.$$

To express $\dfrac{dP}{dt}$ as a function of t, we substitute $4 + 2t$ for x to obtain

$$\frac{dP}{dt} = \frac{400(100-(4+2t)^2)}{(100+(4+2t)^2)^2}.$$

c. When $t = 8$, $\dfrac{dP}{dt} = \dfrac{400(100-(4+16)^2)}{(100+(4+16)^2)^2} = -.48.$

Profits are falling at the rate of 480 dollars per week.

55. Since $\dfrac{d}{dx} f(g(x)) = f'(g(x)) \cdot g'(x)$,

$$\frac{d}{dx} f(g(x)) \bigg|_{x=1} = f'(g(1)) \cdot g'(1).$$

Use $g(1) = 5$, $f'(5) = 4$, and $g'(1) = 6$ to obtain

$$f'(g(1)) \cdot g'(1) = f'(5) \cdot 6 = 4 \cdot 6 = 24.$$

3.3 Implicit Differentiation and Related Rates

The material in this section is not used in the rest of the text. However, the two techniques introduced here are fundamental concepts of calculus and are commonly found in applications. Both techniques involve using the chain rule in situations where we don't know the specific formula for the inner part of a composite function.

1.   We will differentiate $x^2 - y^2 = 1$ term by term. The first term x^2 has derivative $2x$. We think of the second term y^2 as having the form $[g(x)]^2$. To differentiate we use the chain rule

$$\frac{d}{dx}[g(x)]^2 = 2[g(x)]g'(x).$$

Hence,

$$\frac{d}{dx}y^2 = 2y\cdot\frac{dy}{dx}.$$

On the right side of the original equation the derivative of the constant function 1 is zero. Thus implicit differentiation of $x^2 - y^2 = 1$ yields

$$2x - 2y\cdot\frac{dy}{dx} = 0.$$

Solving for $\frac{dy}{dx}$, we have

$$-2y\cdot\frac{dy}{dx} = -2x.$$

If $y \neq 0$,

$$\frac{dy}{dx} = \frac{x}{y}.$$

7.   We will differentiate $2x^3 + y = 2y^3 + x$ term by term. The derivative at $2x^3$ is $6x$. We write $\frac{dy}{dx}$ for the derivative of y. On the right side of the equation, $2y^3$ has derivative $6y^2\cdot\frac{dy}{dx}$ and x has derivative 1. Thus implicit differentiation of $2x^3 + y = 2y^3 + x$ yields

$$6x^2 + \frac{dy}{dx} = 6y^2\cdot\frac{dy}{dx} + 1.$$

Solving for $\frac{dy}{dx}$ we have

$$(1-6y^2)\frac{dy}{dx} = 1 - 6x^2,$$

$$\frac{dy}{dx} = \frac{1 - 6x^2}{1 - 6y^2}.$$

13. To differentiate x^3y^2, use the product rule, treating y as a function of x:

$$\frac{d}{dx}x^3y^2 = x^3 \cdot \frac{d}{dx}(y^2) + y^2 \cdot \frac{d}{dx}(x^3)$$

$$= x^3 2y \cdot \frac{dy}{dx} + y^2(3x^2)$$

$$= 2x^3y\frac{dy}{dx} + 3x^2y^2.$$

Hence implicit differentiation of $x^3y^2 - 4x^2 = 1$ yields

$$2x^3y\frac{dy}{dx} + 3x^2y^2 - 8x = 0.$$

Solving for $\frac{dy}{dx}$ we have

$$2x^3y\frac{dy}{dx} = 8x - 3x^2y^2,$$

$$\frac{dy}{dx} = \frac{8x - 3x\ y}{2x^3y} = \frac{8 - 3xy}{2x^2y}.$$

19. Implicit differentiation of $4y^3 - x^2 = -5$ yields

$$12y^2 \cdot \frac{dy}{dx} - 2x = 0.$$

Solving for $\frac{dy}{dx}$ gives

$$12y^2\frac{dy}{dx} = 2x,$$

$$\frac{dy}{dx} = \frac{2x}{12y^2}.$$

Hence, $\qquad \left.\frac{dy}{dx}\right|_{\substack{x=3 \\ y=1}} = \frac{2(3)}{12(1)^2} = \frac{1}{2}.$

25. A two-step procedure is required.

(a) Find the slope at each point.

(b) Use the point-slope formula to obtain the equation of the tangent line.

For (a), note that

$$\frac{d}{dx}x^2y^4 = x^2 \cdot \frac{d}{dx}y^4 + y^4 \cdot \frac{d}{dx}x^2 = x^2 \cdot 4y^3 \frac{dy}{dx} + y^4 \cdot 2x.$$

Thus implicit differentiation of $x^2y^4 = 1$ yields

$$4y^3x^2 \frac{dy}{dx} + 2y^4x = 0,$$

$$4y^3x^2 \frac{dy}{dx} = -2y^4x,$$

$$\frac{dy}{dx} = \frac{-2y^4x}{4y^3x^2} = \frac{-y}{2x}.$$

At the point $\left(4, \frac{1}{2}\right)$, the slope of the curve is given by

$$\frac{dy}{dx}\bigg|_{\substack{x=4 \\ y=1/2}} = \frac{-1/2}{2(4)} = -\frac{1}{16}.$$

Hence the equation of the tangent line at $\left(4, \frac{1}{2}\right)$ is

$$y - \frac{1}{2} = -\frac{1}{16}(x - 4).$$

At the point $\left(4, -\frac{1}{2}\right)$, the slope of the curve is given by

$$\frac{dy}{dx}\bigg|_{\substack{x=4 \\ y=-1/2}} = \frac{-(-1/2)}{2(4)} = \frac{1}{16}.$$

Hence the equation of the tangent line at $\left(4, -\frac{1}{2}\right)$ is

$$y + \frac{1}{2} = \frac{1}{16}(x - 4).$$

31. We will differentiate $x^4 + y^4 = 1$ term by term. Since x is a function of t, the general power rule gives

$$\frac{d}{dt}x^4 = 4x^3 \cdot \frac{dx}{dt}.$$

Similarly,

$$\frac{d}{dt}y^4 = 4y^3 \cdot \frac{dy}{dt}.$$

And

$$\frac{d}{dt}(1) = 0.$$

Hence $4x^3 \frac{dx}{dt} + 4y^3 \frac{dy}{dt} = 0$. Solving for $\frac{dy}{dt}$ we have

$$4y^3 \frac{dy}{dt} = -4x^3 \frac{dx}{dt},$$

$$\frac{dy}{dt} = \frac{-x^3}{y^3} \frac{dx}{dt}.$$

37. First we compute $\frac{dy}{dt}$. Differentiating $x^2 - 4y^2 = 9$ term by term, we have

$$2x \frac{dx}{dt} - 8y \frac{dy}{dt} = 0.$$

Solving for $\frac{dy}{dt}$ we have

$$-8y \frac{dy}{dt} = -2x \frac{dx}{dt},$$

$$\frac{dy}{dt} = \frac{x}{4y} \frac{dx}{dt}.$$

The problem tells us that at the point (5,-2), the x-coordinate is increasing at the rate of 3 units per second, that is, $\frac{dx}{dt} = 3$. Hence,

$$\frac{dy}{dt} = \frac{5}{4(-2)}(3) = -\frac{15}{8} \text{ units per second.}$$

43. $\frac{d}{dt}P^5V^7 = P^5 \cdot \frac{d}{dt}V^7 + V^7 \cdot \frac{d}{dt}P^5$

$$= P^5 7V^6 \frac{dV}{dt} + V^7 5P^4 \frac{dP}{dt}.$$

$\frac{d}{dx}(k) = 0$ (since k is a constant).

Hence $7P^5V^6 \frac{dV}{dt} + 5P^4V^7 \frac{dP}{dt} = 0$. Solving for $\frac{dV}{dt}$ we have

$$7P^5V^6 \frac{dV}{dt} = -5P^4V^7 \frac{dP}{dt},$$

$$\frac{dV}{dt} = \frac{-5P^4V^7}{7P^5V^6}\frac{dP}{dt},$$

$$= \frac{-5V}{7P}\frac{dP}{dt}.$$

The problem tells us that when V = 4 liters, P = 200 units and $\frac{dP}{dt}$ = 5 units per second. Hence

$$\frac{dV}{dt} = \frac{-5(4)}{7(200)}(5) = -\frac{1}{14}.$$

Therefore the volume is decreasing at the rate of $\frac{1}{14}$ liters per second.

Chapter 3: Supplementary Exercises

The techniques of differentiation presented in the first two sections of this chapter must be mastered. They will be used throughout the text.

You may need to review curve sketching and optimization problems because these problems can be more difficult when they involve the product rule or quotient rule. On an exam that covers both Chapters 2 and 3 (or on the final exam) you may see a problem similar to Exercises 39 and 40 in Section 3.1 or Exercises 23 and 24 in Section 3.2.

1. $\frac{d}{dx}[(4x-1)(3x+1)^4] = (4x-1)\cdot\frac{d}{dx}(3x+1)^4 + (3x+1)^4\cdot\frac{d}{dx}(4x-1)$

    [Product Rule]

    $= (4x-1)4(3x+1)^3\cdot3 + (3x+1)^4\cdot4.$

If we factor $4(3x+1)^3$ from each term, we have

$\frac{d}{dx}[(4x-1)(3x+1)^4] = 4(3x+1)^3[3(4x-1) + (3x+1)]$

$= 4(3x+1)^3[12x-3+3x+1]$

$= 4(3x+1)^3(15x-2).$

7. If $y = 3(x^2-1)^3(x^2+1)^5$, then

$$\frac{dy}{dx} = 3(x^2-1)^3 \cdot \frac{d}{dx}(x^2+1)^5 + (x^2+1)^5 \cdot \frac{d}{dx}3(x^2-1)^3 \quad [\text{Prod. Rule}]$$

$$= 3(x^2-1)^3 5(x^2+1)^4 2x + (x^2+1)^5 9(x^2-1)^2 2x.$$

If we factor $6x(x^2-1)^2(x^2+1)^4$ from each term, we have

$$\frac{dy}{dx} = 6x(x^2-1)^2(x^2+1)^4(5(x^2-1)+3(x^2+1))$$

$$= 6x(x^2-1)^2(x^2+1)^4(8x^2-2)$$

$$= 12x(x^2-1)^2(x^2+1)^4(4x^2-1).$$

13. If $f(x) = (3x+1)^4(3-x)^5$, then

$$f'(x) = (3x+1)^4 \cdot \frac{d}{dx}(3-x)^5 + (3-x)^5 \cdot \frac{d}{dx}(3x+1)^4 \quad [\text{Prod. Rule}]$$

$$= (3x+1)^4 5(3-x)^4(-1) + (3-x)^5 4(3x+1)^3 3$$

$$= (3x+1)^3(3-x)^4[-5(3x+1) + 12(3-x)]$$

$$= (3x+1)^3(3-x)^4(-27x+31).$$

Set $f'(x) = 0$ and solve for x:

$$(3x+1)^3(3-x)^4(-27x+31) = 0.$$

$$x = -\frac{1}{3}, \ x = 3, \ \text{and} \ x = \frac{31}{27}.$$

19. We want to evaluate $\frac{dC}{dt}$. The problem tells us that daily sales are rising at the rate of three lamps per day. This means $\frac{dx}{dt} = 3$. Now if $C = 40x + 30$, then $\frac{dC}{dx} = 40$. Hence by the chain rule,

$$\frac{dC}{dt} = \frac{dC}{dx} \cdot \frac{dx}{dt} = 40(3) = 120.$$

Costs are rising by $120 per day.

25. $h(x) = f(g(x))$,

   $h(1) = f(g(1))$, and since $g(1) = 2$, $h(1) = f(2) = 1$,

$$h'(x) = f'(g(x)) \, g'(x) \quad \text{[Chain rule]}.$$
$$h'(1) = f'(g(1)) \, g'(1)$$
$$= f'(2) \, g'(1).$$

The slope of the tangent line at $x = 2$ on the graph of $f(x)$ is -1. This is clear from an examination of the "graph paper" background in Fig. 2. Therefore, $f'(2) = -1$. Similarly, Fig. 2 shows that the slope of the tangent line at $x = 1$ on the graph of $g(x)$ is $\frac{3}{2}$, so

$$g'(1) = \frac{3}{2},$$

$$h'(1) = (-1)\frac{3}{2} = -\frac{3}{2}.$$

31. If $g(x) = \sqrt{x} = x^{1/2}$, then $g'(x) = \frac{1}{2}x^{-1/2}$. Since $f'(x) = x\sqrt{1-x^2}$, $\frac{d}{dx}f(g(x)) = f'(g(x))g'(x) = (x^{1/2})\sqrt{1-x}\left(\frac{1}{2}x^{-1/2}\right)$

$$= \frac{1}{2}\sqrt{1-x}.$$

37. If $u = \sqrt{x} = x^{1/2}$, then $\frac{du}{dx} = \frac{1}{2}x^{-1/2}$. Since $\frac{dy}{du} = \frac{u}{\sqrt{1+u^4}}$,

$$\frac{dy}{dx} = \frac{dy}{du}\cdot\frac{du}{dx} = \frac{u}{\sqrt{1+u^4}}\left(\frac{1}{2}x^{-1/2}\right).$$

To express $\frac{dy}{dx}$ as a function of x alone, we substitute $x^{1/2}$ for u to obtain

$$\frac{dy}{dx} = \frac{x^{1/2}}{(1+x^2)^{1/2}}\left(\frac{1}{2}x^{-1/2}\right) = \frac{1}{2\sqrt{1+x^2}}.$$

43. By the product rule,

$$\frac{d}{dx}x^2y^2 = x^2\cdot\frac{d}{dx}y^2 + y^2\cdot\frac{d}{dx}x^2 = x^2 2y\frac{dy}{dx} + y^2 2x.$$

Hence implicit differentiation of $x^2y^2 = 9$ yields

$$2x^2y\frac{dy}{dx} + 2xy^2 = 0.$$

Solving for $\frac{dy}{dx}$ we have

$$2x^2y\frac{dy}{dx} = -2xy^2$$

$$\frac{dy}{dx} = \frac{-2xy^2}{2x^2y} = -\frac{y}{x}.$$

If $x = 1$ and $y = 3$, then $\frac{dy}{dx} = -\frac{3}{1} = -3$.

49. First, to find $\frac{dx}{dt}$, we differentiate $6p + 5x + xp = 50$ term by term, with respect to t, using the produce rule on xp.

$$6\frac{dp}{dt} + 5\frac{dx}{dt} + x\frac{dp}{dt} + p\frac{dx}{dt} = 0.$$

Solving for $\frac{dx}{dt}$ we have

$$5\frac{dx}{dt} + p\frac{dx}{dt} = -6\frac{dp}{dt} - x\frac{dp}{dt},$$

$$(5+p)\frac{dx}{dt} = -(6+x)\frac{dp}{dt},$$

$$\frac{dx}{dt} = -\left(\frac{6+x}{5+p}\right)\frac{dp}{dt}.$$

If $x = 4$, $p = 3$, and $\frac{dp}{dt} = -2$, then

$$\frac{dx}{dt} = \left(\frac{6+4}{5+3}\right)2 = \frac{10}{4} = \frac{5}{2} = 2.5.$$

Therefore, the quantity x is increasing at the rate of 2.5 units per unit time.

Chapter 4

The Exponential and Natural Logarithm Functions

4.1 Exponential Functions

The exercises in Section 4.1 focus on the specific skills you need later in Chapter 4. If you need more practice, go back to Section 0.5.

It will be helpful to make a table that lists the laws of exponents shown on page 232 and to add to it the "reverse" laws listed in the study guide notes for Section 0.5. (Use x and y in the exponents now instead of r and s.) You definitely need to memorize this enlarged list of laws. Working scores of problems will help, of course, because you will have to refer to your list. Here is an additional method. Write only the left side of each law in the table on page 232. Maybe mix up the order of the laws. On a separate sheet of paper, write the left side of the laws listed in the study guide for Section 0.5 (with x,y in place of r,s). Put these partial lists aside for a day or two while you work exercises from Section 4.1. Later, try to fill in the lists of laws without any help. You may need to do this more than once.

1. $4^x = (2^2)^x = 2^{2x}$,

   $(\sqrt{3})^x = (3^{1/2})^x = 3^{(1/2)x}$,

   $(\frac{1}{9})^x = (3^{-2})^x = 3^{-2x}$.

7. $6^x \cdot 3^{-x} = (2 \cdot 3)^x \cdot 3^{-x} = 2^x \cdot 3^x \cdot 3^{-x} = 2^x \cdot 3^0 = 2^x \cdot 1 = 2^x$,

   $\frac{15^x}{5^x} = (\frac{15}{5})^x = 3^x$, or $\frac{15^x}{5^x} = (3 \cdot 5)^x \cdot 5^{-x} = 3^x \cdot 5^x \cdot 5^{-x} = 3^x$,

   $\frac{12^x}{2^{2x}} = 12^x \cdot 2^{-2x} = (3 \cdot 2^2)^x \cdot 2^{-2x} = 3^x \cdot 2^{2x} \cdot 2^{-2x} = 3^x \cdot 2^0 = 3^x$,

$$\text{or} \quad \frac{12^x}{2^{2x}} = \frac{12^x}{4^x} = \left(\frac{12}{4}\right)^x = 3^x.$$

13. $(2^{-3x} \cdot 2^{-2x})^{2/5} = (2^{-5x})^{2/5} = 2^{(-5x)(2/5)} = 2^{-2x},$

$(9^{1/2} \cdot 9^4)^{x/9} = 9^{(9/2)(x/9)} = 9^{x/2} = (3^2)^{x/2} = 3^x,$

or $(9^{1/2} \cdot 9^4)^{x/9} = \left[3 \cdot (3^2)^4\right]^{x/9} = (3^9)^{x/9} = 3^x.$

19. If $(2.5)^{2x+1} = (2.5)^5,$ then equating exponents,

$2x+1 = 5, \quad 2x = 4, \quad x = 2.$

25. If $(2^{x+1} \cdot 2^{-3})^2 = 2,$ then

$(2^{(x+1)-3})^2 = 2, \quad (2^{x-2})^2 = 2, \quad 2^{2x-4} = 2^1.$

Equating exponents, we have $2x - 4 = 1$ and hence $x = \frac{5}{2}.$

31. Since $2^{3+h} = 2^3(2^h),$ the missing factor is $2^h.$

37. Set $Y_1 = 2^{\wedge}X.$ Part C in the Appendix section **Derivatives, Slopes, and Tangent Lines** describes how to compute the slope of the graph of $Y_1.$ Alternatively, if Y_4 is the derivative of $Y_1,$ then evaluate $Y_4(0),$ as described in part C of the Appendix section **Special Points on the Graph of Y_1** (and apply the steps to Y_4 in place of Y_1). You should obtain .69314724.

39. Apply the methods for Exercise 37 to $b^{\wedge}X$ in place of $2^{\wedge}X.$ Try different numbers for b, such as 2.5 and 3.0.

4.2 The Exponential Function e^x

The purpose of this brief section and its exercises is to introduce the function e^x and to help you get used to working with it. Here are the main facts about $e^x.$ The number e is between 2 and 3; the graph of the function e^x is similar to the graphs of 2^x and 3^x and lies between them. The number e is chosen so that the slope of $y = e^x$ is 1 at $x = 0.$ The slope of $y = e^x$ at an arbitrary point (x, e^x) on the graph has the same numerical value as the y-coordinate of the point. That is (see Figure 3 on page 238),

$$[\text{slope at } (x, e^x)] = [\text{y-coord. of } (x, e^x)]$$

$$\frac{d}{dx} e^x = e^x.$$

1. If $y = 3^x$, then the slope of the secant line through $(0,1)$ and $(h, 3^h)$ is

$$\frac{3^h - 1}{h}.$$

As h approaches zero, the slope of the secant line approaches the slope of $y = 3^x$ at $x = 0$; i.e.,

$$\frac{d}{dx} 3^x \Big|_{x=0}.$$

If $h = .1$, then $\dfrac{3^h - 1}{h} = \dfrac{1.11612 - 1}{.1} = 1.1612$.

If $h = .01$, then $\dfrac{3^h - 1}{h} = \dfrac{1.01105 - 1}{.01} = 1.105$.

If $h = .001$, then $\dfrac{3^h - 1}{h} = \dfrac{1.00110 - 1}{.001} = 1.10$.

Therefore, $\dfrac{d}{dx} 3^x \Big|_{x=0} = \lim_{x \to 0} \dfrac{3^h - 1}{h} \approx 1.1$.

Helpful Hint: The calculations in Exercise 1 can be automated in various ways on a graphing calculator. Even if such calculators are not required in your course, you should consider learning how to perform simple computations. For instance, set $Y_1 = (3^\wedge X - 1)/X$ and then evaluate $Y_1(.1)$, $Y_1(.01)$, and $Y_1(.001)$. Or, in the home screen, compute $(3^\wedge.1 - 1)/.1$. Then use the key that recalls the last computation and edit the command, replacing .1 by .01. Repeat, with .001 in place of .01. See the Appendix Sections, **Functions** and **Special Points on the Graph of** Y_1.

7. a. $\dfrac{d}{dx} e^{4x} = \dfrac{d}{dx}(e^x)^4 = 4(e^x)^3 \cdot \dfrac{d}{dx} e^x$ $\begin{bmatrix} \text{General} \\ \text{power rule} \end{bmatrix}$

$$= 4(e^x)^3 \cdot e^x = 4e^{3x} \cdot e^x = 4e^{4x}.$$

b. $\dfrac{d}{dx} e^{kx} = \dfrac{d}{dx}(e^x)^k = k(e^x)^{k-1} \cdot \dfrac{d}{dx} e^x$

$$= k(e^x)^{k-1} \cdot e^x = ke^{kx-x} \cdot e^x = ke^{kx}.$$

13. $(e^{4x} \cdot e^{6x})^{3/5} = (e^{10x})^{3/5} = e^{(10x)(3/5)} = e^{6x}$.

$$\frac{1}{e^{-2x}} = e^{-(-2x)} = e^{2x}.$$

19. By the product rule,

$$\frac{d}{dx} xe^x = x \cdot \frac{d}{dx} e^x + e^x \cdot \frac{d}{dx} x = xe^x + e^x.$$

25. Note that each grid line along the x-axis represents 2 kilometers, while each grid line vertically represents 100 units. The units for f(x) are g/cm^2 (pressure), and the units for f'(x) are g/cm^2 per kilometer (rate of change of pressure per kilometer of altitude).

   a. "Pressure" is a value of f(x). A point on the graph of f(x) where x = 2 is about (2,800). The pressure is about 800 g/cm^2 at an altitude of 2 km.

   b. A point on the graph of f(x) where y = 200 is close to (13,200). The pressure is 200 g/cm^2 at an altitude of approximately 14 km.

   c. Rate questions involve the graph of f'(x). When x = 8, f'(8) is about -50. At an altitude of 8 km, the pressure is falling at the rate of about 50 g/cm^2 per kilometer.

   d. Here the rate is negative 100 because the pressure is falling. A point on the graph of f'(x) where y = -100 is about (2,-100). The pressure is falling at the rate of one hundred g/cm^2 per kilometer at an altitude of about 2 km.

31. Set $Y_1 = (10\wedge X - 1)/X$, and deselect all other functions. Then compute values of Y_1 for various values for X, such as .1, .01, .001, and so on until you obtain a limiting value up to three or four decimal places. For X = .000001, you should get $Y_1 = 2.3025877$.

   To compute Y_1 on the TI-83 or TI-86, use the TABLE command in the "Ask" mode. For the TI-85, you can use the MATH MISC menu. On that menu, press MORE to display the eval command. Press [F5] for eval, type a number such as .001 on the home screen, and press ENTER. The value of Y_1 will appear, and you can repeat the process by pressing eval again.

   For X = .01,   Y1 = 2.32929
   For X = .001,   Y1 = 2.30523
   For X = .0001, Y1 = 2.30285

For X = .00001, Y_1 = 2.30261
For X = .000001, Y_1 = 2.30259

A description of the derivative formula for an exponential function such as 10^X is given in (6) on page 238:

$$\frac{d}{dx} 10^X = m \cdot 10^X, \quad \text{where} \quad m = \frac{d}{dx} 10^X \bigg|_{x=0} \approx 2.3.$$

4.3 Differentiation of Exponential Functions

Everything in this section is important. It is essential that you not fall behind the class at this point. Make every effort to completely finish the work in Sections 4.1-4.3 before the class begins Section 4.4.   You may have difficulty with the material on logarithms in Sections 4.4-4.6 if you try to learn it while you are still uncertain about exponential functions. Be sure to read the boxes on pages 241-42.   The importance of the differential equation $y' = ky$ will not be apparent until you reach Chapter 5, but it is desirable to think a little bit now about questions such as Exercises 41-44.

1. $\frac{d}{dx} 4e^{2x} = 4 \cdot \frac{d}{dx} e^{2x} = 4(2e^{2x}) = 8e^{2x}.$

7. Begin with the general power rule.

$$\frac{d}{dx}(e^x + e^{-x})^3 = 3(e^x + e^{-x})^2 \cdot \frac{d}{dx}(e^x + e^{-x})$$

$$= 3(e^x + e^{-x})^2 (e^x - e^{-x}).$$

13. Use the chain rule for $e^{g(x)}$:

$$\frac{d}{dx}(e^{x^2-5x+4}) = e^{x^2-5x+4} \cdot \frac{d}{dx}(x^2 - 5x + 4) = e^{x^2-5x+4} \cdot (2x - 5).$$

19. Use the product rule, then the chain rule for e^{-x+2}:

$$\frac{d}{dx}(x + 1)e^{-x+2} = (x + 1) \cdot \frac{d}{dx} e^{-x+2} + e^{-x+2} \cdot \frac{d}{dx}(x + 1)$$

$$= (x + 1) \cdot e^{-x+2}(-1) + e^{-x+2} \cdot 1$$

$$= e^{-x+2}(-x -1 + 1) = -xe^{-x+2}$$

25. Write $1/x$ as x^{-1} and use the product rule:

$$\frac{d}{dx}(x^{-1} + 3)e^{2x} = (x^{-1} + 3)\cdot\frac{d}{dx}e^{2x} + e^{2x}\cdot\frac{d}{dx}(x^{-1} + 3)$$

$$= (x^{-1} + 3)\cdot 2e^{2x} + e^{2x}\cdot(-x^{-2})$$

$$\text{or } (6 + 2x^{-1} - x^{-2})e^{-2}$$

31. $f(x) = (5x - 2)e^{1-2x}$. Use the product rule:

$$f'(x) = (5x - 2)\cdot\frac{d}{dx}e^{1-2x} + e^{1-2x}\cdot\frac{d}{dx}(5x - 2)$$

$$= (5x - 2)\cdot e^{1-2x}\cdot(-2) + e^{1-2x}\cdot 5.$$

Simplify f'(x) first, and then find f"(x):

$$f'(x) = (-10x + 4)e^{1-2x} + 5e^{1-2x} = (-10x + 4 + 5)e^{1-2x}$$

$$= (9 - 10x)e^{1-2x}$$

$$f''(x) = (9 - 10x)\cdot e^{1-2x}(-2) + e^{1-2x}\cdot(-10).$$

To find values of x at which f(x) has a possible relative max or min, set the derivative equal to zero, and solve for x:

$$(9 - 10x)e^{1-2x} = 0 \Rightarrow 9 - 10x = 0 \text{ and } x = 9/10.$$

Here we used the fact that e^{1-2x} is never zero. To check the concavity of the graph of f(x) at x = .9, compute f"(.9). Looking at f"(x), notice that the first term is zero when 9 - 10x = 0, so

$$f''(.9) = 0 + e^{1-2(.9)}\cdot(-10) < 0,$$

because every value of e^{x} is positive. The graph is con-cave down at x = .9, and so f(x) has a relative maximum point at x = .9 or 9/10.

Helpful Hint: Simplify f'(x) before computing f"(x), but don't simplify f"(x). When you find an x that makes f'(x) = 0, this value of x may satisfy some equation that will make part of the formula for f"(x) equal to 0. In Exercise 31 above, the equation was 9 - 10x = 0. This fact simplifies calculations when you check f"(x) for concavity.

37. The phrase "after 7 weeks" means that 7 weeks have passed since t was zero; that is, t = 7. The rate of growth involves the derivative, so we compute:

$$f(t) = (.05 + e^{-.4t})^{-1}$$

$$f'(t) = (-1)(.05 + e^{-.4t})^{-2} \cdot \frac{d}{dt}(.05 + e^{-.4t})$$

$$= -(.05 + e^{-.4t})^{-2} \cdot e^{-.4t}(-.4).$$

There is no need to simplify $f'(t)$, because further differentiation is not required.

$$f'(7) = -(.05 + e^{-2.8})^{-2} \cdot e^{-2.8}(-.4) \approx 1.98.$$

The plant was growing at the rate of nearly 2 inches per week after 7 weeks.

43. This question relies on the basic fact discussed just before Example 5. If $y' = -.5y$, then y must be a function of the form $f(t) = Ce^{-.5x}$, for some constant C. If, in addition, $f(0) = 1$, then $Ce^{-.5(0)} = 1$, which shows that $C = 1$ (because $e^0 = 1$). Thus, $f(t) = e^{-.5x}$.

49. Set $Y_1 = 1.825^3*(1 - 1.6*e^{\wedge}(-.4196X))^{\wedge}3$, set Y_4 to be the derivative (possibly a numerical derivative) of Y_1, and set Y_5 to be the derivative of Y_2.

   a. A suitable window for graphing is [1,15] by [0,8]. The graph seems to have a horizontal asymptote close to $y = 6$ milliliters. As X grows, the negative exponential goes to zero, and values of Y_1 approach 1.825^3, which equals 6.0784, to four decimal places.

   b. Use TRACE or function evaluation to find $Y_1(5) \approx 3.16$ milliliters at X = 5 weeks.

   c. Set $Y_2 = 5$ (a constant function), and use Intersect, to find the X at which the graphs of Y_1 and Y_2 cross. You should obtain $X \approx 7.71$ weeks.

   d. Graph Y_4 and use TRACE, or evaluate $Y_4(5)$, to find the rate of growth when X = 5. You should find that $Y_4(5)$ is about .97 milliliters per week.

   e. The growth is fastest when the derivative has a maximum, which can happen only if the second derivative is zero. So use a Solver command to find when $Y_5 = 0$. You should obtain $X \approx 3.74$ weeks.

   f. Evaluate Y_4 at the value of X found in part (e). You should obtain $Y_4(3.74) \approx 1.13$ ml/wk.

4.4 The Natural Logarithm Function

The natural logarithm function is defined by its graph, and this is what you should think of when you are trying to understand what the ln x function really is. Study Fig. 2 in Section 4.4. The natural logarithm is a function whose graph is defined only for x > 0; the graph is increasing, passes through (1,0), and is concave downward. The graph of ln x is obtained by interchanging the x- and y-coordinates of points on the graph of $y = e^x$. This fact leads immediately to the fundamental relations (numbered below as in the text):

$$e^{\ln x} = x \qquad \text{(all positive x)} \qquad\qquad (2)$$

$$\ln e^x = x \qquad \text{(all x)} \qquad\qquad\qquad (3)$$

The main purpose of Section 4.4 is to teach you how to use these relations to solve equations involving ln x and e^x.

1. $\ln(\sqrt{e}) = \ln e^{1/2} = \frac{1}{2}$ [Relation (3)]

7. $\ln e^{-3} = -3$ [Relation (3)]

13. If $e^{2x} = 5$, we take the (natural) logarithm of each side to obtain:

$$\ln e^{2x} = \ln 5,$$

$$2x = \ln 5, \qquad \text{[Relation (3)]}$$

$$x = \frac{1}{2} \ln 5.$$

19. The first step is to isolate the term $e^{-.00012x}$ so we can use the logarithm function to undo the effect of the exponentiation. Given $6e^{-.00012x} = 3$, we divide by 6 to obtain:

$$e^{-.00012x} = .5.$$

Taking the natural logarithm of each side, we have

$$\ln e^{-.00012x} = \ln .5,$$

$$-.00012x = \ln .5,$$

$$x = \frac{\ln .5}{-.00012}.$$

25. If $2e^{x/3} - 9 = 0$ then

$$2e^{x/3} = 9,$$

$$e^{x/3} = \frac{9}{2},$$

$$\ln(e^{x/3}) = \ln\frac{9}{2},$$

$$\frac{x}{3} = \ln\frac{9}{2}, \text{ or } x = 3\ln\frac{9}{2}.$$

31. Given $4e^x \cdot e^{-2x} = 6$, observe that x occurs in two places. Use a property of exponents to write

$$4e^{-x} = 6.$$

Now proceed as in Exercise 19.

$$e^{-x} = \frac{6}{4} = \frac{3}{2},$$

$$\ln e^{-x} = \ln\frac{3}{2},$$

$$-x = \ln\frac{3}{2}, \text{ or } x = -\ln\frac{3}{2}.$$

Warning: A slight change in Exercise 31 can make it seem harder. Consider the equation

$$e^x = \frac{3}{2}e^{2x}.$$

Taking logarithms at this point is of no help because the equation $x = \ln(\frac{3}{2}e^{2x})$ expresses x in terms of something involving x. The correct step is to get x on only one side of the equation. There are two ways to do this:

$$\text{(i)} \quad e^x = \frac{3}{2}e^{2x}, \qquad \text{or} \qquad \text{(ii)} \quad e^x = \frac{3}{2}e^{2x},$$

$$e^x - \frac{3}{2}e^{2x} = 0. \qquad\qquad\qquad e^x \cdot e^{-2x} = \frac{3}{2}e^{2x} \cdot e^{-2x}.$$

Equation (i) leads nowhere because you can't take the logarithm of each side, since $\ln 0$ is not defined. Also, $\ln(e^x - \frac{3}{2}e^{2x})$ cannot be simplified. Equation (ii) is the correct approach, since a property of exponents leads to $e^{-x} = \frac{3}{2}e^0$, that is, $e^{-x} = \frac{3}{2}$. This can be solved for x as in Exercise 31, yielding $x = -\ln\frac{3}{2}$.

37. If $f(t) = 5(e^{-.01t} - e^{-.51t})$, then

$$f'(t) = 5(e^{-.01t}(-.01) - e^{-.51t}(-.51))$$

$$= 5(-.01e^{-.01t} + .51e^{-.51t}).$$

Set $f'(t) = 0$ and solve for t:

$$5(-.01e^{-.01t} + .51e^{-.51t}) = 0,$$

$$-.01e^{-.01t} + .51e^{-.51t} = 0.$$

Thus,

$$-.01e^{-.01t} = -.51e^{-.51t},$$

$$e^{-.01t} \cdot e^{.51t} = \frac{-.51}{-.01} e^{-.51t} \cdot e^{.51t},$$

$$e^{.5t} = 51,$$

$$\ln e^{.5t} = \ln 51,$$

$$.5t = \ln 51, \text{ or } t = 2 \ln 51.$$

43. Set $Y_1 = \ln(5X)$ and $Y_2 = 2$. Graph Y_1 and Y_2 in a window such as $[0,10]$ *by* $[-10,10]$. Use the intersection command on your calculator (see the Appendix) to find the x-coordinate of the intersection point. (You should obtain $X \approx 1.478$.) On paper, solve the equation $\ln 5x = 2$, to find $5x = e^2$ and $x = e^2/5$. Evaluate $e^x/5$ on your calculator to see if the value agrees with the intersection point you found.

4.5 The Derivative of ln x

The exercises in this section combine the derivative formula for ln x with a review of the product rule, the quotient rule, and the chain rule. You should memorize the chain rule for the logarithm function:

$$\boxed{\frac{d}{dx}[\ln g(x)] = \frac{1}{g(x)} \cdot g'(x) = \frac{g'(x)}{g(x)}}$$

This rule is used in Exercises 1, 7, 13, and 19, discussed below.

1. $\dfrac{d}{dx} \ln 2x = \dfrac{1}{2x} \cdot \dfrac{d}{dx}(2x) = \dfrac{1}{2x}(2) = \dfrac{1}{x}.$

7. $\dfrac{d}{dx}e^{\ln x + x} = e^{\ln x + x} \cdot \dfrac{d}{dx}(\ln x + x) = \left(\dfrac{1}{x} + 1\right)e^{\ln x + x}.$

13. $\dfrac{d}{dx}\ln(kx) = \dfrac{1}{kx} \cdot \dfrac{d}{dx}(kx) = \dfrac{1}{kx}(k) = \dfrac{1}{x}.$

19. $\dfrac{d}{dx}\ln(e^{5x} + 1) = \dfrac{1}{e^{5x} + 1} \cdot \dfrac{d}{dx}(e^{5x} + 1)$

$$= \dfrac{1}{e^{5x} + 1} \cdot e^{5x}(5)$$

$$= \dfrac{5e^{5x}}{e^{5x} + 1}.$$

25. For the equation of the tangent line we need a point on the line and the slope of the line. We use the original equation $y = \ln(x^2 + e)$ to find a point. If $x = 0$, then $y = \ln(0^2 + e) = \ln e = 1$, and hence $(0,1)$ is on the line. For the slope of the tangent line, we first find the general slope formula.

$$\dfrac{dy}{dx} = \dfrac{1}{x^2 + e} \cdot \dfrac{d}{dx}(x^2 + e)$$

$$= \dfrac{1}{x^2 + e}(2x) \qquad [\text{e is a constant}]$$

$$= \dfrac{2x}{x^2 + e}.$$

The slope of the tangent line when $x = 0$ is $\dfrac{2(0)}{0^2 + e} = 0$.

Therefore the tangent line is the horizontal line passing through the point $(0,1)$. The equation of this line is $y - 1 = 0(x - 0)$; that is, $y = 1$.

Warning: Exercises 25—30 make good exam questions because they review important concepts and skills from Chapters 1—3 as well as testing your ability to differentiate $\ln g(x)$.

31. The marginal cost at $x = 10$ is $C'(10)$. Using the quotient rule, we first find

$$C'(x) = \dfrac{d}{dx}\left(\dfrac{100 \ln x}{40 - 3x}\right)$$

$$= \frac{(40-3x) \cdot \frac{d}{dx}(100 \ln x) - (100 \ln x) \cdot \frac{d}{dx}(40-3x)}{(40-3x)^2}$$

$$= \frac{(40-3x)(\frac{100}{x}) - (100 \ln x)(-3)}{(40-3x)^2} .$$

$$\text{Now } C'(10) = \frac{(40-3(10))\frac{100}{10} + 300 \ln 10}{(40-3(10))^2}$$

$$= \frac{100 + 300 \ln 10}{(10)^2} \qquad = 1 + 3 \ln 10.$$

37. Set $Y_1 = \ln(\text{abs}(X))$ and set Y_4 to be the derivative of Y_1. For the "abs" command, you can either type the lowercase letters or use the CATALOG command to find "abs" in the list of all commands. Graph both functions in the ZDecimal window (found in the Zoom menu). Use TRACE on the graph of Y_4 to check the values of Y_4 at -4, -2, -1, 1, 2, and 4. (You should obtain $-.25$, $-.5$, -1, 1, -5, and $.25$.) What happens at $x = 0$?

4.6 Properties of the Natural Logarithm Function

Just as with laws of exponents, it is essential to know the properties of logarithms "backwards and forwards." You will find it helpful to add the following properties to the list on page 255.

LI′	$\ln x + \ln y = \ln xy$
LII′	$-\ln x = \ln(\frac{1}{x})$
LIII′	$\ln x - \ln y = \ln(\frac{x}{y})$
LIV′	$b \ln x = \ln(x^b)$

Unfortunately, many students make up additional "laws" that are not true. A study of the following facts will help you avoid the most common incorrect "laws".

a. $\ln(x + y)$ is not equal to $\ln x + \ln y$.

b. $\ln(e^x + e^y)$ is not equal to $x + y$.

c. $(\ln x)(\ln y)$ is <u>not</u> equal to $\ln x + \ln y$.

d. $\dfrac{\ln x}{\ln y}$ is <u>not</u> equal to $\ln x - \ln y$.

1. $\ln 5 + \ln x = \ln 5x$. (LI')

7. $e^{2\ln x} = e^{\ln x^2} = x^2$. (LIV')

13. We have $2\ln 5 = \ln 5^2 = \ln 25$, (LIV')

    and $\quad 3\ln 3 = \ln 3^3 = \ln 27$. (LIV')

    Since the graph of the natural logarithm function is in-creasing, and since $25 < 27$, we know that $\ln 25 < \ln 27$. Therefore, $3\ln 3$ is larger.

Helpful Hint: Whenever you have a function to differentiate, you should pause and check if the form of the function can be simplified *before* you begin to differentiate. Exercises 19-26 illustrate how much this will simplify your work.

19. $y = \ln[(x+5)(2x-1)(4-x)] = \ln(x+5) + \ln(2x-1) + \ln(4-x)$.
    (LI')

    $\dfrac{dy}{dx} = \dfrac{d}{dx}\ln(x+5) + \dfrac{d}{dx}\ln(2x-1) + \dfrac{d}{dx}\ln(4-x)$

    $\quad = \dfrac{1}{x+5} + \dfrac{1.(2)}{2x-1} + \dfrac{1.(-1)}{4-x}$

    $\quad = \dfrac{1}{x+5} + \dfrac{2}{2x-1} + \dfrac{1}{x-4}$.

25. $y = \ln(5x+1) + \ln(4x+1) + \ln(\ln x) - \ln(\sqrt{2x+1})$

    $\quad = \ln(5x+1) + \ln(4x+1) + \ln(\ln x) - \dfrac{1}{2}\ln(2x+1)$.

    $\dfrac{dy}{dx} = \dfrac{d}{dx}\ln(5x+1) + \dfrac{d}{dx}\ln(4x+1) + \dfrac{d}{dx}\ln(\ln x)$

    $\qquad - \dfrac{1}{2}\dfrac{d}{dx}\ln(2x+1)$

    $\quad = \dfrac{1}{5x+1}\cdot 5 + \dfrac{1}{4x+1}\cdot 4 + \dfrac{1}{\ln x}\cdot\dfrac{d}{dx}\ln(x) - \dfrac{1}{2}\cdot\dfrac{1}{2x+1}\cdot 2$

    $\quad = \dfrac{5}{5x+1} + \dfrac{4}{4x+1} + \dfrac{1}{x\ln x} - \dfrac{1}{2x+1}$.

Warning: Remember that the natural logarithm converts products and quotients into sums and differences. But a *product* of logarithms *cannot* be simplified by a standard logarithm rule. Be on guard when you work Exercises 27 and 28.

31. $f(x) = \dfrac{(x + 1)(2x + 1)(3x + 1)}{(4x + 1)^{1/2}}$,

$\ln f(x) = \ln\left[\dfrac{(x + 1)(2x + 1)(3x + 1)}{(4x + 1)^{1/2}}\right]$

$\qquad = \ln(x+1) + \ln(2x+1) + \ln(3x+1) - \dfrac{1}{2}\ln(4x+1).$

Differentiate both sides with respect to x:

$\dfrac{f'(x)}{f(x)} = \dfrac{1}{x+1} + \dfrac{1}{2x+1}\cdot 2 + \dfrac{1}{3x+1}\cdot 3 - \dfrac{1}{2}\cdot\dfrac{1}{4x+1}\cdot 4$

$\qquad = \dfrac{1}{x+1} + \dfrac{2}{2x+1} + \dfrac{3}{3x+1} - \dfrac{2}{4x+1}.$

So

$f'(x) = f(x)\cdot\left[\dfrac{1}{x+1} + \dfrac{2}{2x+1} + \dfrac{3}{3x+1} - \dfrac{2}{4x+1}\right]$

$\qquad = \dfrac{(x + 1)(2x + 1)(3x + 1)}{(4x + 1)^{1/2}}\left[\dfrac{1}{x+1} + \dfrac{2}{2x+1} + \dfrac{3}{3x+1} - \dfrac{2}{4x+1}\right].$

37. $\ln y = k\ln x + \ln c,$

$e^{\ln y} = e^{k\ln x + \ln c} = e^{k\ln x}e^{\ln c}$ (by laws on p. 280 of text)

$\qquad\qquad = e^{\ln x^k}e^{\ln c}$ (LIV′)

Since $e^{\ln y} = y$, $e^{\ln x^k} = x^k$, and $e^{\ln c} = c$, the last equation becomes:

$\qquad y = cx^k.$

Review of Chapter 4

There are many facts in this chapter to remember and keep straight. The learning process requires time and lots of practice. Don't wait until the last minute to review. Your efforts to master this chapter will be rewarded later, since the exponential and natural logarithm functions appear in nearly every section in the rest of the text.

By now you should have constructed the expanded lists of properties of exponents and logarithms. To these lists add notes about common mistakes—yours and the ones mentioned in the study guide notes for this chapter. Here is another common error: If you take logarithms of each side of an equation of the form

$$A = B + C,$$

you *cannot* write $\ln A = \ln B + \ln C$.   The correct form is

$$\ln A = \ln(B + C).$$

Similarly, if you exponentiate each side of $A = B + C$, you *cannot* write $e^A = e^B + e^C$.   The correct form is

$$e^A = e^{(B + C)}.$$

Here are four problems that contain "traps" for the unwary student.   Try them now.   You will find answers later in the manual   as   you   work   through   the   supplementary   exercises. *Please* don't look for the answers until you have done your best to work the problems.

    (A) Solve for y in terms of x: $\ln y - \ln x^2 = \ln 5$.

    (B) Solve for y in terms of x: $e^y - e^{-3} = e^{2x}$.

    (C) Solve for x: $\dfrac{\ln 10x^3}{\ln 2x^2} = 1$.

    (D) Simplify, if possible: $\ln(x^3 - x^2)$.

Chapter 4: Supplementary Exercises

In Exercises 9-14 and 35-40, *"simplify"* means to use the laws of exponents and logarithms to write the expression in another form that either is less complicated or at least is more useful for some purposes.

1. $27^{4/3} = (27^{1/3})^4 = 3^4 = 81.$

7. $\dfrac{9^{5/2}}{9^{3/2}} = 9^{5/2-3/2} = 9^{2/2} = 9.$

13. $(e^{8x} + 7e^{-2x})e^{3x} = e^{8x} \cdot e^{3x} + 7e^{-2x} \cdot e^{3x}$

$$= e^{11x} + 7e^x.$$

19. $\dfrac{d}{dx}10e^{7x} = 10\dfrac{d}{dx}e^{7x} = 10e^{7x}(7) = 70e^{7x}.$

25. $\dfrac{d}{dx}\left(\dfrac{x^2 - x + 5}{e^{3x} + 3}\right) = \dfrac{(e^{3x}+3)\cdot(2x-1) - (x^2-x+5)\cdot 3e^{3x}}{(e^{3x} + 3)^2}$ $\quad\left[\begin{matrix}\text{Quot.}\\\text{rule}\end{matrix}\right]$

Helpful Hint: In Exercises 27-30, the solution is a *function*, not a number. An equation in which both the unknown function and its (unknown) derivative appear is called a *differential equation*. The differential equations that appear here are solved with the boxed result (3) of Section 4.3.

31. $y = e^{-x} + x$, $y' = -e^{-x} + 1$, $y'' = e^{-x}$.

Now set $y' = 0$ and solve for x:

$$-e^{-x} + 1 = 0,$$
$$e^{-x} = 1,$$
$$\ln e^{-x} = \ln(1),$$
$$-x = 0, \text{ or } x = 0.$$

If $x = 0$, then $y = e^{-0} + 0 = 1$ and $y'' = e^{-0} = 1 > 0$, hence the graph is concave up at $(0,1)$. Thus the graph has a relative minimum at $(0,1)$. Since $y'' = e^{-x} > 0$ for all x, the graph is concave up for all x and there are no inflection points. As x becomes large: e^{-x} approaches 0, and for this case $e^{-x} + x$ is only slightly larger than x. Hence for large positive values of x, the graph of $y = e^{-x} + x$ has $y = x$ as an asymptote. The graph is shown in the answer section of the text.

Warning: Be careful with Exercise 35. Don't use an incorrect property of logarithms, and don't look at the answer until you have tried the problem!

37. $e^{-5\ln 1} = e^{-5(0)} = e^0 = 1$.

43. $2 \ln t = 5$, then
$$\ln t = \frac{5}{2},$$
$$e^{\ln t} = e^{5/2},$$
$$t = e^{5/2}.$$

49. $\dfrac{d}{dx}(\ln x)^2 = 2(\ln x)\cdot\dfrac{d}{dx}(\ln x) = 2(\ln x)\left(\dfrac{1}{x}\right) = \dfrac{2\ln x}{x}$.

55. $\dfrac{d}{dx} \ln(\ln\sqrt{x}) = \dfrac{1}{\ln\sqrt{x}} \cdot \dfrac{d}{dx}\ln\sqrt{x} = \dfrac{1}{\ln x^{1/2}} \cdot \dfrac{d}{dx}\ln x^{1/2}$

$$= \dfrac{1}{(1/2)\ln x} \cdot \dfrac{d}{dx}\left[\dfrac{1}{2}\ln x\right]$$

$$= \dfrac{2}{\ln x} \cdot \dfrac{1}{2} \cdot \dfrac{d}{dx}\ln x = \dfrac{1}{\ln x} \cdot \dfrac{1}{x} = \dfrac{1}{x\ln x}.$$

Helpful Hint: Always be alert to the possibility of simplifying a function before you differentiate it. This is particularly important when the function involves $\ln x$ or e^x. Observe that

$$\ln(\ln\sqrt{x}) = \ln(\ln x^{1/2}) = \ln(\tfrac{1}{2}\ln x) = \ln\tfrac{1}{2} + \ln(\ln x).$$

Thus

$$\dfrac{d}{dx}\ln(\ln\sqrt{x}) = \dfrac{d}{dx}\ln\tfrac{1}{2} + \dfrac{d}{dx}\ln(\ln x)$$

$$= 0 + \dfrac{1}{\ln x} \cdot \dfrac{d}{dx}\ln x = \dfrac{1}{\ln x} \cdot \dfrac{1}{x} = \dfrac{1}{x\ln x}.$$

Hints for extra problems:

(A) Get $\ln y$ by itself on the left, and use a property of logarithms to simplify $\ln 5 + \ln x^2$.

(B) Write $e^y = e^{2x} + e^{-3}$ and then take the logarithm of each side. Be careful!

(C) You made a mistake if you obtained any of the following equations from problem (C):

$$\dfrac{10x^3}{2x^2} = 1, \quad \ln\left(\dfrac{10x^3}{2x^2}\right) = 1, \quad \ln(10x^3 - 2x^2) = 1.$$

None of these equations is equivalent to the original equation. The correct first step is to multiply both sides of the equation in (C) by $\ln 2x^2$ and obtain $\ln 10x^3 = \ln 2x^2$. _Now_ can you solve for x?

(D) Is it true that $\ln(x^3 - x^2)$ is the same as $\dfrac{\ln x^3}{\ln x^2}$?

The correct solutions to (A) – (D) are at the end of this supplementary exercise set.

61. First take the natural logarithm of each side.

$$\ln f(x) = \ln[(x^2+5)^6(x^3+7)^8(x^4+9)^{10}]$$

$$= \ln(x^2+5)^6 + \ln(x^3+7)^8 + \ln(x^4+9)^{10} \qquad \text{(LI)}$$

$$= 6 \cdot \ln(x^2+5) + 8 \cdot \ln(x^3+7) + 10 \cdot \ln(x^4+9). \qquad \text{(LIV)}$$

Now, take the derivative of each side and solve for $f'(x)$.

$$\frac{f'(x)}{f(x)} = 6\left[\frac{1}{x^2+5} \cdot 2x\right] + 8\left[\frac{1}{x^3+7} \cdot 3x^2\right] + 10\left[\frac{1}{x^4+9} \cdot 4x^3\right]$$

$$= \frac{12x}{x^2+5} + \frac{24x^2}{x^3+7} + \frac{40x^3}{x^4+9}.$$

$$f'(x) = f(x)\left[\frac{12x}{2} + \frac{24x^2}{3} + \frac{40x^3}{4}\right]$$

$$= (x^2+5)^6(x^3+7)^8(x^4+9)^{10}\left[\frac{12x}{x^2+5} + \frac{24x^2}{x^3+7} + \frac{40x^3}{x^4+9}\right].$$

67. $y = (\ln x)^2,$

$$y' = 2(\ln x) \cdot \frac{d}{dx}\ln x = \frac{2 \ln x}{x}.$$

$$y'' = \frac{x \cdot \frac{d}{dx}(2 \ln x) - (2 \ln x)\frac{d}{dx}x}{x^2} = \frac{x \cdot 2\left(\frac{1}{x}\right) - 2 \ln x}{x^2}$$

$$= \frac{2 - 2 \ln x}{x^2}.$$

Set $y' = 0$ and solve for x:

$$\frac{2 \ln x}{x} = 0.$$

A fraction is zero only when its numerator is zero. Thus $2 \ln x = 0$, and $\ln x = 0$. Then $e^{\ln x} = e^0 = 1$, so $x = 1$. If $x = 1$, then $y = (\ln 1)^2 = 0$, and

$$y'' = \frac{2 - 2 \ln 1}{1^2} = 2 > 0.$$

Hence, the curve is concave up at $(1,0)$. Now, set $y'' = 0$ and solve for x to find the possible inflection points.

$$\frac{2 - 2 \ln x}{x^2} = 0,$$

$$2 - 2 \ln x = 0,$$

$$-2 \ln x = -2, \text{ or } \ln x = 1.$$

So,

$$e^{\ln x} = e^1, \text{ or } x = e.$$

If $x = e$, then $y = (\ln e)^2 = 1$, hence $(e,1)$ is the only possible inflection point. We have seen that the second derivative is positive at $x = 0$. When x is large, then $y = 2 \ln x$ is negative, so the second derivative is negative. Thus the concavity must change somewhere, which shows that $(e,1)$ is the inflection point. The graph is shown in the answer section of the text.

Solutions to Extra Problems

(A) $\ln y - \ln x^2 = \ln 5$,

$\ln y = \ln 5 + \ln x^2$,

$\ln y = \ln 5x^2$.

Exponentiate each side to obtain $y = x^2$.

(B) $e^y = e^{2x} + e^{-3}$,

$\ln e^y = \ln(e^{2x} + e^{-3})$, $\quad \begin{bmatrix} \text{Note: The right side} \\ \text{cannot be simplified.} \end{bmatrix}$

$\quad y = \ln(e^{2x} + e^{-3})$.

(C) $\ln 10x^3 = \ln 2x^2$. Exponentiate to obtain

$\quad 10x^3 = 2x^2$.

Notice that x cannot be zero, since $\ln 10x^3$ is not defined when $x = 0$. So we may divide by $2x^2$ and obtain $5x = 1$ and hence $x = 1/5$.

(D) If you answered "yes" to the "Hint", then you have made one of the most common mistakes involving logarithms. The logarithm of a sum or difference *cannot be simplified*, unless that sum or difference can be written somehow as a product or quotient. For instance, you *may* write

$\quad \ln(x^3 - x^2) = \ln[x^2(x - 1)] \quad$ [now the expression inside
$\qquad\qquad\qquad\qquad\qquad\qquad$ the logarithm is a product]

$\qquad\qquad = \ln x^2 + \ln(x - 1)$

$\qquad\qquad = 2 \ln x + \ln(x - 1).$

Whether or not this answer is "simplified" depends on the use to be made of the expression. See our remark at the beginning of the Supplementary Exercises.

Chapter 5

Applications of the Exponential and Natural Logarithm Functions

5.1 Exponential Growth and Decay

The basic differential equation $y' = ky$ was introduced in Section 4.3, just before Example 5. You should review that now. All the exercises in this section refer either to that differential equation or to the general form of functions that satisfy the equation, namely, $f(x) = Ce^{kx}$. In this chapter, we usually use t in place of x, because most of the applications involve functions of time.

The first question to ask when considering an exponential growth and decay problem is, "Does the quantity increase or decrease with time?" For instance, populations increase and radioactive substances decrease. The formula for the quantity present after t units of time will have the form $P(t) = P_0 e^{kt}$ if increasing and $P(t) = P_0 e^{-\lambda t}$ if decreasing. The problems are primarily of the following types:

1. Given P_0 and k (or λ), find the value of $P(t)$ for a specific time t. These problems are solved by just substituting the value of t into the formula.

2. Given P_0 and k (or λ), find the time when $P(t)$ assumes a specific value, call it A. That is, solve $P(t) = A$ for t. Problems of this type are solved by replacing $P(t)$ by its formula, dividing by P_0 and using logarithms. Sometimes A is given as a multiple of P_0, in which case the P_0's cancel each other.

3. Given P_0 and the value of $P(t)$ at some specific time t, solve for k (or λ). This problem reduces to one of the form "solve $P_0 e^{kt} = A$," where A is the value of $P(t)$.

This equation is solved by the method of 2 above.

4. The problem gives enough information to solve for k (or λ), but only asks for the value of P(t) at a future time or asks for the time at which P(t) attains a given size. The important point to realize here is that the problem really consists of two parts First, find k (or λ) and second, answer the question asked. Exercises 9 and 19 are of this type. Students usually have difficulty with such problems on exams since they try to answer the question posed immediately without doing the intermediate step.

5. Determine the *rate of change* of P(t) at a time when P(t) is a certain size. The actual time is not specified, so you cannot compute P'(t) and evaluate at t. Instead, you must use the differential equation P'(t) = k·P(t). Assuming that k is known, you can determine P'(t) from P(t) (for the same t), and vice-versa. You'll find this type of problem in Exercises 1, 13, and elsewhere.

1. a. The differential equation P'(t) = .02P(t) has the form y' = ky, with k = .02, so the general solution P(t) has the form $P(t) = P_0 e^{.02t}$. Also,

$$P(0) = P_0 e^{.02(0)} = P_0,$$

so the condition P(0) = 3 shows that $P(t) = 3e^{.02t}$.

   b. *Initial population* is the population when t = 0, which in this problem refers to 1990: 3 million persons.

   c. The *growth constant* is the constant .02 that appears in the differential equation P'(t) = .02P(t).

   d. 1998 corresponds to t = 8. The population then was $P(8) = 3e^{.02(8)} = 3.52053261298$ million. Of course, writing the answer in this form is silly. Even the answer 3,520,533 persons is inappropriate. A problem such as this exercise purports to be a *model* of population growth, but it is only an approximation at best. Since the initial population is given with only the single digit "3", a rounded answer such as 3.5 million, or perhaps 3.52 million, would be more realistic.

   e. Assume that t_0 is the time when $P(t_0) = 4$ (million). At that value of t, the differential equation says that

$$P'(t_0) = .02P(t_0) = .02 \cdot 4 = .08 .$$

5-2

The population is growing at the rate of .08 million (or 80,000) people per year.

f. The unit of measurement of the population is millions of people, so convert 70,000 to .07 million. If t represents the time when $P'(t) = .07$ million people per year, then the differential equation

$$P'(t) = .02P(t)$$

shows that $.07 = .02P(t)$ and hence $P(t) = .07/.02 = 3.5$. The population is approximately 3.5 million.

Helpful Hint: In Exercises 5, 6, 9, and 10, the phrase "growing at a rate proportional to its size" describes the differential equation $y' = ky$. You may assume that the solution of this equation has the form $y = P_0e^{kt}$, or $P(t) = P_0e^{kt}$. This fact was discussed at the beginning of the chapter.

7. See the notes about problem type #2 on page 5-1 in this *Study Guide*. The phrase "growing exponentially" is another way of saying that the model for the growth is $P(t) = P_0e^{kt}$. Here k is .05, so $P(t) = P_0e^{.05t}$. The population will be triple its initial size when $P(t) = 3P_0$. To find the time when this happens, set the formula for $P(t)$ equal to $3P_0$ and solve for t:

$$P_0e^{.05t} = 3P_0$$

$$e^{.05t} = 3 \quad \text{(dividing both sides by } P_0\text{)}.$$

Apply the natural logarithm to each side:

$$\ln e^{.05t} = \ln 3$$

$$.05t = \ln 3$$

$$t = \frac{\ln 3}{.05} \approx 22 \text{ years} \quad \text{(rounding off 21.97 to 22)}.$$

13. a. From the differential equation $P'(t) = -.021\,P(t)$, you know that $P(t)$ has the form $P(t) = P_0e^{-.021t}$. The initial amount is 8 grams, so $P(t) = 8e^{-.021t}$.

b. $P(0) = P_0 = 8$ grams.

c. The decay constant is .021 (not -.021).

d. Compute $P(10) = 8e^{-.021(10)} \approx 6.5$ grams.

e. $P'(t) = -.021\,P(t)$. If $P(t) = 1$, then at this same time, $P'(t) = -.021(1) = -.021$ grams/year. The sample is disintegrating at the rate of .021 grams/year.

f. The time is not specified directly, but it described by the property that $P(t)$ is "disintegrating at the rate of .105 grams per year," that is, $P'(t_0) = -.105$ for some particular time t_0. From the differential equation, you can conclude that

$$P'(t_0) = -.021P(t_0)$$

that is,

$$-.105 = -.021 \cdot P(t_0)$$

Hence, $P(t_0) = \frac{-.105}{-.021} = 5$. Thus 5 grams of material remain at the time when the disintegration rate is .105 grams per year.

g. A half-life of 33 years means that half of any given amount will remain in 33 years. Of the original 8 grams, 4 will remain in 33 years, of that amount 2 grams will remain after another 33 years, and 1 gram will remain after another 33 years (a total of 99 years).

19. This problem is the problem type #4 discussed on page 5-1. The first step is to find the decay constant, using the fact that 5 grams decay to 2 grams in 100 days. We may assume that $P(0) = 5$, and $P(t) = 5e^{-\lambda t}$. Set $P(100) = 2$ and solve for λ:

$$5e^{-\lambda(100)} = 2$$

$$e^{-100\lambda} = \frac{2}{5} = .4$$

$$-100\lambda = \ln(.4)$$

$$\lambda = \frac{\ln(.4)}{-100} \approx .00916291 \text{ or } .00916 .$$

Once λ is determined, write the explicit formula for $P(t)$, that is, $P(t) = 5e^{-.00916t}$. The second step is to find the value of t at which $P(t)$ is 1 gram. Set $P(t) = 1$ and solve for t:

$$5e^{-.00916t} = 1$$

$$e^{-.00916t} = .2$$

$$-0.00916t = \ln(.2)$$

$$t = \frac{\ln(.2)}{-.00916} \approx 175.70.$$

The material will decay to 1 gram in about 176 days.

Helpful Hint: It is wise to keep at least two or three significant figures in a decay constant or growth constant. Otherwise, the answers to other parts of the problem can vary somewhat. In the solution to Exercise 19, above, a value of .009 for λ leads to the answer that 1 gram will remain in 179 days.

25. Let P_0 be the original level of ^{14}C in the charcoal. Since the decay constant for ^{14}C is $\lambda = .00012$, the amount of ^{14}C remaining after t years is $P(t) = P_0 e^{-.00012t}$. The discovery in 1947 found that the amount of ^{14}C found in the charcoal is $.20P_0$, assuming that the original ^{14}C level in the charcoal was the same as the level in living organisms today. That is, we assume that the time t satisfies $P(t) = .20P_0$, which says that

$$P_0 e^{-.00012t} = .2P_0.$$

Solving for t,

$$e^{-.00012t} = .2$$

$$-.00012t = \ln(.2)$$

$$t = (\ln .2)/(-.00012) \approx 13,412 \text{ years.}$$

That was the estimated age of the cave paintings more than 50 years ago. The estimated age now is about 13,500 years.

31. Read through the answers and note that in some cases such as (c) and (d) a function is evaluated at a specified value of t, that is, the time t is known but the value of the function must be computed. In other cases such as (a) and (f), the time t is unknown and an equation is solved to find t.

    Next, note that some answers such as (b) and (c) involve the function $P(t)$, the amount of material present, while other answers such as (d) and (f) involve the derivative $P'(t)$, the *rate* at which the amount of material is changing. Finally, answers (g) and (h) relate to the specific type of function and differential equation that are associated with the model for radioactive decay.

Now, before you read further in this solution, go back to the text, read each question, and try to find the appropriate answer. *After you have done this*, read the solutions that follow.

A. The only differential equation is in (g).

B. The question "How fast?" indicates an answer involving the derivative (rate of change). The time is known, so the answer is (d), compute $P'(.5)$.

C. The general form of the function $P(t)$ is in (h).

D. Half-life is the time at which $P(t)$ is half of the original amount, $P(0)$. The answer is (a).

E. "How many grams?" relates to $P(t)$, not $P'(t)$. The time is known, so the answer is (c), compute $P(.5)$.

F. The phrase "disintegrating at the rate" relates to $P'(t)$, and the question "When?" forces us to find t. The answer is (f).

G. The question "When?" implies that the answer is either (a), (b) or (f). Rate of change is not involved, so (f) is ruled out. To choose between (a) and (b), you need to realize that the .5 in (b) is the *value* of $P(t)$ while the .5 in (a) only *compares* the value of $P(t)$ to $P(0)$. So the answer is (b).

H. "How much" relates to $P(t)$, and "present initially" actually gives the time, namely $t = 0$, although the word "year" is not mentioned. The answer is (e).

Helpful Hint: Exercise 31 provides a good review of basic concepts of exponential decay. Similar questions for exponential growth are in Exercise 25 of Section 5.2 and Exercise 13 of the Supplementary Exercises.

Helpful Hint: Use estimation to check whether your answer to a growth or decay problem is reasonable.

(a) Suppose a population doubles every 24 years and you compute that it will increase tenfold in 100 years. Is this reasonable? Round the doubling time to 25 years and notice that in 100 years, the initial population P_0 will double four times, from P_0 to $2P_0$, then to $4P_0$, $8P_0$ and finally $16P_0$, which is much more than just ten times P_0. Therefore, the answer is not reasonable.

(b) Suppose that a radioactive material has a half-life of 5 years and you compute that 1/10 of the material will remain after 22 years. Is this reasonable? Consider the following table which was constructed solely from the fact that the material will halve every five years.

Number of years	5	10	15	20
Fraction of original remaining	$\frac{1}{2}$	$\frac{1}{4}$	$\frac{1}{8}$	$\frac{1}{16}$

Since 1/10 is between 1/8 and 1/16, the time lies between 15 and 20 years. Therefore, the answer of 22 is not reasonable.

5.2 Compound Interest

The exercises in this section are similar to those in Section 5.1. A problem involving continuously compounded interest can be thought of as a problem about a population of money that is growing exponentially. The exercises in this section are of the same five types discussed in the notes for Section 5.1.

1. a. The initial amount deposited is $A(0) = \$5000$.

    b. The interest rate is .04 or 4% interest per year.

    c. After 10 years, the amount in the account is

    $$A(10) = 5000e^{.04(10)} \approx \$7459.12.$$

    d. $A(t)$ satisfies the differential equation
    $$A'(t) = .04A(t)$$
    which is also written as $y' = .04y$.

    e. From the differential equation and part (c),

    $$A'(10) = .04 \cdot A(10) = .04 \cdot (7459.12)$$
    $$\approx 298.36$$

    After 10 years, the savings account balance is growing at the rate of about $298.36 per year.

    f. Let t_0 be the time at which $A'(t_0) = \$280$ per year. From the differential equation, $A(t_0)$ must satisfy

    $$280 = .04 \cdot A(t_0)$$

    so that $A(t_0) = 280/.04 = \$7000$. The account balance will be about $7000 when it is growing at the rate of $280 per year.

Helpful Hint: The phrase "after 10 years" in Exercise 1 means "after (exactly) 10 years of time have passed" This is a fairly common way of specifying t = 10. (The number 10, of course, could be replaced by any positive number.)

7. The initial amount and the interest rate are given. So $A(t) = 1000e^{.06t}$. To find when $A(t) = 2500$, set the formula for A(t) equal to 2500, and solve for t:

$$1000e^{.06t} = 2500$$
$$e^{.06t} = 2.5$$

Apply the natural logarithm to both sides:

$$\ln e^{.06t} = \ln 2.5$$
$$.06t = \ln 2.5$$
$$t = \frac{\ln 2.5}{.06} \approx 15.27 \text{ (to two decimal places).}$$

About fifteen and one-quarter years are required for the account balance to reach $2500.

13. Since $A(t) = Pe^{rt}$, the fact that an initial investment P triples to 3P in 15 years means that the interest rate r satisfies

$$Pe^{r(15)} = 3P$$

Divide by P and take the natural logarithm of each side:

$$e^{15r} = 3$$
$$15r = \ln 3$$
$$r = (\ln 3)/15 \approx .07324.$$

Interest rates are usually reported to two or three significant figures. In this case, we estimate the rate either as 7.3% or 7.32%.

Helpful Hint: Exercises 15—18 are two-step problems, similar to Exercise 19 in Section 5.1.

Step 1: Find the interest rate r. Keep at least two or preferably three significant figures in r. Otherwise, the answer to part 2 will have less accuracy.

Step 2: Write the formula for A(t) with the value of r filled in, and use A(t) to find the time required for the investment to grow to a certain amount.

19. The text supplies a formula for present value, but you may find it easier just to remember the equation $A = Pe^{rt}$ in the form:

$$[\text{future } \underline{\text{A}}\text{mount}] = [\underline{\text{P}}\text{resent value}] \cdot e^{rt}.$$

If P, r, and t are given, you can compute A. If A, r, and t are given, you can compute P (the "present value"). In Exercise 19 we are told the value of the investment at a future time (3 years), so that value is A. Thus A = $1000, t = 3 years, r is .08, and

$$1000 = Pe^{.08(3)}$$
$$P = 1000/e^{.24} \approx \$786.63 \quad \text{(to the nearest cent)}.$$

25. This exercise is analogous to Exercise 31 in Section 5.1, with the function $A(t) = Pe^{rt}$ in place of P(t). You might review that exercise before continuing here.

For most of the questions in this exercise, you need to decide (1) whether the question involves A(t) or the rate of change of A(t) and (2) whether the time t is known or unknown.

A. "How fast?" relates to A'(t), the rate of growth of the balance A(t). Since the time is known, the answer is (d), compute A'(3).

B. Answer: (a), the general form of A(t) is Pe^{rt}.

C. The question involves the amount A(t) in the account and its relation to the initial amount A(0). The question, "How long?" indicates we must solve to find t. Answer: (h), solve A(t) = 3A(0) for t.

D. "The balance" refers to A(t). The phrase "after 3 years" means that t = 3. Answer: (b), compute A(3).

E. The question concerns A(t). "When?" means that t must be found. Answer: (f), solve A(t) = 3 for t.

F. The phrase, "the balance...growing...rate" relates to A'(t). "When?" means that t must be found. Answer: (e), solve A'(t) = 3 for t.

G. Answer: (c), *principal amount* means initial amount.

H. The differential equation is in (g), y' = ry.

Helpful Hint: Use estimation to check that the answer to a compound interest problem is reasonable.

(a) Suppose $1000 is invested at 5% interest and you compute it will grow to about $1103 in two years. Is this reasonable? Well, the deposit will earn .05($1000) or $50 interest the first year and a little more than that (due to interest on the interest) during the second year. Therefore, it will earn a little more than $100 in interest in two years, and so the result is reasonable.

(b) Suppose an investment doubles every eight years and you compute that it will increase tenfold in 20 years. Is this reasonable? Well, the investment will increase fourfold in 16 years and eightfold in 24 years. Therefore, the answer is not reasonable.

(c) Bankers have a *Rule of 70* that can be used to estimate the doubling time of an investment (because 70 is approximately 100 times ln 2). The *Rule of 70* says that an investment earning an interest rate of r % will double in about 70/r years. For instance, an investment earning 7 percent interest will double in about 70/7 or 10 years. Similarly, an investment doubling in d years has earned an interest rate of about 70/d percent per year. (In former times, bankers used a *rule of 72*, because they relied on mental arithmetic, and 72 is easily divisible by many common interest rates.)

31. Set $Y_1 = 1200*e^{(-3X)} + 800*e^{(-4X)} + 500*e^{(-5X)}$. Then use the SOLVER command to solve the equation $Y_1 - 2000 = 0$. (Refer to Part A of the Appendix section, **Special Points on the Graph of Y_1.**) A good initial guess is X = .10 (a 10% interest rate). The answer to six decimal places is X = .060276, so the interest rate is about 6.0%.

5.3 Applications of the Natural Logarithm Function to Economics

The material in this section is not used in any other part of the book. Elasticity is one of the most important concepts of economics and provides insights into the pricing of goods and services. In addition to being able to compute the elasticity of demand, you should be able to interpret what it means for the demand to be, say, elastic. The box on page 284 summarizes this. Here is another more informal way to remember it. When demand is elastic, an increase in price causes such a decline in sales that the total revenue falls. When demand is inelastic, an increase in price causes only a relatively small decline in sales, so that the total revenue still increases.

1. $f(t) = t^2$, so $f'(t) = 2t$.

Thus at $t = 10$, $\frac{f'(10)}{f(10)} = \frac{2(10)}{10^2} = \frac{20}{100} = .2 = 20\%$.

At $t = 50$, $\frac{f'(50)}{f(50)} = \frac{2(50)}{50^2} = \frac{100}{2500} = .04 = 4\%$.

7. $f(p) = \frac{1}{p + 2}$, thus $f'(p) = \frac{-1}{(p + 2)^2}$.

So at $p = 2$, $\frac{f'(2)}{f(2)} = \frac{-\frac{1}{16}}{\frac{1}{4}} = -\frac{4}{16} = -.25 = -25\%$.

And at $p = 8$, $\frac{f'(8)}{f(8)} = \frac{-\frac{1}{100}}{\frac{1}{10}} = -\frac{10}{100} = -.1 = -10\%$.

13. $f(p) = q = 700 - 5p$, so $f'(p) = -5$.

$$E(p) = \frac{-pf'(p)}{f(p)} = \frac{-p(-5)}{700 - 5p} = \frac{5p}{700 - 5p} = \frac{p}{140 - p}.$$

So at $p = 80$, $E(80) = \frac{80}{140 - 80} = \frac{80}{60} = \frac{4}{3}$.

Since $\frac{4}{3} > 1$, demand is elastic.

19. a. $f(p) = q = 600(5 - \sqrt{p}) = 3000 - 600p^{1/2}$, and thus

$f'(p) = -300p^{-1/2}$.

$$E(p) = \frac{-pf'(p)}{f(p)} = \frac{-p(-300p^{-1/2})}{3000 - 600p^{1/2}} = \frac{300p^{1/2}}{3000 - 600p^{1/2}}$$

$$= \frac{p^{1/2}}{10 - 2p^{1/2}}.$$

Thus at $p = 4$, $E(4) = \frac{4^{1/2}}{10 - 2(4)^{1/2}} = \frac{2}{10 - 2(2)} = \frac{1}{3}$.

Since $\frac{1}{3} < 1$, demand is inelastic.

b. Since demand is inelastic, an increase in price will bring about an increase in revenue. Thus, the price of a ticket should be raised.

25. $E_c(x) = \dfrac{\frac{d}{dx} \ln C(x)}{\frac{d}{dx} \ln x} = \dfrac{\frac{C'(x)}{C(x)}}{\frac{1}{x}} = \dfrac{xC'(x)}{C(x)}$.

29. Use X for the variable p, and set $Y_1 = 60000e^{(-.5X)}$. If Y_4 is the first derivative of Y_1, then use Y_2 for the elasticity of demand function and set $Y_2 = -X*Y_4/Y_1$. To solve $Y_2 = 1$, apply the Solver program to the equation $0 = Y_2 - 1$. See part A of the Appendix section, **Special Points on the Graph of Y_1.**

5.4 Further Exponential Models

This section illustrates the wide variety of applications in which exponential functions appear. The material in this section is not needed for any other part of the book. The logistic curve will be studied further in Chapter 10. However, the discussion there is completely independent of the discussion in Section 5.4.

1. **a.** $f(x) = 5(1 - e^{-2x}) = 5 - 5e^{-2x}$, $x \geq 0$. Thus $f'(x) = 10e^{-2x}$. Since $e^{-2x} > 0$ for every value of x, $10e^{-2x} > 0$ for every value of x, in particular when $x \geq 0$. Thus $f(x)$ is increasing. $f''(x) = -20e^{-2x}$. Again, since $e^{-2x} > 0$, we have $-20e^{-2x} < 0$ for all values of x, in particular when $x \geq 0$. Thus $f(x)$ is concave down.

b. $f(x) = 5(1 - e^{-2x})$, $x \geq 0$.
Note that as x gets larger, $e^{-2x} = \frac{1}{e^{2x}}$ gets closer and closer to zero. Hence when x is very large the values of $f(x)$ are very close to 5. (The values of $f(x)$ are slightly less than 5 because $1 - e^{-2x}$ is slightly less than 1.)

c. See the graph in the answer section of the text.

7. The number of people who have heard about the indictment by time t is given by $f(t) = P(1 - e^{-kt})$, where P is the total population. Since after one hour, one quarter of the citizens had heard the news, we have
$f(1) = P(1 - e^{-k(1)}) = \frac{1}{4}P = .25P$. Hence

$$1 - e^{-k} = .25,$$

$$e^{-k} = .75,$$

$$-k = \ln .75 \approx -.29, \text{ or } k = .29.$$

Before continuing with the solution, write out the formula for f(t) for future reference.

$$f(t) = P(1 - e^{-.29t}).$$

Now we must find time t when $f(t) = \frac{3}{4}P = .75P$, that is,

$$P(1 - e^{-.29t}) = .75P.$$

Thus,

$$1 - e^{-.29t} = .75,$$

$$e^{-.29t} = .25,$$

$$-.29t = \ln .25 \approx -1.4,$$

$$t = \frac{-1.4}{-.29} = \frac{1.4}{.29} \approx 4.8 \text{ hours.}$$

13. Set $Y_1 = 122(e^{\wedge}(-.2X) - e^{\wedge}(-X))$. We assume that Y_4 and Y_5 are the first two derivatives of Y_1.

   a. See the graph in the text's answer section.

   b. Evaluate $Y_1(7) \approx 29.97$. About 30 units are present.

   c. Evaluate $Y_4(1) \approx 24.90$. The drug level is increasing at the rate of about 25 units per hour.

   d. Solve $Y_1 - 20 = 0$. If you use the SOLVER command, you'll need to look first at the graph of Y_1 and use TRACE to find an approximate initial guess for X, on the part of the graph where the level is decreasing. Another method is to graph Y_1 and $Y_2 = 20$ in the same window and use the **intersect** command. You can choose an initial guess for X while in the graphing window. In any case, you should obtain $X \approx 9.038$. So the level of the drug is 20 units at about t = 9 hours.

   e. You can use TRACE to estimate the maximum point on the graph of Y_1. On the TI-83, with the suggested window, you should find (2.04, 65.26). A more accurate method is to use SOLVER on the equation $Y_4 = 0$. You should obtain $X \approx 2.0118$. Evaluating $Y_1(X)$, with the exact value of X produced by SOLVER, yields $Y_1 \approx 65.269$. In either case, you might report that after about 2 hours the drug reaches its maximum level of about 65.3 units.

   f. The point of steepest decline on the graph of Y_1 is the inflection point. That's practically impossible to estimate on the graph of Y_1 using TRACE. The two reasonable choices are either to use TRACE on Y_4 and look for the minimum point, or to use SOLVER to find where the second derivative Y_5 is zero. SOLVER will work on Y_5, but only if your initial guess for X is small enough. (If you try X = 12 on the TI-83, the calculator will work for about 2 minutes and give the answer as X = 9.99...E98, or about 10^{99}, which is the calculator's view of heaven.)

For this graph, the best method is to use TRACE on the graph of Y_4, and find that its minimum point occurs when X $\approx$ 4.08. So the drug level is decreasing the fastest when t = 4 hours.

Chapter 5: Supplementary Exercises

1. $P'(x) = -.2P(x)$ implies that $P(x)$ is an exponential function of the form $P(x) = P_0e^{-.2x}$, where $P_0 = P(0)$ is the atmospheric pressure at sea level. Thus $P_0 = 29.92$, and $P(x) = 29.92e^{-.2x}$.

7. **a.** $P(t) = 17e^{kt}$, where t = 0 corresponds to January 1, 1990. To find the growth constant, set $P(7) = 19.3$ and solve for k:

$$17e^{k(7)} = 19.3$$

$$e^{7k} = 19.3/17$$

$$7k = \ln(19.3/17)$$

$$k = \frac{1}{7}\ln(19.3/17) \approx .0181274 \text{ or } .0181.$$

Thus $P(t) = 17e^{.0181t}$.

b. The year 2000 corresponds to t = 10. At that time,

$$P(10) = 17e^{.0181(10)} \approx 20.4 \text{ million.}$$

c. The population reaches 25 million when t satisfies

$$17e^{.0181t} = 25$$

$$e^{.0181t} = 25/17$$

$$.0181t = \ln(25/17)$$

$$t = \frac{1}{.0181}\ln(25/17) \approx 21.3$$

Since t = 0 corresponds to 1990, the population will reach 25 million 21 years later, in 2011.

13. A. "How fast" concerns P′(t). The time is known, so the answer is (c).

B. The general form of the function is in (g), P_0e^{kt}.

C. The question involves the population P(t) and the time is unknown, so the answer is either (a) or (f). The actual size of the population is not given. Rather, it is described as twice the current population. So the answer is (f), which involves 2P(0).

D. The question involves the population P(t), the time is known, and the answer to "what size" requires a value of P(t), not a time. The answer is is (b).

E. The initial size is P(0), which is answer (h).

F. The exact value of P(t) is specified, and the time is unknown, so the answer is (a).

G. The question involves the *rate* of growth, P′(t), and the time is unknown, so the answer is (d).

H. The differential equation is in (e), y′ = ky.

19. This question is based on the elasticity of demand, discussed at the end of Section 5.3. If the elasticity at p = 8 is 1.5, then the demand is *elastic*, because E(p) is greater than 1. In this case, the change in revenue is in the *opposite* direction of the change in price, for prices close to p = 8. So if the price is increased to $8.16, the revenue will decrease. Furthermore, from the discussion before Example 4 in Section 5.3,

$$\frac{[\text{relative rate of change of quantity}]}{[\text{relative rate of change of price}]} = -1.5.$$

The relative increase of price from $8.00 to $8.16 is .16/8.00 = .02. Therefore the relative change (decrease) of quantity demanded is (.02)(-1.5) = -.03. So the demand will fall by about 3%.

25. a. The temperature "after 11 seconds" means the temperature at t = 11. This temperature is the y-coordinate of the point on the graph of f(t) at which t is 11, namely, 400° F. (Each horizontal square represents 1 second, and each vertical square represents 100°.)

b. The "rate of temperature" involve the graph of f′(t). "After 6 seconds" means that t = 6. The corresponding y-coordinate is at about -100° per second.

c. The temperature of the rod is 200 degrees at the time corresponding to a y-coordinate of 200 on the graph of f(t), namely, at t = 16 seconds.

d. The rod is cooling at the *rate* of 200°/sec when the y-coordinate of f'(t) is -200, namely, when t = 2 sec.

Chapter 6

The Definite Integral

6.1 Antidifferentiation

To find an antiderivative, first make an educated guess and then differentiate the guess. (This may be done mentally if the differentiation is simple.) Your guess should be based on your experience with derivatives. In most cases, functions and their antiderivatives are the same basic type, such as power functions or exponential functions. If your first guess for the antiderivative is correct, you are finished (after you add "+C"). With some practice, your guess usually will be correct except for a constant factor, and you will only need to multiply the guess by a suitable constant. Exercises 7 to 22 show the correct form of the antiderivative. All you have to do is to adjust the constant k correctly.

1. By the constant multiple rule, $\frac{d}{dx} \frac{1}{2} x^2 = \frac{1}{2} \cdot \frac{d}{dx} x^2 = \frac{1}{2} \cdot 2x = x$.

    Hence one antiderivative of $f(x) = x$ is $F(x) = \frac{1}{2} x^2$, and

    all antiderivatives are of the form $F(x) = \frac{1}{2} x^2 + C$.

7. The equation $\int x^{-5} \, dx = kx^{-4} + C$ reminds you that x^{-4} is the correct type of function to use as an antiderivative. In fact,

    $$\frac{d}{dx} \left(kx^{-4} + c \right) = -4kx^{-5}.$$

    Your task is to choose k so that the −4k in front of x^{-5} is a 1. So, to make −4k = 1, take k = −1/4. Now, check your work:

    $$\frac{d}{dx} \left(-\frac{1}{4}\right) x^{-4} = \left(-\frac{1}{4}\right) \cdot \frac{d}{dx} x^{-4} = \left(-\frac{1}{4}\right) \cdot (-4) x^{-5} = x^{-5}.$$

    $\uparrow$──constant multiple rule

Thus k = -1/4 is correct, and $(-1/4)x^{-4}$ is an antiderivative of x^{-5}. All the others are formed by adding an arbitrary constant, C.

13. The equation $\int 5e^{-2t} dt = ke^{-2t} + C$ reminds you that e^{-2t} is the correct type of function to use as an antiderivative—you only have to adjust the constant multiple in front of it. After some practice, you will be able to guess immediately what k should be. At first, however, just compute

$$\frac{d}{dt} ke^{-2t} = -2ke^{-2t}.$$

You want k to make -2k equal to 5 (because there is a factor 5 inside the indefinite integral). To make -2k = 5, choose k = 5/(-2), or k = -5/2. Check:

$$\frac{d}{dt} (\frac{5}{-2})e^{-2t} = (\frac{5}{-2}) \cdot \frac{d}{dt} e^{-2t}$$

$$= (\frac{5}{-2}) \cdot (-2)e^{-2t} = 5e^{-2t}.$$

Thus k = -5/2 is correct, and $(-5/2)e^{-2t}$ is an antiderivative of $5e^{-2t}$. The -2 in the denominator of $\frac{5}{-2}$ antici-pates the -2 that will appear when e^{-2t} is differentiated. Once you have the antiderivative $(-5/2)e^{-2t}$, don't forget to add "C" to generate all the other antiderivatives.

19. The formula $\int (4-x)^{-1} dx = k \ln|4-x| + C$ reminds you of the type of antiderivative you need. If you guess that k = 1, then you have forgotten about the -1 that appears when $\ln|4-x|$ is differentiated:

$$\frac{d}{dx} \ln|4-x| = (4-x)^{-1} \cdot (-1).$$

The -1 is the derivative of the function 4 - x inside the logarithm. To compensate for the -1, take k = -1. A check will show why that works:

$$\frac{d}{dx} (-1) \cdot \ln|4-x| = (-1) \cdot \frac{d}{dx} \ln|4-x|$$

$$= (-1) \cdot (4-x)^{-1}(-1)$$

$$= (4-x)^{-1}.$$

Thus $-\ln|4-x|$ is an antiderivative of $(4-x)^{-1}$, and the others are found by adding an arbitrary constant.

Helpful Hint: The antiderivatives in Exercises 15—17 and 19—22 are a little harder to find because you must remember how the chain rule works. (Later we will study a general method for handling such problems. For now, however, you may use the technique of simply guessing the general form of an antiderivative.) For instance, to handle Exercise 21, compute

$$\frac{d}{dx}k(3x+2)^5 = 5k(3x+2)^4 \cdot \frac{d}{dx}(3x+2)$$

$$= 5k(3x+2)^4 \cdot 3$$

$$= 15k(3x+2)^4.$$

You want $15k = 1$, so take $k = 1/15$. Perhaps you can do the calculation above mentally. In any case, once you "see" the 5 and the 3 appearing after the differentiation is performed, you can guess how to choose k so that

$$\frac{d}{dx}k(3x+2)^5 = (3x+2)^4.$$

Remember that you can check your final answer by differentiating what you think is the correct antiderivative.

25. Rewriting the integral, we have

$$\int\left(\frac{2}{\sqrt{x}} - 3\sqrt{x}\right) dx = \int (2x^{-1/2} - 3x^{1/2})\, dx.$$

Since $\frac{d}{dx}4x^{1/2} = 2x^{-1/2}$, and $\frac{d}{dx}2x^{3/2} = 3x^{1/2}$, we have

$$\int(2x^{-1/2} - 3x^{1/2})\, dx = 4x^{1/2} - 2x^{3/2} + C$$

$$= 4\sqrt{x} - 2x^{3/2} + C.$$

31. From Theorem II, we see that if $f'(t) = 0$ for all t, then $f(t) = C$ for some constant C.

Helpful Hint: In Exercises 33-36 and 47-53, each answer is a single function. This function is found by first antidifferentiating and then using additional information to find the proper value of C. On an exam or homework assignment, this value of C should be substituted for C in the antiderivative to obtain the answer.

37. f(x) is an antiderivative of $\frac{2}{x}$. Since $\frac{d}{dx} \ln x = \frac{1}{x}$, we have $\frac{d}{dx} (2 \ln x) = \frac{2}{x}$. So $2 \ln x$ is an antiderivative of $\frac{2}{x}$, and f(x) = 2 ln x + C for some C. To make the graph of f(x) pass through (1,2), we want f(1) = 2. That is,

$$2 \ln 1 + C = 2.$$

Since ln 1 = 0, we find C = 2. Thus f(x) = 2 ln x + 2.

43. g(x) = f(x) + 3,

g'(x) = f'(x),

$g'(5) = f'(5) = \frac{1}{4}.$

49. We let f(t) represent the temperature in degrees Celsius of the strawberries at time t. Then $f'(t) = 10e^{-.4t}$, and f(0) = -5 (since the initial temperature of the strawberries is -5°C). Thus $f(t) = \int 10e^{-.4t}\, dt = -25e^{-.4t} + C$. To find C, we use the fact that f(0) = -25 + C = -5. Hence C = 20, and $f(t) = -25e^{-.4t} + 20 = 20 - 25e^{-.4t}$.

55. C'(x) = 1000 + 50x.
Find the antiderivative, F(x), of this expression. Noting that

$$\frac{d}{dx}(1000x) = 1000,$$

and

$$\frac{d}{dx}(x^2) = 2x, \text{ so } \frac{d}{dx}(25x^2) = 50x.$$

Therefore, $\frac{d}{dx}(1000x + 25x^2) = 1000 + 50x$, giving us the antiderivative as $F(x) = 1000x + 25x^2 + K$ (K constant). But $C(x) = F(x) = 1000x + 25x^2 + K$, and with the condition C(0) = 10,000, we can evaluate K: K = 10,000. Therefore, finally the cost function is:

$$C(X) = 25x^2 + 1000x + 10,000.$$

6.2 Areas and Riemann Sums

Riemann (pronounced "Reemahn") sums are introduced here in order to approximate the area under the graph of a nonnegative function, but their importance extends far beyond that. As we shall see later, Riemann sums are used to derive some important formulas in applications.

Computations with Riemann sums can be time-consuming, but some numerical homework is necessary for a proper understanding. Check with your instructor about how far to carry calculations on an exam. In some cases you may only have to write down the complete Riemann sum (using numbers and not symbols such as Δx), and omit the final arithmetic computation.

One goal of this section is to suggest how the change in a function over some interval is related to the area under the graph of the derivative of that function. See Example 4 and the Table on page 317. This concept will be made precise in Section 6.3.

1. $a = 0$, $b = 2$, $n = 4$, so $\Delta x = \dfrac{b-a}{n} = \dfrac{2-0}{4} = .5$.

The first midpoint is $a + \Delta x/2 = 0 + .5/2 = .25$. Subsequent midpoints are found by adding Δx repeatedly. So the other midpoints are:
$$.25 + .5 = .75,$$
$$.75 + .5 = 1.25,$$
$$1.25 + .5 = 1.75.$$

Helpful Hint: You may use fractions, if you wish, and write 1/4 in place of .25, and so on. However, you can use a calculator more efficiently if you convert to decimals.

Helpful Hint: To draw a partition that has 5 subintervals, draw a horizontal line and, beginning at one end, mark off five equal subintervals. This is easier than trying to divide one larger interval into five equal pieces. (See Exercises 3,4, and 7-10.)

7. $\Delta x = (b - a)/n = (3 - 1)/5 = 2/5 = .4$ The first left endpoint is $x_1 = a = 1$. Subsequent left endpoints are found by adding Δx repeatedly.

Thus the area is approximated by the Riemann sum:

$$\Delta x \, [f(1) + f(1.4) + f(1.8) + f(2.2) + f(2.6)]$$

$$= (.4.)[(1)^3 + (1.4)^3 + (1.8)^3 + (2.2)^3 + 2.6)^3]$$

$$= (.4)[1 + 2.744 + 5.832 + 10.648 + 17.576]$$

$$= (.4)[37.8] = 15.12.$$

13. Since $\Delta x = (9 - 4)/5 = 1$, the subintervals have length 1. The first right endpoint is at $4 + \Delta x = 5$. Focus your attention on the five right endpoints by placing small dots on the x-axis at 5, 6, 7, 8, and 9.

From the figure in the text, estimate the y-coordinates of the points on the curve where $x = 5, 6, \ldots, 9$, and compute

$$A \approx [f(5) + \cdots + f(9)]\Delta x$$

$$= [6 + 4 + 2 + 1 + 2] \cdot 1 = 15.$$

19. For $0 \le x \le 2$ and $n = 5$, $\Delta x = 2/5 = .4$. The first midpoint is at $\Delta x/2 = .2$ The next midpoint is at $.2 + \Delta x = .6$, and so on.

In the figure for Exercise 19, the interval $0 \le x \le 1$ is divided into five segments, so each represents .2 second, which means that Δx is the length of two segments:

From the figure, read the heights of the curve above .2, .6,..., 1.8. The Riemann sum is

$$[f(.2) + \cdots + f(1.8)]\Delta x = [.2 + .7 + .8 + .7 + .3](.4)$$

$$= (2.7)(.4) = 1.08.$$

The heights of the rectangles represent flow rate, in liters/second; the widths of the rectangles represent time, in seconds; the product of the height and the width represents (liters/second)·(seconds) = liters. Thus the total volume of air during exhalation is approximately 1.08 liters.

25. To understand the answer, it might help to consider the units involved. Consider a rectangle that approximates part of the area under the curve. Its height represents *rate* of soil erosion, in tons/day, and its width represents time, in days. So, the area of the rectangle, which is the product of the height and width, represents [(tons of soil)/day]·[days] = [tons of soil].

Thus, the area under the rate curve equals the total number of tons of soil that has eroded during the five days from t = 0 to t = 5.

31. Here $\Delta x = [2 - (-2)]/100 = .04$. The left endpoint of the first subinterval is $x_1 = -2$. The left endpoint of the last subinterval is $x_{100} = 2 - \Delta x = 2 - .04 = 1.96$. Consult the Appendix section, **Riemann Sums**, which shows how to compute the Riemann sum in the form

$$[f(x_1) + f(x_2) + \cdots + f(x_{100})](.04).$$

The **seq** command creates the sequence of terms

$$f(x_1), \ f(x_2), \ \ldots, \ f(x_{100}).$$

The **sum** command adds the terms and computes

$$f(x_1) + f(x_2) + \cdots + f(x_{100}).$$

After that, multiply the result by $\Delta x = .04$. You should find that

$$\texttt{sum(seq(e\^{}(-X}^2\texttt{),X,-2,1.96,.04)*.04} \approx 1.764143.$$

6.3 Definite Integrals and the Fundamental Theorem

Although definite integrals are defined by Riemann sums, they are usually calculated as the net change in an antiderivative. Since you have computed a few Riemann sums, you probably appreciate the value of the Fundamental Theorem of Calculus.

1. The function is $f(x) = 1/x$. The interval is $.5 \leq x \leq 2$, which is determined by the x-coordinates of the points

shown in the figure. The area is the value of $\displaystyle\int_{.5}^{2} \frac{1}{x}\,dx$.

7. $\displaystyle\int_{-1}^{1} x\,dx = \frac{1}{2}x^2\Big|_{-1}^{1} = \frac{1}{2}(1)^2 - \left(\frac{1}{2}(-1)^2\right) = \frac{1}{2} - \frac{1}{2} = 0.$

13. $\displaystyle\int_0^1 4e^{-3x}\,dx = -\frac{4}{3}e^{-3x}\Big|_0^1 = [-\frac{4}{3}e^{-3}] - [-\frac{4}{3}]$

$$= \frac{4}{3} - \frac{4}{3}e^{-3}, \quad \text{or} \quad \frac{4}{3}(1 - e^{-3}).$$

19. $\displaystyle\int_3^6 x^{-1}\,dx = \ln|x|\Big|_3^6 = \ln 6 - \ln 3 = \ln\frac{6}{3} = \ln 2.$

25. $\displaystyle\int_0^3 (x^3+x-7)\,dx = (\frac{1}{4}x^4 + \frac{1}{2}x^2 - 7x)\Big|_0^3 = [\frac{81}{4} + \frac{9}{2} - 21] - [0]$

$$= \frac{81}{4} + \frac{18}{4} - \frac{84}{4} = \frac{15}{4} = 3\frac{3}{4}.$$

31. The desired area is

$$\int_0^1 e^{x/2}\,dx = 2e^{x/2}\Big|_0^1 = 2e^{1/2} - 2 = 2(e^{1/2}-1).$$

37. Number of cigarettes sold from 1980 to 1998 is

$$= \int_{20}^{38} (.1t + 2.4)\,dt$$

$$= \left(\frac{.1t^2}{2} + 2.4t\right)\Big|_{20}^{38} \quad \left(\text{note: } \frac{.1}{2} = .05\right)$$

$$= .05(38)^2 + 2.4(38) - [.05(20)^2 + 2.4(20)]$$

$$= 95.4 \text{ trillion.}$$

43. This represents the increase in profits by increasing the production level from x = 44 to x = 48 units.

49. As explained at the bottom of page 394, A'(x) = f(x). Hence A'(3) = f(3) = 3^2 + 1 = 10.

51. The command **fnInt** is discussed in Part A of the Appendix section, **Definite Integrals and Antiderivatives.** You should find that

$$\text{fnInt}(1/X, X, 2, 3) \approx .4055.$$

55. fnInt(ln(X),X,1,4) $\approx$ 2.5452.

6.4 Areas in the xy-Plane

1. $\displaystyle\int_{1}^{2} f(x)\, dx + \int_{3}^{4} [-f(x)]\, dx$ (Fig. 10)

7. The graph of $y = x^2 - 6x + 12$ is a parabola that opens upward. Its minimum point occurs where $y' = 2x - 6 = 0$, that is, at $x = 3$. The minimum point is $(3,3)$. So the parabola lies entirely above the horizontal line $y = 1$. So $f(x) = x^2 - 6x + 12$ and $g(x) = 1$. The area between the two curves from $x = 0$ to $x = 4$ is equal to,

$$\int_{0}^{4} [(x^2 - 6x + 12) - (1)]\, dx$$

$$= \int_{0}^{4} (x^2 - 6x + 11)\, dx = \frac{x^3}{3} - 3x^2 + 11x \Big|_{0}^{4}$$

$$= \left(\frac{64}{3} - 48 + 44\right) - \left(0\right) = \frac{60}{3} = 20.$$

13. Only a rough sketch is needed. The graph of $y = -x^2 + 6x - 5$ is a parabola that opens downward. (You can see this from the $-x^2$ term.) Also, the graph of $y = 3 - x$ is a line with negative slope. Without plotting any points or using a coordinate system, you can visualize the two possible locations of the parabola and line:

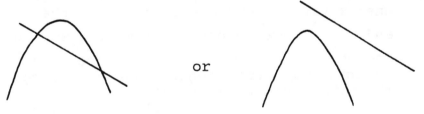

or

Hopefully, the line intersects the parabola. Otherwise there will be no region "bounded" by the graphs. To find the x-values of the intersection points, if any, equate the y-values of the two curves and solve for x:

$$-x^2 + 6x - 5 = 2x - 5,$$
$$-x^2 + 4x = 0,$$
$$-x(x - 4) = 0,$$
$$x = 0, \text{ or } x = 4.$$

The rough sketch shows that the parabola is the top curve between $x = 0$ and $x = 4$. So the area bounded by the curves is

$$\int_0^4 [(-x^2 + 6x - 5) - (2x - 5)]\, dx$$

$$= \int_0^4 (-x^2 + 4x)\, dx = \left.\frac{-x^3}{3} + 2x^2\right|_0^4 = \frac{-64}{3} + 32 = \frac{32}{3}.$$

19. The graph of $y = x^2 - 3x$ is obviously a parabola that opens upward. It crosses the x-axis at values of x that satisfy $x^2 - 3x = 0$, i.e., $x(x - 3) = 0$. Thus $x = 0$, or $x = 3$.

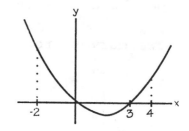

a. The x-axis is the graph of the (constant) function $y = 0$. Since this graph is above the parabola from $x = 0$ to $x = 3$, the area of the region for part (a) is

$$\int_0^3 [0 - (x^2 - 3x)]\, dx = \int_0^3 3x - x^2\, dx$$

$$= \left.\frac{3}{2}x^2 - \frac{1}{3}x^3\right|_0^3 = \left(\frac{27}{2} - 9\right) - 0 = \frac{9}{2}.$$

b. When x varies from $x = 0$ to $x = 4$, the two curves $y = 0$ and $y = 3x - x^2$ cross. We must consider two regions, one where $y = 0$ is on top and one where $y = 3x - x^2$ is on top. The first region was considered in part (a). The total area is equal to

$$[\text{Area found in (a)}] + \int_3^4 [(x^2 - 3x) - 0]\, dx$$

$$= \frac{9}{2} + \left.\left[\frac{1}{3}x^3 - \frac{3}{2}x^2\right]\right|_3^4$$

$$= \frac{9}{2} + \left(\frac{64}{3} - 24\right) - \left(9 - \frac{27}{2}\right)$$

$$= \frac{27}{6} + \frac{128}{6} - 24 - 9 + \frac{81}{6}$$

$$= \frac{236}{6} - 33 = \frac{38}{6} = \frac{19}{3}.$$

c. This is similar to part (b). When x is between -2 and 0, the graph of $y = 3x - x^2$ is on top; when x is between 0 and 3, the x-axis is on top. Thus the total area is

$$\int_{-2}^{0} [(x^2 - 3x) - 0] \, dx + [\text{Area found in (a)}]$$

$$= \left(\frac{1}{3}x^3 - \frac{3}{2}x^2\right)\Bigg|_{-1}^{0} + \frac{9}{2}$$

$$= 0 - \left(\frac{1}{3}(-2)^3 - \frac{3}{2}(-2)^2\right) + \frac{9}{2}$$

$$= -\left(-\frac{8}{3} - 6\right) + \frac{9}{2} = \frac{26}{3} + \frac{9}{2} = \frac{52}{6} + \frac{27}{6} = \frac{79}{6}.$$

25. $\begin{bmatrix} \text{amount of} \\ \text{depletion} \end{bmatrix} = \begin{bmatrix} \text{amount of} \\ \text{consumption} \end{bmatrix} - \begin{bmatrix} \text{amount of} \\ \text{new growth} \end{bmatrix}$

$$= \begin{bmatrix} \text{area of region} \\ \text{under consump-} \\ \text{tion curve} \end{bmatrix} - \begin{bmatrix} \text{area of region} \\ \text{under new} \\ \text{growth curve} \end{bmatrix}$$

$$= \begin{bmatrix} \text{area of region} \\ \text{between the curves} \end{bmatrix}$$

$$= \int_{0}^{20} [76.2e^{.03t} - (50 - 6.03e^{.09t})] \, dt$$

$$= \int_{0}^{20} (76.2e^{.03t} - 50 + 6.03e^{.09t}) \, dt.$$

31. Set $Y_1 = 5 - (X - 2)^2$ and $Y_2 = e^{\wedge}X$. Deselect all functions except Y_1 and Y_2. You will need a window to the graph the functions. Start with one of the basic windows that are predefined on the ZOOM window, and then adjust the range of x-values and y-values as needed. Notice that between the two intersection points, the graph of Y_1 is above the graph of Y_2.

The desired area is the definite integral of $Y_1 - Y_2$ from a to b, where a and b are the x-coordinates of the intersection points. For high accuracy, you can find the values of a and b. To do so, refer to Part B of the Appendix section, **Special Points on the Graph of** Y_1. You should be able to find intersection points at x = 0 and at approximately x = 1.572.) Then use the command **fnInt** to find the definite integral. See Part A of the Appendix section, **Definite Integrals and Antiderivatives**.

You can also get a fairly good estimate of the desired area without explicitly finding a and b. The Appendix shows how to "Shade a region under the graph of a function and find its area," using the command ∫**f(x)dx** on the CALC menu.   See Part B in **Definite Integrals and Antideriva-tives**.   Adjust the window to [-1,2] by [-1,2] and apply the command ∫**f(x)dx** to the function $Y_3 = Y_1 - Y_2$. (Before you integrate Y_3, deselect Y_1 and Y_2.)   The area should turn out to be approximately 1.403.

6.5 Applications of the Definite Integral

Although the derivations of the formulas presented in this section rely on Riemann sums, the exercises are worked by sub-stitution into the formulas and do not require analysis in terms of Riemann sums.   Example 1 is important.

1. $f(x) = x^2$.   By definition, the average value of $f(x)$ be-tween a and b is given by:

$$\text{Average value} = \frac{1}{b-a} \int_a^b f(x) \, dx$$

$$= \frac{1}{3-0} \int_0^3 x^2 \, dx = \frac{1}{3} \int_0^3 x^2 \, dx$$

$$= \frac{1}{3} \left[\frac{x^3}{3} \Big|_0^3 \right] = \frac{1}{3} \left[\frac{3^3}{3} \right] = 3.$$

7. $\text{Average temperature} = \frac{1}{12-0} \int_0^{12} \left(47 + 4t - \frac{1}{3}t^2 \right) dt$

$$= \frac{1}{12} \left[47t + 2t^2 - \frac{1}{9}t^3 \Big|_0^{12} \right]$$

$$= \frac{1}{12} \left[47(12) + 2(12)^2 - \frac{1}{9}(12)^3 \right]$$

$$= 47 + 2(12) - \frac{1}{9}(12)^2 = 55°.$$

13. $\text{Consumer's surplus} = \int_0^A [f(x) - B] \, dx, \quad B = f(A).$

$$f(x) = \frac{500}{x+10} - 3,$$

$$f(40) = \frac{500}{40+10} - 3 = \frac{500}{50} - 3 = 7,$$

$$\text{so the surplus} = \int_0^{40} \left(\frac{500}{x+10} - 3 - 7 \right) dx$$

$$= 500 \int_0^{40} \frac{dx}{x+10} - \int_0^{40} 10\, dx$$

$$= 500 \ln(x+10) \Big|_0^{40} - 10x \Big|_0^{40}$$

$$= 500 \ln 50 - 500 \ln 10 - 400$$

$$= 500 \ln 5 - 400$$

$$\approx \$404.72.$$

19. To find (A,B) set $12 - \dfrac{x}{50} = \dfrac{x}{20} + 5$

$$7 = \frac{x}{20} + \frac{x}{50} = \frac{7x}{100} \Rightarrow x = 100.$$

Thus A = 100, and $B = 12 - \dfrac{100}{50} = 10.$

To find the consumer's surplus $= \int_0^{100} \left(12 - \dfrac{x}{50} - 10\right) dx$

$$= \int_0^{100} \left(2 - \frac{x}{50}\right) dx = 2x - \frac{x^2}{100} \Big|_0^{100}$$

$$= 200 - 100 = \$100.$$

Producers surplus $= \int_0^{A} (f(A) - f(x))\, dx$

$$= \int_0^{100} \left[10 - \left(\frac{x}{20} + 5\right)\right] dx$$

$$= \int_0^{100} \left(5 - \frac{x}{20}\right) dx = 5x - \frac{x^2}{40} \Big|_0^{100}$$

$$= 500 - \frac{10000}{40} = \$250.$$

25. Future amount $= \int_0^{N} P\, e^{r(N-t)}\, dt.$

We don't know N, and this is what we wish to evaluate. So

$$140{,}000 = \int_0^{N} 5000\, e^{.1(N-t)}\, dt$$

$$= 5000 \int_0^{N} e^{.1N}\, e^{-.1t}\, dt$$

hence,

$$\frac{240,000}{5,000} = 28 = \int_0^N e^{.1N} e^{-.1t} \, dt$$

$$= e^{.1N} \int_0^N e^{-.1t} \, dt = e^{.1N} \left[\frac{e^{-.1t}}{-.1} \Big|_0^N \right]$$

$$= -10e^{.1N} \left[e^{-.1N} - 1 \right].$$

So,

$$28 = -10 + 10e^{.1N},$$

$$38 = 10e^{.1N},$$

$$3.8 = e^{.1N}.$$

Taking the logarithm of both sides, we have $\ln 3.8 = .1N$. Then $10 \ln 3.8 = N$ and $N \approx 13.35$ years.

31. The volume is given by

$$\int_1^2 \pi(x^2)^2 \, dx = \int_1^2 \pi x^4 \, dx = \frac{\pi}{5} x^5 \Big|_1^2 = \frac{31\pi}{5} \text{ cubic units.}$$

37. The Riemann sum tells us that $f(x) = x^3$, $n = 4$, and $\Delta x = .5$. Since $a = 8$ and $\Delta x = \frac{b-a}{n}$, we have

$$.5 = \frac{b-8}{4},$$

so

$$2 = b-8, \text{ or } b = 10.$$

43. a. At interest rate r, the average value of the amount in the account over three years is

$$\frac{1}{3} \int_0^3 1000e^{rt} \, dt = \frac{1}{3} \cdot \frac{1000}{r} e^{rt} \Big|_0^3 = \frac{1000}{3r} e^{3r} - \frac{1000}{3r}.$$

b. For the average balance to be $1070.60, the rate r must satisfy the equation

$$\frac{1000}{3r} e^{3r} - \frac{1000}{3r} = 1070.60$$

or

$$1000e^{3r} - 1000 = 3211.8r$$

To solve for r, set $Y_1 = 1000*e\wedge(3X) - 1000 - 3211.8X$, and use the SOLVER command, with an initial guess of

X = .10 (a 10% interest rate). (Make sure that "3x" is inside the exponential function. Refer to Part A of the Appendix section, **Special Points on the Graph of Y_1**. The equation solver produces x = .04497.., so the desired interest rate is about 4.45%.

Chapter 6: Supplementary Exercises

(for *Calculus and Its Applications, 8th Edition.*)

1. Since $\frac{d}{dx}(-2e^{-x/2}) = e^{-x/2}$, we have

$$\int e^{-x/2} \, dx = -2e^{-x/2} + c.$$

7. $\int_1^4 \frac{1}{x^2} \, dx = \int_1^4 x^{-2} \, dx = -x^{-1} \Big|_1^4 = -\frac{1}{4} + 1 = \frac{3}{4}.$

Warning: A common error is to think that $\frac{1}{x^3}$ is an antiderivative of $\frac{1}{x^2}$. You avoid this mistake when you switch to the negative exponent notation, $\frac{1}{x^2} = x^{-2}$.

13. A sketch of the graph reveals three points of intersection. Equating the two expressions in x we obtain

$$x^3 - 3x + 1 = x + 1,$$
$$x^3 - 4x = 0,$$
$$x(x^2-4) = 0,$$
$$x(x-2)(x+2) = 0.$$

Hence, x = 0, 2, or -2. The total area bounded by the curves is the sum of the areas of the two regions.

$$\text{Area} = \int_{-2}^{0} [(x^3-3x+1) - (x+1)] \, dx + \int_0^2 [(x+1) - (x^3-3x+1)] \, dx$$

$$= \int_{-2}^{0} (x^3 - 4x) \, dx + \int_0^2 (-x^3 + 4x) \, dx$$

$$= (\tfrac{1}{4}x^4 - 2x^2)\Big|_{-2}^{0} + (-\tfrac{1}{4}x^4 + 2x^2)\Big|_{0}^{2}$$

$$= 0 - (4 - 8) + (-4 + 8) - 0$$

$$= 8.$$

19. The cost of producing x tires a day is an antiderivative of the marginal cost function .04x + 150. Hence, if we denote the cost function by C(x), we have

$$C(x) = \int (.04x + 150)\, dx = .02x^2 + 150x + C.$$

If fixed costs are \$500 per day, then the cost of producing no tires is \$500 per day. That is,

$$C(0) = 0 + 0 + C = C = 500.$$

Hence

$$C(x) = .02x^2 + 150x + 500.$$

25. We have $\Delta x = \dfrac{b-a}{n} = \dfrac{2-0}{2} = 1$, so the midpoints of the two subintervals are given by

$$x_1 = a + \frac{\Delta x}{2} = 0 + \frac{1}{2} = \frac{1}{2},$$

$$x_2 = \frac{1}{2} + \Delta x = \frac{1}{2} + 1 = \frac{3}{2}.$$

Using the midpoint rule, we have

$$\text{Area} \approx [f(\tfrac{1}{2}) + f(\tfrac{3}{2})](1) = \left[\frac{1}{1/2 + 2} + \frac{1}{3/2 + 2}\right]$$

$$= \frac{2}{5} + \frac{2}{7} = \frac{24}{35} \approx .68571.$$

Computing the integral directly, we have

$$\int_0^2 \frac{1}{x+2}\, dx \approx \ln |x+2|\,\Big|_0^2$$

$$= \ln 4 - \ln 2 = \ln \frac{4}{2} = \ln 2 = .69315.$$

31. The region corresponding to $\int_a^c f(x)\, dx$ contains one part above the x-axis, with area .68, and one part below the x-axis, with area .42. From Section 6.2, $\int_a^c f(x)\, dx = .68 - .42 = .26$. Similarly, $\int_a^d f(x)\, dx = .68 - .42 + 1.70 = 1.96$, because the part from b to c is below the x-axis.

37. Observe that the sum is a Riemann sum for the function $f(t) = 5000e^{-.1t}$ from $t = 0$ to $t = 3$. This sum is approximately equal to the value of the definite integral:

$$\int_0^3 5000e^{-.1t}\,dt = -50{,}000e^{-.1t}\Big|_0^3$$

$$= -50{,}000e^{-.3} + 50{,}000$$

$$\approx 13{,}000.$$

43. Amount of water used between 1960 and 1995:

$$= \int_0^{35} 860\,e^{.04t}\,dt$$

$$= 860\,\frac{e^{.04t}}{.04}\Big|_0^{35} = 21{,}500\left(e^{.04(35)} - e^0\right)$$

$$= 21{,}500\left(e^{1.4} - 1\right) \approx 65{,}700 \text{ km}^3.$$

6.6   Techniques of Integration (Brief Edition)

The technique of integration by substitution is best learned by trial and error. The more problems you work the fewer errors you will make in your first guess at a substitution. The basic strategy is to arrange the integrand in the form $f(g(x))g'(x)$. Look for the most complicated part of the integrand that may be expressed as a composite function, and let u be the "inside" function $g(x)$.

Exercises 21-30 are all solved using integration by parts. Once you have mastered integration by parts and by substitution, you are ready to try Exercises 31-46. These problems are harder because you have to decide which method to use!

a. Always consider the method of substitution first. This will work if the integrand is the product of two functions and one of the functions is the derivative of the "inside" of the other function (except maybe for a constant multiple).

b. If the integrand is the product of two unrelated functions, try integration by parts.

c. Some antiderivatives cannot be found by either of the methods we have discussed. We will never give you such a problem to solve, but you should be careful if you look in another text for more problems to work.

Remember that you can check your answers to an antidifferentiation problem by differentiating your answer. (You ought to do this at least mentally for every indefinite integral you find.) We urge you to work *all* the problems (odd and even) in Section 6.6. Use the solutions in this guide to check your work, *not* to show you how to start a problem.

1.   Let $u = x^2 + 4$. Then $du = \frac{d}{dx}(x^2+4)\ dx = 2x\ dx$.

$$\int 2x(x^2+4)^5\ dx = \int u^5\ du$$

$$= \frac{1}{6}u^6 + C$$

$$= \frac{1}{6}(x^2+4)^6 + C.$$

7.   Let $u = x^3 - 1$. Then $du = 3x^2\ dx$, and

$$\int \frac{3x^2}{x^3-1}\ dx = \int \frac{1}{x^3-1} \cdot 3x^2\ dx = \int \frac{1}{u}\ du$$

$$= \ln|u| + C = \ln|x^3-1| + C.$$

13. Let $u = x^3 + 3x + 2$. Then $du = 3x^3 + 3\ dx$, and

$$\int \frac{x^2+1}{x^3+3x+2}\ dx = \frac{1}{3}\int \frac{1}{x^3+3x+2}\cdot 3(x^2+1)\ dx = \frac{1}{3}\int \frac{1}{u}\ du$$

$$= \frac{1}{3}\ln|u| + C = \frac{1}{3}\ln|x^3+3x+2| + C.$$

19. Let $u = -x^2$. Then $du = -2x\ dx$, and

$$\int \frac{x}{e^{x^2}}\ dx = \int xe^{-x^2}\ dx = \frac{1}{-2}\int e^{-x^2}\cdot(-2x)\ dx$$

$$= -\frac{1}{2}\int e^u\ du = -\frac{1}{2}e^u + C = -\frac{1}{2}e^{-x^2} + C.$$

25. Let $f(x) = x$, $g(x) = \sqrt{x + 1} = (x + 1)^{1/2}$,

$f'(x) = 1$, $G(x) = \frac{2}{3}(x + 1)^{3/2}$.

Then $\int x\sqrt{x + 1}\ dx = \frac{2}{3}x(x + 1)^{3/2} - \int \frac{2}{3}(x + 1)^{3/2}\ dx$

$$= \frac{2}{3}x(x + 1)^{3/2} - \frac{2}{3}\int (x + 1)^{3/2}\ dx$$

$$= \frac{2}{3}x(x + 1)^{3/2} - \frac{2}{3}\cdot\frac{2}{5}(x + 1)^{5/2} + C$$

$$= \frac{2}{3}x(x + 1)^{3/2} - \frac{4}{15}(x + 1)^{5/2} + C.$$

31. Since xe^{2x} is the product of two unrelated functions, we try integration by parts. Let

$$f(x) = x, \quad g(x) = e^{2x},$$

$$f'(x) = 1, \quad G(x) = \tfrac{1}{2}e^{2x}.$$

Then
$$\int xe^{2x}\,dx = \tfrac{1}{2}xe^{2x} - \int \tfrac{1}{2}e^{2x}\,dx$$

$$= \tfrac{1}{2}xe^{2x} - \tfrac{1}{2}\int e^{2x}\,dx$$

$$= \tfrac{1}{2}xe^{2x} - \tfrac{1}{2}\cdot\tfrac{1}{2}e^{2x} + C$$

$$= \tfrac{1}{2}xe^{2x} - \tfrac{1}{4}e^{2x} + C.$$

Helpful Hint: The various steps in your calculation of an integral such as $\int xe^{2x}\,dx$ should be connected by equals signs, showing how you move from one step to the next. It requires a little more effort to rewrite the first term $\tfrac{1}{2}xe^{2x}$ on each line, but the solution is not correct otherwise. A careless student might write

$$\int xe^{2x}\,dx = \tfrac{1}{2}xe^{2x} - \int \tfrac{1}{2}e^{2x}\,dx$$

$$\boxed{=} \qquad - \tfrac{1}{2}\int e^{2x}\,dx$$

$$\boxed{errors} \rightarrow \boxed{=} \qquad - \tfrac{1}{2}\cdot\tfrac{1}{2}e^{2x} + C$$

$$\boxed{=} \qquad - \tfrac{1}{4}e^{2x} + C.$$

Avoid such "shortcuts" in your *homework* as well as on tests. Develop the habit of writing proper mathematical solutions on your homework. This will help to generate correct patterns of thought when you take an exam.

37. Let $u = 6x^2 + 9x$, then $du = (12x + 9)\,dx = 3(4x+3)\,dx$.

$$\int (4x+3)(6x^2+9x)^{-7}\,dx = \tfrac{1}{3}\int (6x^2+9x)^{-7}\cdot 3(4x+3)\,dx$$

$$= \tfrac{1}{3}\int u^{-7}\,du = \tfrac{1}{3}\left(-\tfrac{1}{6}u^{-6}\right) + C$$

$$= -\tfrac{1}{18}(6x^2+9x)^{-6} + C.$$

43. $\int \ln x^4 \, dx = \int 4 \ln x \, dx.$ Use integration by parts with $f(x) = \ln x$ and $g(x) = 4$, and so $f'(x) = 1/x$ and $G(x) = 4x$.

$$\int \ln x^4 \, dx = (\ln x) \cdot 4x - \int \frac{1}{x} \cdot 4x \, dx = 4x \ln x - \int 4 \, dx$$

$$= 4x \ln x - 4x + C.$$

You could also use integration by parts on the original integral, with $f(x) = \ln x^4$ and $g(x) = 1$. (You might think of this method when you read Example 11.) In this case, $f'(x) = 4/x$ (using the chain rule) and $G(x) = x$. The antiderivative you find should be $x \ln x^4 - 4x + C$, which equals the antiderivative found above, by a property of $\ln x$.

49. Use the formula for the present value P of an income stream with $K(t) = 300t + 500$, $N = 5$ years, and $r = .10$.

$$P = \int_0^5 (300t+500) e^{-.1t} \, dt.$$

We use integration by parts, with

$$f(t) = 300t + 500, \qquad g(t) = e^{-.1t},$$
$$f'(t) = 300, \qquad G(t) = -10e^{-.1t}.$$

Then

$$\int (300t+500) e^{-.1t} \, dt = (300t+500)(-10e^{-.1t})$$
$$- \int 300(-10e^{-.1t}) \, dt$$
$$= (-3000t-5000) e^{-.1t} + 3000 \int e^{-.1t} \, dt$$
$$= (-3000t-5000) e^{-.1t} + 3000(-10e^{-.1t})$$
$$= (-3000t-5000-30,000) e^{-.1t}$$
$$= (-3000t-35000) e^{-.1t}.$$

Finally,

$$P = (-3000t-35000) e^{-.1t} \Big|_0^5$$
$$= (-15,000-35,000) e^{-.5} - (-35,000) e^0$$
$$= -50,000(.60653) + 35,000$$
$$= 4673.47 \text{ (dollars)}$$

6.7 Improper Integrals (Brief Edition)

This section in the Brief Edition is the same as Section 9.6 in *Calculus and Its Applications, 8th edition.* The remarks and exercise solutions for this section may be found later in the *Study Guide*, with the other material for Chapter 9.

6.8 Applications of Calculus to Probability (Brief Edition)

A probability density function on an interval $A \le x \le B$ is a function $f(x)$ such that, for $A \le x \le B$, the graph of $f(x)$ lies above or on the x-axis and the area of the region under the graph equals 1.

1. Let X be the outcome of an experiment whose probability density function is $f(x) = 6(x-x^2) = 6x - 6x^2$.

   a. $Pr(\frac{1}{4} \le X \le \frac{1}{2}) = \int_{1/4}^{1/2} (6x-6x^2)\, dx = (3x^2-2x^3) \Big|_{1/4}^{1/2}$

   $$= [3(\tfrac{1}{2})^2 - 2(\tfrac{1}{2})^3] - [3(\tfrac{1}{4})^2 - 2(\tfrac{1}{4})^3]$$

   $$= \frac{1}{2} - \frac{10}{64} = \frac{22}{64} = \frac{11}{32}.$$

   b. $Pr(0 \le X \le \frac{1}{3}) = \int_{0}^{1/3} (6x-6x^2)\, dx = (3x^2-2x^3) \Big|_{0}^{1/3}$

   $$= [3(\tfrac{1}{3})^2 - 2(\tfrac{1}{3})^3] - 0$$

   $$= \frac{3}{9} - \frac{2}{27} = \frac{7}{27}.$$

   c. Since the values of X lie between 0 and 1, the probability that X is at least 1/4 is the same (by definition) as the probability that X is between 1/4 and 1.

   $$Pr(\tfrac{1}{4} \le X) = Pr(\tfrac{1}{4} \le X \le 1) = \int_{1/4}^{1} (6x-6x^2)\, dx$$

   $$= (3x^2 - 2x^3) \Big|_{1/4}^{1} = [3-2] - [3(\tfrac{1}{4})^2 - 2(\tfrac{1}{4})^3]$$

   $$= 1 - [\frac{3}{16} - \frac{2}{64}] = 1 - \frac{10}{64} = \frac{54}{64} = \frac{27}{32}.$$

   d. $Pr(X \le \frac{3}{4}) = Pr(0 \le X \le \frac{3}{4}) = \int_{0}^{3/4} (6x-6x^2)\, dx.$

$$= (3x^2-2x^3)\Big|_0^{3/4} = [3(\tfrac{3}{4})^2 - 2(\tfrac{3}{4})^3] - 0$$

$$= \frac{27}{16} - \frac{27}{32} = \frac{27}{32}.$$

7. a. The fact that the value of X is determined by a "ran-
        dom" arrival time means that X has a uniform probabil-
        ity density function, $f(x) = k$, where k is a suitable
        constant.   The values of X lie between 0 and 3 minutes.
        We must choose k so that the area of the region under
        the graph of $f(x)$ is 1.   Since the graph is a horizon-
        tal line at height k, over the interval $0 \le x \le 3$, the
        region is a rectangle with area [base]·[height] = 3·k.
        So we need $3k = 1$ and $k = 1/3$.   Thus

    $$f(x) = \frac{1}{3}, \ 0 \le x \le 3.$$

    b. Since the values of X do not exceed 3,

    $$Pr(1 \le X) = Pr(1 \le X \le 3) = \int_1^3 \frac{1}{3}\,dx = \frac{1}{3}x\Big|_1^3$$

    $$= \frac{1}{3}(3) - \frac{1}{3}(1) = 1 - \frac{1}{3} = \frac{2}{3}.$$

    c. Since the values of x are not less than 0,

    $$Pr(X \le 1) = Pr(0 \le X \le 1) = \int_0^1 \frac{1}{3}\,dx = \frac{1}{3}x\Big|_0^1$$

    $$= \frac{1}{3}(1) - 0 = \frac{1}{3}.$$

13. The exponential probability density function for x has the
    form $f(x) = \lambda e^{-\lambda x}$.   We find λ from the fact that

    $$\lambda = \frac{1}{[\text{average value of X}]}.$$

    In this exercise, the average service time is 4 minutes,
    so $\lambda = 1/4$ and

    $$f(x) = \frac{1}{4}e^{-(1/4)x} = \frac{1}{4}e^{-x/4}.$$

    a. $Pr(X \le 2) = Pr(0 \le X \le 2) = \displaystyle\int_0^2 \frac{1}{4}e^{-x/4}\,dx$

$$= -e^{-x/4} \Big|_0^2 = -e^{-2/4} - (-e^0)$$

$$= 1 - e^{-1/2} = 1 - .60657 = .39347.$$

b. $Pr(4 \leq X) = Pr(4 \leq X < \infty) = \int_4^\infty \frac{1}{4} e^{-x/4} \, dx.$

We have

$$\int_4^b \frac{1}{4} e^{-x/4} \, dx = -e^{-x/4} \Big|_4^b = -e^{-b/4} - (-e^{-4/4})$$

$$= e^{-1} - e^{-b/4} \to e^{-1} \text{ as } b \to \infty.$$

Thus,

$$Pr(4 \leq X) = \int_4^\infty \frac{1}{4} e^{-x/4} \, dx = e^{-1} = .36788.$$

19. $Pr(X \geq 5) = 1 - Pr(X < 5) = 1 - \int_0^5 k e^{-kx} \, dx$

$$= 1 - \left(-e^{-kx} \Big|_0^5 \right) = 1 - \left(-e^{-5k} - 1 \right) = e^{-5k}.$$

If this probability is .90, then $e^{-5k} = .90$. Taking the natural logarithm of both sides, $-5k = \ln .90$, and $k = (\ln .90)/(-5) \approx .02107$ or about .0211.

Chapter 6: Supplementary Exercises (Brief Edition)

1. By inspection, $\int e^{-x/2} \, dx = -2e^{-x/2} + C.$ Always remember to check your answer.

7. The second function in the integrand is the derivative of the "inside" of the first function, so we use the substitution $u = e^x + 4$, $du = e^x \, dx$:

$$\int (e^x + 4)^3 \cdot e^x \, dx = \int u^3 \, du = \frac{1}{4} u^4 + C = \frac{1}{4}(e^x + 4)^4 + C.$$

13. Since $x(2x + 3)^7$ is the product of two unrelated functions, we use integration by parts. Let

$$f(x) = x, \quad g(x) = (2x + 3)^7,$$
$$f'(x) = 1, \quad G(x) = \frac{1}{8 \cdot 2}(2x + 3)^8 = \frac{1}{16}(2x + 3)^8.$$

Don't forget to check that $G(x)$ is a correct antiderivative of $g(x)$. (Differentiate $G(x)$.) Then

$$\int x(2x + 3)^7 \, dx = x \cdot \frac{1}{16}(2x + 3)^8 - \int \frac{1}{16}(2x + 3)^8 \, dx$$

$$= \frac{x}{16}(2x + 3)^8 - \frac{1}{16} \cdot \frac{1}{9 \cdot 2}(2x + 3)^9 + C$$

$$= \frac{x}{16}(2x + 3)^8 - \frac{1}{288}(2x + 3)^9 + C.$$

19. Since x^4 is almost (up to a multiple) the derivative of $x^5 - 1$, we use the substitution $u = x^5 - 1$, $du = 5x^4$. Then

$$\int x^4 e^{x^5 - 1} \, dx = \frac{1}{5}\int 5x^4 e^{x^5 - 1} \, dx = \frac{1}{5}\int e^u \, du$$

$$= \frac{1}{5}e^u + C = \frac{1}{5}e^{x^5 - 1} + C.$$

Finally,

$$\int_{-1}^{1} x^4 e^{x^5 - 1} \, dx = \frac{1}{5} e^{x^5 - 1}\Big|_{-1}^{1} = \frac{1}{5} e^0 - \frac{1}{5} e^{(-1)^5 - 1} = \frac{1}{5} - \frac{1}{5} e^{-2}.$$

25. The graph of $y = 16 - x^2$ is a parabola that opens downward. The graph of $y = 10 - t$ is a line with negative slope. Since the two curves determine a bounded region, the two curves must intersect. The general shape of the region is shown at the right. Clearly the parabola lies above the line for this region. We find the x-coordinates of the intersection points by solving the equation:

$$10 - x = 16 - x^2,$$
$$x^2 - x - 6 = 0,$$
$$(x-3)(x+2) = 0.$$

Hence $x = -2$ or $x = 3$. The area of the region is

$$\int_{-2}^{3} [(16 - x^2) - (10 - x)] \, dx = \int_{-2}^{3} (-x^2 + x + 6) \, dx$$

$$= (-\frac{1}{3}x^3 + \frac{1}{2}x^2 + 6x)\Big|_{-2}^{3}$$

$$= [-9+\frac{9}{2}+18] - [\frac{8}{3}+2-12]$$

$$= \frac{125}{6}.$$

31. With the demand curve $p = \sqrt{25 - .04x}$, the sales level $x = 400$ corresponds to the price $p = \sqrt{25 - .04(400)} = \sqrt{25 - 16} = 3$. The consumer's surplus is the area of the region below the demand curve and above the horizontal line $p = 3$, from $x = 0$ to $x = 400$. This area is given by

$$\int_0^{400} (\sqrt{25 - .04x} - 3)\, dx.$$

You should be able by now to guess that an antiderivative of $(25 - .04x)^{1/2}$ has the form $k(25 - .04x)^{3/2}$. To find k, we differentiate

$$\frac{d}{dx} k(25 - .04x)^{3/2} = \frac{3}{2} k(25 - .04x)^{1/2} \cdot (-.04).$$

In order for this derivative to be exactly $(25 - .04x)^{1/2}$, we need

$$\frac{3}{2} k(-.04) = 1,$$

$$k = \frac{2}{3} \cdot \frac{1}{-.04} = -\frac{2}{3} \cdot 25 = -\frac{50}{3}.$$

Thus the consumer's surplus equals

$$\int_0^{400} (\sqrt{25 - .04x} - 3)\, dx = \left[-\frac{50}{3}(25 - .04x)^{3/2}) - 3x \right]\Big|_0^{400}$$

$$= \left[-\frac{50}{3}(9)^{3/2} - 1200 \right] - \left[-\frac{50}{3}(25)^{3/2} - 0 \right]$$

$$= \left[-\frac{50}{3}(27) - 1200 \right] + \frac{50}{3}(125)$$

$$= -1650 + \frac{6250}{3} = \frac{1300}{3} = 433.33.$$

The consumer's surplus is \$433.33.

37. From Section 6.5, the volume of the solid of revolution obtained by revolving about the x-axis the region under the graph of $g(x) = 1 - x^2$ from $x = 0$ to $x = 1$ is given by

$$\int_0^1 \pi(1 - x^2)^2\, dx = \pi \int_0^1 (1 - 2x^2 + x^4)\, dx$$

$$= \pi \left(x - \frac{2}{3}x^3 + \frac{1}{5}x^5 \right) \Big|_0^1$$

$$= \pi \left(1 - \frac{2}{3} + \frac{1}{5} \right) - 0 = \frac{8\pi}{15}.$$

43. For any $b > 0$, we compute

$$\int_0^b e^{6-3x} \, dx = -\frac{1}{3}e^{6-3x} \Big|_0^b$$

$$= [-\frac{1}{3}e^{6-3b}] - [-\frac{1}{3}e^6] = \frac{1}{3}e^6 - \frac{1}{3}e^{6-3b}.$$

We observe that

$$\frac{1}{3}e^{6-3b} = \frac{e^6}{3e^{3b}} \to 0 \text{ as } b \to \infty.$$

Thus

$$\int_0^\infty e^{6-3x} \, dx = \lim_{b\to\infty} \int_0^b e^{6-3x} \, dx = \lim_{b\to\infty} [\frac{1}{3}e^6 - \frac{1}{3}e^{6-3b}]$$

$$= \frac{1}{3}e^6.$$

49. The average life span (or mean) is given by $E(X) = \frac{1}{k} = 72$. Hence $k = \frac{1}{72}$, and the probability density function is $f(x) = \frac{1}{72}e^{-(1/72)x}$. The probability that a component lasts for more than 24 months is given by

$$Pr(24 \le X) = \int_{24}^\infty \frac{1}{72}e^{-(1/72)x} \, dx$$

$$= \lim_{b\to\infty} \int_{24}^b \frac{1}{72}e^{-(1/72)x} \, dx$$

$$= \lim_{b\to\infty} \left[\left(-e^{-(1/72)x} \right) \Big|_{24}^b \right]$$

$$= \lim_{b\to\infty} \left[e^{-1/3} - e^{-b/72} \right]$$

$$= e^{-1/3}.$$

Chapter 7

Functions of Several Variables

7.1 Examples of Functions of Several Variables

You should be sure that you completely understand the meanings of the variables in Examples 2 and 3. These examples will be used to illustrate the concepts introduced in later sections.

1. $f(x,y) = x^2 - 3xy - y^2$. So

$$f(5,0) = (5)^2 - 3(5)(0) - (0)^2 = 25,$$
$$f(5,-2) = (5)^2 - 3(5)(-2) - (-2)^2$$
$$= 25 + 30 - 4 = 51,$$
$$f(a,b) = (a)^2 - 3(a)(b) - (b)^2.$$

7. [Cost] = [Cost of top and bottom] + [Cost of four sides]

   = [Total area of top & bottom]·[Cost per sq. ft.]
   + [Total area of four sides]·[Cost per sq. ft.]

   = [xy + xy]·3 + [xz + yz + xz + yz]·5

   = 6xy + 10xz + 10yz

   = C(x,y,z)

13. a. $v = 200,000$, $x = 5000$, $r = 2.5$,

$$T = \frac{r}{100} [.4v - x],$$
$$T = \frac{2.5}{100} [.4(200,000) - 5000]$$
$$= \$1875.00.$$

   b. If $r = 3.00$,

$$T = \frac{3.00}{100} [.4(200,000) - 5000]$$
$$= \$2250.$$

The tax due also increases by 20% (or $\frac{1}{5}$), since

$$1875.00 + \frac{1}{5}(1875.00) = \$2250.00$$

19. A level curve has the form $f(x,y) = C$ (C is arbitrary). Rearrange the equation $y = 3x - 4$ so that all terms of x and y are on the left-hand side:

$$y - 3x = -4.$$

So,

$$y - 3x = C, \text{ some constant.}$$

Thus $f(x,y) = y - 3x$.

25. The graph in Exercise 25 is matched with the level curves in (c). Imagine slicing "near the top" of the four humps. We obtain a cross section of four circular-like figures and as we move further down the z-axis these circular-like figures become larger and larger.
Similarly, Exercise 23 is matched with (d),
Exercise 24 is matched with (b),
Exercise 26 is matched with (a).

7.2 Partial Derivatives

Any letter can be used as a variable of differentiation, even y. As a warm-up to this section, look over the following ordinary derivatives.

$$\text{If } f(y) = ky^2, \text{ then } \frac{df}{dy} = 2ky.$$

$$\text{If } g(y) = 3y^2x, \text{ then } \frac{dg}{dy} = 6yx.$$

Notice that x is a constant in the formula for g(y) because the notation g(y) means that y is the only variable in the function.

1. $\frac{\partial}{\partial x} 5xy = \frac{\partial}{\partial x}[5y]x = 5y$, [we treat 5y as a constant]

$\frac{\partial}{\partial y} 5xy = \frac{\partial}{\partial y}[5x]y = 5x.$ [we treat 5x as a constant]

7. $\frac{\partial}{\partial x}(2x-y+5)^2 = 2(2x-y+5) \cdot \frac{\partial}{\partial x}(2x-y+5)$

$= 2(2x-y+5) \cdot (2-0+0)$ [we treat y as a constant]

$= 4(2x-y+5).$

$$\frac{\partial}{\partial y}(2x-y+5)^2 = 2(2x-y+5)\cdot\frac{\partial}{\partial y}(2x-y+5)$$

$$= 2(2x-y+5)\cdot(0-1+0) \quad \text{[we treat 2x as}$$
$$\text{a constant]}$$

$$= -2(2x-y+5).$$

13. $f(L,K) = 3\sqrt{LK} = 3(LK)^{1/2} = 3L^{1/2}K^{1/2}$. So

$$\frac{\partial}{\partial L} 3L^{1/2}K^{1/2} = \frac{\partial}{\partial L}[3K^{1/2}]L^{1/2} = [3K^{1/2}]\frac{1}{2}L^{-1/2}$$

$$= \frac{3}{2}K^{1/2}L^{-1/2} = \frac{3\sqrt{K}}{2\sqrt{L}}.$$

19. $\frac{\partial}{\partial x}(x^2 + 2xy + y^2 + 3x + 5y) = 2x + 2y + 0 + 3 + 0$
$$= 2x + 2y + 3.$$

Thus $\frac{\partial f}{\partial x}(2,-3) = 2(2) + 2(-3) + 3 = 4 - 6 + 3 = 1.$

$\frac{\partial}{\partial y}(x^2 + 2xy + y^2 + 3x + 5y) = 0 + 2x + 2y + 0 + 5$
$$= 2x + 2y + 5.$$

Thus $\frac{\partial f}{\partial y}(2,-3) = 2(2) + 2(-3) + 5 = 4 - 6 + 5 = 3.$

25. a. Marginal productivity of labor is given by $\frac{\partial f}{\partial x}$.

$$f(x,y) = 200\sqrt{6x^2+y^2} = 200(6x^2 + y^2)^{1/2}.$$

$$\frac{\partial f}{\partial x} = 200(\tfrac{1}{2})(6x^2+y^2)^{-1/2}\cdot\frac{\partial}{\partial x}(6x^2+y^2)$$

$$= 100(6x^2+y^2)^{-1/2}(12x) = \frac{1200x}{\sqrt{6x^2+y^2}}.$$

$$\frac{\partial f}{\partial x}(10,5) = \frac{1200(10)}{\sqrt{6(10)^2+(5)^2}} = \frac{12,000}{\sqrt{625}} = \frac{12,000}{25} = 480.$$

Here is what the value 480 of the marginal productivity of labor really means:

> At $(x,y) = (10,5)$, production changes at a rate 480 times the change in labor, when the amount x of labor changes slightly from 10 units and y stays fixed at 5 units.

See the discussion in Example 5.

Marginal productivity of capital is given by $\frac{\partial f}{\partial y}$.

$$\frac{\partial f}{\partial y} = 200\left(\frac{1}{2}\right)(6x^2+y^2)^{-1/2} \cdot \frac{\partial}{\partial y}(6x^2+y^2)$$

$$= 100(6x^2+y^2)^{-1/2} \cdot (2y) = \frac{200y}{\sqrt{6x^2+y^2}}.$$

$$\frac{\partial f}{\partial y}(10,5) = \frac{200(5)}{\sqrt{6(10)^2+(5)^2}} = \frac{1000}{\sqrt{625}} = \frac{1000}{25} = 40.$$

The value 40 for the marginal productivity of capital means that:

> For $(x,y) = (10,5)$, production changes at a rate 40 times the change in capital, when x stays fixed at 10 units and the amount y of capital changes slightly from 5 units.

This interpretation and the one above illustrate what is written in the box preceding Example 6. The next two parts of the exercise make this discussion more concrete.

b. Let h represent a small number (positive or negative). If labor is changed by h units from 10 to 10+h units and if capital is fixed at 5 units, then the quantity of goods produced will change by approximately 480·h units of goods.

c. Suppose labor decreases from 10 to 9.5 units (while capital stays fixed at 5 units). Then the h from part (b) is -.5, and production will change by approximately 480(-.5) units. That is, production will *decrease* by about 240 units.

31. $V = \frac{.08T}{P} = .08TP^{-1}$,

$$\frac{\partial V}{\partial P} = -(.08)TP^{-2},$$

$$\frac{\partial V}{\partial P}(20,300) = -(.08)(300)(20)^{-2} = \frac{-(.08)(300)}{400} = -.06,$$

$$\frac{\partial V}{\partial T} = .08P^{-1},$$

$$\frac{\partial V}{\partial T}(20,300) = .08(20)^{-1} = \frac{.08}{20} = .004,$$

$\frac{\partial V}{\partial P}(20,300)$ represents the rate of change of volume, when temperature is fixed at 300 and pressure is allowed to vary near 20. That is, if the pressure is increased by one small unit, volume will decrease by about .06 units.

$\frac{\partial V}{\partial T}(20,300)$ represents the rate of change of volume when pressure is fixed at 20 and temperature is allowed to vary near 300. That is, if temperature is increased by one small unit, volume will increase by approximately .004 units.

37. $f(x,y) = 3x^2 + 2xy + 5y,$

$$f(1+h,4) - f(1,4) = 3(1+h)^2 + 2(1+h)(4) + 5(4)$$
$$-[3(1)^2 + 2(1)(4) + 5(4)]$$
$$= 3(1+h^2+2h) + 8 + 8h + 20 - 3 - 8 - 20$$
$$= 3 + 3h^2 + 6h + 8h - 3$$
$$= 3h^2 + 14h.$$

7.3 Maxima and Minima of Functions of Several Variables

Finding relative extreme points for functions of several variables is accomplished in much the same way as for functions of one variable. In Chapter 2 we found relative maximum and minimum points by differentiating and then solving one equation for x. In this section, we differentiate (with partials) and then solve a system of two equations in two unknowns.

Three types of systems of equations arise in this section.

First type: Each equation involves just one variable.

An example is:

$$\begin{cases} x^2 + 1 = 5, \\ 3y - 4 = 11. \end{cases}$$

To solve this system, solve each equation separately for its variable. The solutions to the system consist of all combinations of these individual solutions. In the example above, the first equation has the two solutions x = 2 and x = -2. The second equation has the single solution y = 5. Therefore, the system has two solutions: x = 2, y = 5 and x = -2, y = 5. [Note: These two solutions can also be written (2,5) and (-2,5).]

Second type: One equation contains both variables, the other equation contains just one variable.

An example is

$$\begin{cases} 2x + 4y = 26, \\ 3y - 4 = 11. \end{cases}$$

To solve this system, solve the equation having just one variable, substitute this value into the other equation, and then solve that equation for the remaining variable. In the example above, the second equation has the solution $y = 5$. Substituting into the first equation, we obtain $2x + 4(5) = 26$ or $x = 3$. Therefore, the system has the solution $x = 3$, $y = 5$.

Third type: Both equations contain both variables.

An example is

$$\begin{cases} -9x + y = 3, \\ y + 2 = 4x. \end{cases}$$

Two methods for solving such systems are the EQUATE METHOD and the SOLVE-SUBSTITUTE METHOD.

With the EQUATE METHOD, both equations are solved for y, the two expressions for y are equated and solved for x, and the value of x is substituted into one of the equations to obtain the value of y. The solution to the system above is

$$\begin{cases} y = 3 + 9x, \\ y = 4x - 2. \end{cases}$$

Equating

$$3 + 9x = 4x - 2,$$
$$5x = -5,$$
$$x = -1.$$

Substituting into the first equation, $y = 3 + 9(-1) = -6$. Therefore, the solution is $x = -1$, $y = -6$.

With the SOLVE-SUBSTITUTE METHOD, one equation is solved for y as an expression in x, this expression is substituted into the other equation, that equation is solved for x, and the value(s) of x is substituted into the expression for y to obtain the value(s) of y. The solution to the system above is found as follows:

Solve first equation for y: $y = 3 + 9x.$
Substitute into 2nd eqn: $(3 + 9x) + 2 = 4x.$
Solve for x: $x = -1.$

Substitute the x value into the equation for y:

$$y = 3 + 9(-1) = -6.$$

1. $\frac{\partial}{\partial x}(x^2 - 3y^2 + 4x + 6y + 8) = 2x - 0 + 4 + 0 + 0 = 2x + 4,$

$\frac{\partial}{\partial y}(x^2 - 3y^2 + 4x + 6y + 8) = 0 - 6y + 0 + 6 + 0 = -6y + 6.$

To find possible relative maxima or minima, set the first partial derivatives equal to zero.

$\frac{\partial f}{\partial x} = 2x + 4 = 0,$ $\qquad\qquad$ $\frac{\partial f}{\partial y} = -6y + 6 = 0,$

$\qquad 2x = -4,$ $\qquad\qquad\qquad\qquad\qquad -6y = -6,$

$\qquad x = -4/2 = -2,$ $\qquad\qquad\qquad\qquad y = 1.$

Thus $f(x,y)$ has a possible relative maximum or minimum at $(-2,1)$.

7. $\frac{\partial}{\partial x}(\frac{1}{3}x^3 - 2y^3 - 5x + 6y - 5) = x^2 - 0 - 5 + 0 - 0 = x^2 - 5,$

$\frac{\partial}{\partial y}(\frac{1}{3}x^3 - 2y^3 - 5x + 6y - 5) = 0 - 6y^2 - 0 + 6 - 0$

$\qquad\qquad\qquad\qquad\qquad\qquad\qquad = -6y^2 + 6.$

Again, we set the first partial derivatives equal to zero.

$\frac{\partial f}{\partial x} = x^2 - 5 = 0,$ $\qquad\qquad$ $\frac{\partial f}{\partial y} = -6y^2 + 6 = 0,$

$\qquad x^2 = 5,$ $\qquad\qquad\qquad\qquad\qquad 6y^2 = 6,$

$\qquad x = \sqrt{5}, \; x = -\sqrt{5},$ $\qquad\qquad\qquad y = 1, \; y = -1.$

Thus we have four values (x,y) where there is a possible relative maximum or minimum:

$$(\sqrt{5},1), \; (-\sqrt{5},1), \; (\sqrt{5},-1), \; (-\sqrt{5},-1).$$

13. $f(x,y) = 2x^2 - x^4 - y^2,$

$\frac{\partial f}{\partial x} = 4x - 4x^3,$ $\qquad\qquad$ $\frac{\partial^2 f}{\partial x^2} = 4 - 12x^2,$

$\frac{\partial f}{\partial y} = -2y,$ $\qquad\qquad$ $\frac{\partial^2 f}{\partial y^2} = -2,$

$\frac{\partial^2 f}{\partial x \partial y} = 0.$

$\qquad D(x,y) = \frac{\partial^2 f}{\partial x^2} \cdot \frac{\partial^2 f}{\partial y^2} - \left(\frac{\partial^2 f}{\partial x \partial y}\right)^2$

$\qquad\qquad = (4 - 12x^2)\cdot(-2) - 0 = -2(4 - 12x^2).$

Use the second-derivative test for functions of two variables. Looking initially at $(-1,0)$:

$$D(-1,0) = -2(4 - 12) \text{ which is positive; and}$$

$$\frac{\partial^2 f}{\partial x^2}(-1,0) = 4 - 12(-1)^2 \text{ which is negative.}$$

Hence $f(x,y)$ has a relative maximum at $(-1,0)$.

For $(0,0)$: $D(0,0) = -2(4 - 0) = -8$ which is negative, so $f(x,y)$ has neither a relative maximum nor a relative minimum at $(0,0)$.

Finally at $(1,0)$: $D(1,0) = -2(4 - 12)$ which is positive; and

$$\frac{\partial^2 f}{\partial x^2}(1,0) = 4 - 12 = -8 \text{ is negative.}$$

Therefore again by the test, $f(x,y)$ has a relative maximum at $(1,0)$.

19. $\frac{\partial}{\partial x}(-2x^2 + 2xy - y^2 + 4x - 6y + 5) = -4x + 2y + 4,$

$\frac{\partial}{\partial y}(-2x^2 + 2xy - y^2 + 4x - 6y + 5) = 2x - 2y - 6.$

Setting these partials equal to zero, we obtain

$$\frac{\partial f}{\partial x} = -4x + 2y + 4 = 0, \qquad\qquad \frac{\partial f}{\partial y} = 2x - 2y - 6 = 0,$$
$$2y = 4x - 4, \qquad\qquad\qquad\qquad 2y = 2x - 6,$$
$$y = 2x - 2, \qquad\qquad\qquad\qquad\quad y = x - 3.$$

Equating these two expressions for y, we have

$$2x - 2 = x - 3,$$
$$x = -1.$$

Substituting $x = -1$ into $y = x - 3$, we obtain $y = x - 3 = (-1) - 3 = -4$. So there is a possible relative maximum or minimum at $(-1,-4)$. We use the second derivative test to determine which, if either, is the case.

$$\frac{\partial^2 f}{\partial x^2} = \frac{\partial}{\partial x}(-4x + 2y + 4) = -4,$$

$$\frac{\partial^2 f}{\partial y^2} = \frac{\partial}{\partial y}(2x - 2y - 6) = -2,$$

$$\frac{\partial^2 f}{\partial x \partial y} = \frac{\partial}{\partial x}(2x - 2y - 6) = 2.$$

Therefore, $D(x,y) = (-4)(-2) - (2)^2 = 8 - 4 = 4$, and hence $D(-1,-4) = 4$. Since $4 > 0$, $f(x,y)$ indeed has a relative maximum or minimum at $(-1,-4)$. Since $\frac{\partial^2 f}{\partial x^2}(-1,-4) = -4 < 0$, $f(x,y)$ has a relative maximum at $(-1,-4)$.

25. $\frac{\partial f}{\partial x} = 4x - 1$, $\frac{\partial f}{\partial y} = 3y^2 - 12$.

Setting the two partials equal to 0 and solving, we obtain

$$4x - 1 = 0, \qquad\qquad\qquad 3y^2 - 12 = 0,$$
$$4x = 1, \qquad\qquad\qquad\quad\; 3y^2 = 12,$$
$$x = 1/4, \qquad\qquad\qquad\quad\; y^2 = 4,$$
$$y = 2, -2.$$

So there are two possible relative maxima and/or minima: $(1/4, 2)$, $(1/4, -2)$. For the second derivative test, we compute

$$\frac{\partial^2 f}{\partial x^2} = \frac{\partial}{\partial x}(4x - 1) = 4,$$

$$\frac{\partial^2 f}{\partial y^2} = \frac{\partial}{\partial y}(3y^2 - 12) = 6y,$$

$$\frac{\partial^2 f}{\partial x \partial y} = \frac{\partial}{\partial x}(3y^2 - 12) = 0.$$

$$D(x,y) = 4(6y) - 0^2 = 24y.$$

Now $D(1/4,2) = 24(2) = 48 > 0$, so $f(x,y)$ does indeed have a relative maximum or minimum at $(1/4,2)$. Since

$$\frac{\partial^2 f}{\partial x^2}(1/4,2) = 4 > 0,$$

there is a relative minimum at $(1/4,2)$. Finally, $D(1/4,-2) = 24(-2) = -48 < 0$, indicating that $(1/4,-2)$ is a saddle point; this is neither a relative maximum nor a relative minimum.

31. We note that the revenue can be expressed by $10x + 9y$, since the company sells x units of product I for 10 dollars each, and y units of product II for 9 dollars each.

Noting also that profit = (revenue) - (cost), we write the profit function:

$$P(x,y) = 10x + 9y - [400 + 2x + 3y + .01(3x^2+xy+3y^2)]$$
$$= 8x + 6y - .03x^2 - .01xy - .03y^2 - 400.$$

We now proceed as in Exercises 19 and 25 above.

$$\frac{\partial P}{\partial x} = 8 - .06x - .01y,$$

$$\frac{\partial P}{\partial y} = 6 - .01x - .06y.$$

$$8 - .06x - .01y = 0, \qquad 6 - .01x - .06y = 0,$$
$$.01y = 8 - .06x, \qquad .06y = 6 - .01x,$$
$$y = 800 - 6x, \qquad y = 100 - (1/6)x.$$

So,

$$800 - 6x = 100 - (1/6)x,$$
$$700 = (35/6)x,$$
$$x = 120.$$

and

$$y = 800 - 6x = 800 - 6(120)$$
$$= 800 - 720 = 80.$$

So (120,80) is the only possible maximum. For the second derivative test, we compute

$$\frac{\partial^2 P}{\partial x^2} = -.06, \quad \frac{\partial^2 P}{\partial y^2} = -.06, \quad \frac{\partial^2 P}{\partial x \partial y} = -.01.$$

Therefore, $D(x,y) = (-.06)(-.06) - (-.01)^2 = .0035$. Thus $D(120,80) = .0035 > 0$ and (120,80) is indeed a maximum or minimum. Since $\frac{\partial^2 P}{\partial x^2}$ (120,80) $= -.06 < 0$, (120,80) is a maximum. Thus profit is maximized by manufacturing and selling 120 units of product I and 80 units of product II.

7.4 Lagrange Multipliers and Constrained Optimization

Any letter of the alphabet can be used as a variable. In this section we introduce the Greek letter λ as a variable. The following results illustrate derivatives using λ.

$$\text{If } f(\lambda) = 5\lambda, \text{ then } \frac{df(\lambda)}{d\lambda} = 5.$$

$$\text{If } f(\lambda) = \lambda k, \text{ then } \frac{df(\lambda)}{d\lambda} = k.$$

Partial derivatives of functions involving λ are not difficult to compute once the unfamiliarity of using a Greek letter is overcome.

The problems in this section require that systems of three and four variables be solved. The method following Example 1 applies to all equations in x, y, and λ. Systems with the additional variable z can usually be solved by mimicking the solution to Example 4.

1. We construct the function

$$F(x,y,\lambda) = x^2 + 3y^2 + 10 + \lambda(8-x-y).$$

Setting the first partial derivatives equal to zero and solving for λ, we obtain

$$\frac{\partial F}{\partial x} = 2x - \lambda = 0, \text{ so } \lambda = 2x,$$

$$\frac{\partial F}{\partial y} = 6y - \lambda = 0, \text{ so } \lambda = 6y,$$

$$\frac{\partial F}{\partial \lambda} = 8 - x - y = 0.$$

Equating $\lambda = 2x$ and $\lambda = 6y$, we obtain $2x = 6y$, or $x = 3y$. Substituting $3y$ for x into the third equation, we have

$$\begin{aligned} 8 - (3y) - y &= 0, \\ 8 - 4y &= 0, \\ 4y &= 8, \\ y &= 2. \end{aligned}$$

Now $x = 3y = 3(2) = 6$ and $\lambda = 2x = 2(6) = 12$.

So the minimum is at $(6,2)$, and the minimum value is

$$F(6,2) = 6^2 + 3(2^2) + 10 = 36 + 12 + 10 = 58.$$

7. Minimize the function, $f(x,y) = x + y$ subject to the constraint

$$xy = 25, \text{ or } xy - 25 = 0.$$

$F(x,y,\lambda) = x + y + \lambda(xy - 25)$ is the Lagrange function. For a relative minimum we set its first partial derivatives equal to zero:

$$\left. \begin{aligned} \frac{\partial F}{\partial F} &= 1 + \lambda x = 0 \\[2mm] \frac{\partial F}{\partial y} &= 1 + \lambda x = 0 \end{aligned} \right\} \Rightarrow \lambda y = \lambda x, \text{ or } y = x \quad (*),$$

$$\frac{\partial F}{\partial \lambda} = xy - 25 = 0 \text{ (substitute in } (*)),$$

$$x^2 - 25 = 0, \text{ or } x = \pm 5.$$

If x = 5 (since we need positive numbers): y = 5 by (*).
Therefore, x = 5, y = 5.

13. Maximize P(x,y) = 3x + 4y subject to the constraint

$$9x^2 + 4y^2 - 18{,}000 = 0.$$

P(x,y,λ) = 3x + 4y + λ(9x^2 + 4y^2 - 18,000).   Setting the first partial derivatives equal to zero:

$$\frac{\partial p}{\partial x} = 3 + 18\lambda x = 0,$$

$$\frac{\partial p}{\partial y} = 4 + 8\lambda y = 0,$$

$$\frac{\partial p}{\partial \lambda} = 9x^2 + 4y^2 - 18000 = 0 \qquad (*).$$

Thus, 3 + 18λx = 0, and 4 + 8λy = 0, which gives:

$$1 + 6\lambda x = 0, \text{ and } 1 + 2\lambda y = 0, \text{ respectively.}$$

Therefore,

$$1 + 6\lambda x = 1 + 2\lambda y,$$
$$6\lambda x = 2\lambda y,$$
$$3x = y.$$

Substituting 3x for y in (*),

$$\text{i.e., } 9x^2 + 4(3x)^2 - 18{,}000 = 0,$$
$$45x^2 = 18{,}000,$$
$$x^2 = 400, \text{ or } x = \pm 20.$$

Since y = 3x, we have y = ±60.   But x, y ≥ 0, so

$$x = 20, \text{ and } y = 60.$$

19. Let F(x,y,z,λ) = 3x + 5y + z - x^2 - y^2 - z^2 + λ(6-x-y-z), and set the first partial derivatives equal to zero.

$$\frac{\partial F}{\partial x} = 3 - 2x - \lambda = 0,$$

$$\frac{\partial F}{\partial y} = 5 - 2y - \lambda = 0,$$

$$\frac{\partial F}{\partial z} = 1 - 2z - \lambda = 0.$$

This gives us three expressions for λ:

$$\lambda = 3 - 2x,$$
$$\lambda = 5 - 2y,$$
$$\lambda = 1 - 2z.$$

Equating the first two equations and solving for x, we have

$$3 - 2x = 5 - 2y,$$
$$-2x = 2 - 2y,$$
$$x = -1 + y.$$

Equating the second two equations and solving for z, we obtain:

$$5 - 2y = 1 - 2z,$$
$$2z = 2y - 4,$$
$$z = y - 2.$$

We now have expressions for x and for z in terms of y, and can substitute these into the equation

$$\frac{\partial F}{\partial \lambda} = 6 - x - y - z = 0.$$

$$6 - (-1+y) - y - (y-2) = 0$$

$$6 + 1 - y - y - y + 2 = 0$$

$$9 - 3y = 0$$

$$9 = 3y, \text{ or } y = 3.$$

Thus, x = -1 + y = -1 + 3 = 2 and z = y - 2 = 3 - 2 = 1. Thus the function is maximized when x = 2, y = 3, and z = 1.

25. Throughout the problem we are not given any specific production function, so we must use the general expression f(x,y) in its place, which we wish to maximize. As a constraint we have that the cost of labor plus the cost of capital is c dollars, that is:

$$ax + by = c, \text{ or } ax + by - c = 0.$$

We then construct the function

$$F(x,y,\lambda) = f(x,y) + \lambda(ax + by - c).$$

We take partial derivatives and set them equal to zero.

$$\frac{\partial F}{\partial x} = \frac{\partial f}{\partial x} + \lambda a = 0,$$

$$\frac{\partial F}{\partial y} = \frac{\partial f}{\partial y} + \lambda b = 0.$$

Solving for λ we get

$$\lambda = \frac{-\frac{\partial f}{\partial x}}{a} \text{ and } \lambda = \frac{-\frac{\partial f}{\partial y}}{b}.$$

And equating these expressions for λ, we conclude that

$$\frac{-\frac{\partial f}{\partial x}}{a} = \frac{-\frac{\partial f}{\partial x}}{b},$$

$$-b\left(\frac{\partial f}{\partial x}\right) = -a\left(\frac{\partial f}{\partial y}\right),$$

$$\frac{\frac{\partial f}{\partial x}}{\frac{\partial f}{\partial y}} = \frac{-a}{-b} = \frac{a}{b}.$$

7.5   The Method of Least Squares

Each problem in this section requires the solution of a system of two equations in two unknowns. These systems differ from those previously studied in three ways.

1. The variables (that is, the unknowns) will always be A and B, rather than x and y.

2. The equations are linear. That is, they have the form aA + bB = c, where a, b, and c are constants.

3. The systems have exactly one solution. This solution is best found by multiplying one equation by a constant and subtracting it from the other equation to eliminate one of the variables. The value of the other variable is then easily found. By substituting this value into one of the equations, the value of the first variable is easily found.

1. $E = E_1^2 + \cdots + E_4^2 = (A + B - 3)^2 + (2A + B - 6)^2$
$$+ (3A + B - 8)^2 + (4A + B - 6)^2.$$
$$= (1.1 + 3 - 3)^2 + (2(1.1) + 3 - 6)^2$$
$$+ (3(1.1) + 3 - 8)^2 + (4(1.1) + 3 - 6)^2$$
$$= 6.7$$

7. $E = (A + B - 9)^2 + (2A + B - 8)^2$
$$+ (3A + B - 6)^2 + (4A + B - 3)^2.$$

To minimize the error E, take partial derivatives with respect to A and B, and set them equal to zero.

$\frac{\partial E}{\partial A} = 2(A + B - 9) + 2(2A + B - 8)\cdot 2$
$$+ 2(3A + B - 6)\cdot 3 + 2(4A + B - 3)\cdot 4$$
$$= (2 + 8 + 18 + 32)A + (2 + 4 + 6 + 8)B - (18 + 32 + 36 + 24)$$
$$= 60A + 20B - 110 = 0.$$

$$\frac{\partial E}{\partial B} = 2(A + B - 9) + 2(2A + B - 8)$$
$$+ 2(3A + B - 6) + 2(4A + B - 3)$$
$$= (2 + 4 + 6 + 8)A + (2 + 2 + 2 + 2)B - (18 + 16 + 12 + 6)$$
$$= 20A + 8B - 52 = 0.$$

To solve the system of simultaneous linear equations

$$60A + 20B = 110$$
$$20A + 8B = 52,$$

multiply the second equation by -3, and add it to the first equation:

$$60A + 20B = 110$$
$$\underline{-60A - 24B = -156}$$
$$ - 4B = -46, \qquad B = 11.5.$$

Then find A by substituting this value of B into the first equation:

$$60A + 20(11.5) = 110, \quad 60A = 110 - 230, \quad A = -2.$$

The least-squares line is $y = -2x + 11.5$.

13. **a.** The data points are $(0, 10.7)$, $(5, 13.9)$, $(10, 16.2)$, $(15, 19.4)$, $(20, 21.3)$, and $(25, 23.0)$. The table for these data is

x	y	xy	x^2
0	10.7	0	0
5	13.9	69.5	25
10	16.2	162	100
15	19.4	291	225
20	21.3	426	400
25	23.0	575	625

$\sum x = 75$ $\sum y = 104.5$ $\sum xy = 1523.5$ $\sum x^2 = 1375$

The formulas for A and B are:

$$A = \frac{6 \cdot 1523.5 - 75 \cdot 104.5}{6 \cdot 1375 - (75)^2} = \frac{1303.5}{2625} \approx .4966$$

$$B = \frac{104.5 - .4966 \cdot 75}{6} \approx 11.2092.$$

The least-squares line is $y = .4966x + 11.2092$. The number of decimal places to use in the equation of the line should be determined by the accuracy of the

original data.   In this problem, the data have three
significant figures, so a reasonable answer for the
least-squares line might be y = .497x + 11.2, or even
y =.50x + 11.2.

b. Since 1993 corresponds to x = 23, the best estimate for
the percent completion in 1993 is .497(23) + 11.2
= 22.631, which we probably should report as 22.6%.   The
same 22.6% answer would come from the line y = .4966x
+ 11.2092.   The line y = .5x + 11.2 produces 22.7%.

c. Solve .497x + 11.2 = 27.1 and obtain x = 31.99, that
is, 32 years after 1970.   The completion rate should
reach 27.1% in 2002.

7.6   Double Integrals

The problems in this section amount to performing two integra-
tions, once with respect to y as the variable and once with
respect to x.   Antidifferentiation with respect to y takes a
little getting used to.   It is just the reverse operation to
taking partial derivatives with respect to y.

1.   We first evaluate the inner integral.

$$\int_0^1 e^{x+y} \, dy = e^{x+y} \Big|_0^1 = e^{x+1} - e^x.$$

[The dy in the integral tells us that y is the variable of
integration in $e^{x+y} \Big|_0^1$.]   We can now evaluate the outer
integral.

$$\int_0^1 (e^{x+1} - e^x) \, dx = (e^{x+1} - e^x) \Big|_0^1$$
$$= (e^2 - e) - (e - 1)$$
$$= e^2 - 2e + 1.$$

7.   We first evaluate the inner integral.

$$\int_x^{2x} (x+y) \, dy = (xy + \frac{1}{2}y^2) \Big|_x^{2x}$$
$$= [x(2x) + \frac{1}{2}(2x)^2] - [x \cdot x + \frac{1}{2}x^2]$$

$$= [2x^2 + 2x^2] - x^2 - \tfrac{1}{2}x^2$$

$$= \tfrac{5}{2}x^2.$$

We can now evaluate the outer integral.

$$\int_{1}^{1} \tfrac{5}{2}x^2 \, dx = \tfrac{5}{6}x^3 \Big|_{-1}^{1} = \tfrac{5}{6} - (-\tfrac{5}{6}) = \tfrac{5}{3} \; .$$

13. The desired volume is given by the double integral:

$$\iint_{R} (x^2 + y^2) \, dx \, dy,$$

which is equivalent to the iterated integral:

$$\int_{1}^{3} \left(\int_{0}^{1} (x^2 + y^2) \, dy \right) dx.$$

Evaluating the inner integral we have

$$\int_{0}^{1} (x^2 + y^2) \, dy = (x^2 y + \tfrac{1}{3}y^3) \Big|_{0}^{1}$$

$$= (x^2 + \tfrac{1}{3}) - (0 + 0) = x^2 + \tfrac{1}{3} \; .$$

Evaluating the outer integral we have

$$\int_{1}^{3} (x^2 + \tfrac{1}{3}) \, dx = (\tfrac{1}{3}x^3 + \tfrac{1}{3}x) \Big|_{1}^{3} = (9+1) - (\tfrac{1}{3} + \tfrac{1}{3}) = 9\tfrac{1}{3} \; .$$

Chapter 7: Supplementary Exercises

1. $f(2,9) = \dfrac{2\sqrt{9}}{1+2} = \dfrac{6}{3} = 2,$

$f(5,1) = \dfrac{5\sqrt{1}}{1+5} = \dfrac{5}{6},$

$f(0,0) = \dfrac{0\sqrt{0}}{1+0} = \dfrac{0}{1} = 0.$

7. $f(x,y) = e^{x/y} = e^{xy^{-1}},$

$\dfrac{\partial f}{\partial x} = y^{-1}e^{xy^{-1}} = \tfrac{1}{y}e^{x/y},$ (we treat y as a constant)

$$\frac{\partial f}{\partial y} = e^{xy^{-1}}[\frac{\partial}{\partial y}xy^{-1}] = -xy^{-2}e^{xy^{-1}} = -\frac{x}{y^2}e^{x/y}, \quad \text{(we treat x as a constant).}$$

13. $f(x,y) = x^5 - 2x^3y + \frac{1}{2}y^4.$

In order to find the second partial derivatives we must first determine the first partial derivatives with respect to x and y.

$$\frac{\partial f}{\partial x} = 5x^4 - 6x^2y,$$

$$\frac{\partial f}{\partial y} = -2x^3 + 2y^3.$$

Differentiating each of these with respect to x and y, we have

$$\frac{\partial^2 f}{\partial x^2} = \frac{\partial}{\partial x}(\frac{\partial f}{\partial x}) = \frac{\partial}{\partial x}(5x^4 - 6x^2y) = 20x^3 - 12xy,$$

$$\frac{\partial^2 f}{\partial y^2} = \frac{\partial}{\partial y}(\frac{\partial f}{\partial y}) = \frac{\partial}{\partial y}(-2x^3 + 2y^3) = 6y^2,$$

$$\frac{\partial^2 f}{\partial x \partial y} = \frac{\partial}{\partial x}(\frac{\partial f}{\partial y}) = \frac{\partial}{\partial x}(-2x^3 + 2y^3) = -6x^2,$$

$$\frac{\partial^2 f}{\partial y \partial x} = \frac{\partial}{\partial y}(\frac{\partial f}{\partial x}) = \frac{\partial}{\partial y}(5x^4 - 6x^2y) = -6x^2.$$

19. $\frac{\partial}{\partial x}(x^3 + 3x^2 + 3y^2 - 6y + 7) = 3x^2 + 6x,$

$\frac{\partial}{\partial y}(x^3 + 3x^2 + 3y^2 - 6y + 7) = 6y - 6.$

To find possible relative maxima or minima, set the first partial derivatives equal to zero.

$$\frac{\partial f}{\partial x} = 3x^2 + 6x = 0, \qquad\qquad \frac{\partial f}{\partial y} = 6y - 6 = 0,$$
$$3x(x+2) = 0, \qquad\qquad\qquad 6y = 6,$$
$$x = 0, \ x = -2, \qquad\qquad\qquad y = 1.$$

Thus f(x,y) has a possible relative maximum or minimum at (0,1) and at (-2,1).

25. We construct the function

$$F(x,y,\lambda) = 3x^2 + 2xy - y^2 + \lambda(5-2x-y).$$

Setting the first partial derivatives equal to zero and solving for λ we obtain

$$\frac{\partial F}{\partial x} = 6x + 2y - 2\lambda = 0,$$

$$2\lambda = 6x + 2y,$$

$$\lambda = 3x + y.$$

$$\frac{\partial F}{\partial y} = 2x - 2y - \lambda = 0,$$

$$\lambda = 2x - 2y.$$

Equating the two expressions for λ we have

$$3x + y = 2x - 2y \quad \text{or} \quad x = -3y.$$

We have $\frac{\partial F}{\partial \lambda} = 5 - 2x - y = 0$ as a constraint, and substituting $-3y$ for x giving:

$$5 - 2(-3y) - y = 0,$$

$$5 + 5y = 0,$$

$$5y = -5, \text{ or } y = -1.$$

Hence, $x = -3y = -3(-1) = 3$, $\lambda = 2x - 2y = 2(3) - 2(-1) = 6 + 2 = 8$, so the maximum is at $(3,-1)$, and the maximum value is $f(3,-1) = 3(9) + 2(3)(-1) - 1 = 27 - 6 - 1 = 20$.

31. Let the straight line be $y = Ax + B$. When $x = 1,2,3$ the corresponding y-coordinates of the points of the line are $A+B$, $2A+B$, $3A+B$, respectively. Therefore, the squares of the vertical distances from the line to the points $(1,1)$, $(2,3)$, and $(3,6)$ are

$$E_1^2 = (A+B - 1)^2,$$

$$E_2^2 = (2A+B - 3)^2,$$

$$E_3^2 = (3A+B - 6)^2.$$

Thus the least-squares error is

$$f(A,B) = E_1^2 + E_2^2 + E_3^2$$

$$= (A + B - 1)^2 + (2A + B - 3)^2 + (3A + B - 6)^2.$$

To minimize $f(A,B)$, we take partial derivatives with respect to A and B, and set them equal to zero.

$$\frac{\partial f}{\partial A} = 2(A + B - 1) + 2(2A + B - 3) \cdot 2 + 2(3A + B - 6) \cdot 3$$

Don't forget these factors ⟶

$$= (2A + 2B - 2) + (8A + 4B - 12) + (18A + 6B - 36)$$

$$= 28A + 12B - 50 = 0.$$

$$\frac{\partial f}{\partial B} = 2(A + B - 1) + 2(2A + B - 3) + 2(3A + B - 6)$$

$$= (2A + 2B - 2) + (4A + 2B - 6) + (6A + 2B - 12)$$

$$= 12A + 6B - 20 = 0.$$

To solve for A and B, we must solve the system of simultaneous linear equations

$$28A + 12B = 50,$$
$$12A + 6B = 20.$$

Subtracting 2 times the second equation from the first equation we have

$$4A = 10, \text{ and } A = 5/2.$$

Hence

$$6B = 20 - 12(5/2) = -10, \text{ and } B = -5/3.$$

Therefore, the straight line that minimizes the least-squares error is $y = (5/2)x - 5/3$.

37. $\iint\limits_R 5 \, dx \, dy$ represents the volume of a box with dimensions

$(4 - 0) \times (3 - 1) \times 5$. So $\iint\limits_R 5 \, dx \, dy = 4 \cdot 2 \cdot 5 = 40.$

Chapter 8

The Trigonometric Functions

Trigonometric functions are useful for describing physical proceses that are cyclical or periodic. The goal of this short chapter is to study basic properties of these functions. We realize that many of our readers have never studied trigonometry, and so we mention a few simple connections with right triangles. However, our main interest is in calculus, not in trigonometry.

8.1 Radian Measure of Angles

All of the exercises in this text use radian measure in connection with trigonometric functions.

1. $30° = \overset{}{\cancel{30}} \times \dfrac{\pi}{\underset{6}{\cancel{180}}}$ radians $= \dfrac{\pi}{6}$ radians

   $120° = \overset{2}{\cancel{120}} \times \dfrac{\pi}{\underset{3}{\cancel{180}}}$ radians $= \dfrac{2\pi}{3}$ radians

   $315° = \overset{7}{\cancel{315}} \times \dfrac{\pi}{\underset{4}{\cancel{180}}}$ radians $= \dfrac{7\pi}{4}$ radians.

7. The angle described by this figure consists of one full revolution plus three quarters of a revolution. That is

$$t = 2\pi + \frac{3}{4}(2\pi) = 2\pi + \frac{3}{2}\pi = \frac{7\pi}{2}.$$

13. See the figures in the answer section of the text. Here is the reasoning that leads to those figures. First, since $\pi/2$ is one quarter-revolution of the circle, $3\pi/2$ is three quarter-revolutions. Next, since $\pi/4$ is one eighth-revolution of the circle, $3\pi/4$ is three eighth-revolutions. Notice also that $3\pi/4$ is exactly one half the angle de-

scribed in the first case. Finally, since π is one half-revolution of the circle, 5π is five half-revolutions or two-and-one-half revolutions.

8.2 The Sine and the Cosine

The most important pictures in this section are on pages 420-21. Years from now if someone asks you what the sine function is, you should think of the graphs in Figures 12 and 13, not the triangles in Figure 3, or even the circle in Figure 7. It is the regular, fluctuating shape of the graphs of $\cos t$ and $\sin t$ that make them useful in mathematical models. Nevertheless, your instructor will want you to have a basic understanding of how $\cos t$ and $\sin t$ are defined, and that is the purpose of the other figures in this section.

Exercises 1—20 help you learn the basic definitions:

$$\cos t = \frac{x}{r}, \quad \text{and} \quad \sin t = \frac{y}{r},$$

where x and y are the coordinates of a point that determines an angle of t radians, and r is the distance of the point from the origin. Exercises 21-38 help you learn the alternative definitions of $\cos t$ and $\sin t$ as the x- and y-coordinates of an appropriate point on the unit circle. The alternative definitions enable you to understand some important properties of the sine and cosine. Be sure to find out which of these properties you must memorize. [Formulas (7) and (8), for example, are only used later for proofs of derivative formulas, so you may not need to learn them.]

1. $\sin t = \dfrac{\text{opposite}}{\text{hypotenuse}} = \dfrac{1}{2}$, $\cos t = \dfrac{\text{adjacent}}{\text{hypotenuse}} = \dfrac{\sqrt{3}}{2}$.

7. First we must compute r.
$$r = \sqrt{x^2 + y^2} = \sqrt{(-2)^2 + 1^2} = \sqrt{4+1} = \sqrt{5}.$$
Then
$$\sin t = \frac{y}{r} = \frac{1}{\sqrt{5}}, \quad \cos t = \frac{x}{r} = \frac{-2}{\sqrt{5}}.$$

13. First compute
$$\sin t = \frac{b}{c} = \frac{5}{13} = .385.$$

One way to find t is to look in the "$\sin t$" column of a table of trigonometric functions. A number in this column close to .385 is .38942, in the row corresponding to t = .4. From this you can conclude that $t \approx .4$. For more accuracy, use a scientific calculator. Check to make sure that angle measurement is set for radians, and use the "inverse sine" function to compute $\sin^{-1} .385 = .39521$.

19. Since we know "a" and it is the side <u>adjacent</u> to the given angle t, we use the formula

$$\cos t = \frac{\text{adjacent}}{\text{hypotenuse}}.$$

We have

$$\cos .5 = \frac{2.4}{c}.$$

From a calculator, $\cos .5 = .87758$, so

$$.87758 = \frac{2.4}{c},$$

$$.87758c = 2.4,$$

$$c = \frac{2.4}{.87758} = 2.7348.$$

One way to find b, now that we know c, is to use the formula

$$\sin t = \frac{b}{c}.$$

That is,

$$\sin .5 = \frac{b}{2.73},$$

$$.47943 = \frac{b}{2.73},$$

$$2.73(.47943) = b,$$

$$b = 1.31.$$

Alternately, using the Pythagorean theorem, we have

$$a^2 + b^2 = c^2, \text{ i.e., } (2.4)^2 + b^2 = (2.73)^2,$$

$$5.76 + b^2 = 7.45,$$

$$b^2 = 1.69,$$

$$b = 1.30.$$

The discrepancy between the two values for b is due to the round-off error in using 2.73 in place of 2.7348. Either value of b is accurate enough for our purposes.

25. On the unit circle we locate the point P that is determined by an angle of $\frac{-5\pi}{8}$ radians. The x-coordinate of P is $\cos(\frac{-5\pi}{8})$. There is another point Q on the unit circle

with the same x-coordinate. (See the figure.) Let t be the radian measure of the angle determined by Q. Then $\cos t = \cos\left(\frac{-5\pi}{8}\right)$ because Q and P have

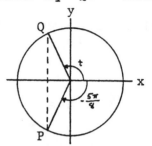

the same x-coordinate. Also, $0 \le t \le \pi$. From the symmetry of the diagram, it is clear that $t = \frac{5\pi}{8}$. Also, since $\cos(-t) = \cos t$ and $0 \le \frac{5\pi}{8} \le \pi$, we have $t = \frac{5\pi}{8}$.

31. The equation $\sin t = -\sin(\pi/6)$ relates the y-coordinates of two points on the unit circle. One point P corresponds to an angle of $\pi/6$ radians. (See the figure.) The other point Q must be on the right half of the unit circle, since $-\frac{\pi}{6} \le t \le \frac{\pi}{2}$. But its y-coordinate must be the nega-

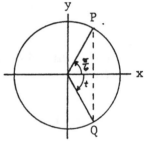

tive of the y-coordinate of P. We conclude from the figure that $t = -\frac{\pi}{6}$. Another method is to recall that $-\sin t = \sin(-t)$. Thus

$$-\sin(\pi/6) = \sin(-\pi/6).$$

Since $-\pi/6$ is between $-\pi/2$ and $\pi/2$, we conclude that $t = -\pi/6$.

37. Thinking of $\sin t$ as the y-coordinate of the point on the unit circle that is determined by an angle of t radians, we find that $\sin 5\pi = 0$ and $\sin(-2\pi) = 0$.

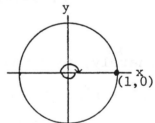

Since $\frac{17\pi}{2} = 8\pi + \frac{\pi}{2} = 4(2\pi) + \frac{\pi}{2}$, $\frac{17\pi}{2}$ is four complete revolutions of the circle plus one quarter-revolution. So P is the point $(0,1)$ and $\sin\frac{17\pi}{2} = 1$.

Since $-\frac{13\pi}{2} = -6\pi - \frac{\pi}{2} = 3(-2\pi) - \frac{\pi}{2}$, $-\frac{13\pi}{2}$ is three complete revolutions of the circle in the negative direction plus one quarter-revolution in the negative direction. So P is the point $(0,-1)$ and $\sin\left(-\frac{13\pi}{2}\right) = -1$.

8.3 Differentiation of sin t and cos t

The significance of the derivative formula

$$\frac{d}{dt}\sin t = \cos t$$

is revealed by Figures 1 and 2 in the text. That is, for each number t, the value of $\cos t$ gives the slope of the sine curve at the specified value of t. This fundamental property of the derivative as a slope function is worth contemplating because it will be crucial for our work in Chapter 10.

Most of the exercises in this section are routine drill problems. Exercises 35-38 are just a "warm-up" to remind you of antiderivatives. We will concentrate on problems such as these in Section 9.1.

Helpful Hint: <u>Don't</u> memorize antiderivative formulas for cos t and sin t, because you might confuse them with the derivative formulas. Just memorize where the minus sign goes in the derivative formulas, and then use this knowledge to check your work whenever you need to "guess" an antiderivative involving a sine or cosine. (See our solution to Exercise 37, below.)

1. By the chain rule we have

$$\frac{d}{dt}(\sin 4t) = (\cos 4t)\cdot\frac{d}{dt}4t = 4\cos 4t.$$

7. $\frac{d}{dt}(t + \cos \pi t) = \frac{d}{dt}t + \frac{d}{dt}\cos \pi t$

$$= 1 + (-\sin \pi t)\frac{d}{dt}\pi t = 1 - \pi \sin \pi t.$$

13. By repeated application of the chain rule we have

$$\frac{d}{dx}\sin\sqrt{x-1} = \cos\sqrt{x-1}\cdot\frac{d}{dx}\sqrt{x-1}$$

$$= \cos\sqrt{x-1}\cdot\frac{d}{dx}(x-1)^{1/2}$$

$$= \cos\sqrt{x-1}\cdot(\tfrac{1}{2}(x-1)^{-1/2})\frac{d}{dx}(x-1)$$

$$= \cos\sqrt{x-1}\cdot(\tfrac{1}{2}(x-1)^{-1/2})$$

$$= \frac{\cos\sqrt{x-1}}{2\sqrt{x-1}}.$$

19. By repeated application of the chain rule we have

$$\frac{d}{dx}\cos^2 x^3 = \frac{d}{dx}(\cos x^3)^2 = 2\cos x^3 \cdot \frac{d}{dx}\cos x^3$$

$$= 2\cos x^3(-\sin x^3)\cdot\frac{d}{dx}x^3 = 2\cos x^3(-\sin x^3)3x^2$$

$$= -6x^2 \cos x^3 \sin x^3.$$

Helpful Hint: Instructors like problems like Exercise 19 because it forces students to understand the notation. To avoid mistakes, be sure to include the first step shown in the solution above.

25. By the quotient rule we have

$$\frac{d}{dt}\left(\frac{\sin t}{\cos t}\right) = \frac{(\cos t)\cdot\frac{d}{dt}\sin t - (\sin t)\cdot\frac{d}{dt}\cos t}{\cos^2 t}$$

$$= \frac{\cos^2 t - (-\sin^2 t)}{\cos^2 t} = \frac{\cos^2 t + \sin^2 t}{\cos^2 t}$$

$$= \frac{1}{\cos^2 t} \quad [\text{because } \cos^2 t + \sin^2 t = 1].$$

An alternate notation for the answer is $\cos^{-2} t$.

31. $y' = -3\sin 3x$. At $x = \frac{13\pi}{6}$ the slope of the tangent line is

$$-3\sin 3\left(\frac{13\pi}{6}\right) = -3\sin\frac{13\pi}{6} = -3\sin\left(6\pi + \frac{\pi}{2}\right) = -3\sin\frac{\pi}{2}$$

$$= -3\cdot 1 = -3.$$

37. Our first guess is that an antiderivative of $\sin(4x+1)$ should involve the cosine function, namely, $\cos(4x+1)$. We may differentiate our guess (<u>not</u> the original function) to check our reasoning:

$$\frac{d}{dx}\cos(4x+1) = -\sin(4x+1)\cdot 4 = -4\sin(4x+1).$$

This derivative is -4 times what it should be. So we adjust our guess by dividing it by -4. Now

$$\frac{d}{dx}\left[-\frac{1}{4}\cos(4x+1)\right] = -\frac{1}{4}\cdot\frac{d}{dx}\cos(4x+1)$$

$$= -\frac{1}{4}\left[-\sin(4x+1)\cdot 4\right] = \sin(4x+1).$$

Thus $-\frac{1}{4}\cos(4x+1)$ _is_ an antiderivative of $\sin(4x+1)$. Hence

$$\int \sin(4x+1)\,dx = -\frac{1}{4}\cos(4x+1) + C.$$

43. Problems of this type expect you to determine the units of measurement on each axis. The tick marks on the t-axis in both parts of Fig. 12 are at ten-week intervals, and five squares lie between the tick marks, so each horizontal square corresponds to 2 weeks. On y-axis of the graph of f(t), the tick marks are 12 degrees apart, and four squares lie between the marks, so each vertical square corresponds to 12/4 = 3 degrees.

On the lower coordinate system in Fig. 12, five squares lie between each unit, so each vertical square represents .2 unit. However, the actual units depend on which function you study. For f'(t), each vertical square represents a change of .2°/week. For f"(t), each vertical square represents a change of .2°/week per week.

a. The average weekly temperature at week 18 is f(18), which you read from the graph as 69°. (Remember that each horizontal square on the graph represents 2 weeks, and each vertical square represents 3°.)

b. Read the rate of temperature change from the graph of f'(t). Since f'(22) = 1, the average weekly temperature is rising at the rate of 1°/week.

c. "When?" means that the time must be found. On the graph of f(t) find the t-coordinate corresponding to 39 degrees. Note that each vertical square represents 3°. Two times are found: t = 6 weeks and t = 44 weeks.

d. The question is answered by solving f'(t) = -1. (Put in the negative sign because the temperature is _falling_.) On the graph of f'(t), the y-coordinate is -1 at two times: t = 28 weeks and t = 48 weeks.

e. The maximum point on the graph of f(t) is easy to see but hard to read. (The peak occurs for t somewhere between 24 and 26). It is easier to estimate that f'(t) = 0 for t = 25.

f. The average weekly temperature is rising fastest at the inflection point on the rising part of the graph of f(t), which occurs when f"(t) = 0. This is at about t = 12. Similarly, the average weekly temperature is falling fastest at the other inflection point, where f'(t) = 0, namely, at t = 38.

8.4 The Tangent and Other Trigonometric Functions

You may need to memorize the discussion of how to get a derivative formula for tan t. (See the bottom of page 436 or the Study Guide solution to Exercise 25 in Section 8.2.) This is a nice application of the quotient rule. Of course you should also memorize the formula:

$$\frac{d}{dt} \tan t = \sec^2 t.$$

1. Since $\cos t = \dfrac{\text{adjacent}}{\text{hypotenuse}}$ and $\sec t = \dfrac{1}{\cos t}$, we have

    $\sec t = \dfrac{\text{hypotenuse}}{\text{adjacent}}$.

7. $\tan t = \dfrac{y}{x} = \dfrac{2}{-2} = -1$. To find $\sec t$ we need r.

    $r = \sqrt{x^2 + y^2} = \sqrt{(-2)^2 + 2^2} = \sqrt{4+4} = \sqrt{8} = 2\sqrt{2}$,

    $\sec t = \dfrac{r}{x} = \dfrac{2\sqrt{2}}{-2} = -\sqrt{2}$.

13. Note that $\sec t = 1/\cos t = (\cos t)^{-1}$. Hence

    $$\frac{d}{dt} \sec t = \frac{d}{dt}(\cos t)^{-1} = (-1)(\cos t)^{-2} \cdot \frac{d}{dt} \cos t$$

    $$= (-1)(\cos t)^{-2}(-\sin t) = \frac{\sin t}{(\cos t)^2}.$$

    This answer is acceptable. It may be written in other equivalent forms, such as $\sin t \, \sec^2 t$, or

    $$\frac{\sin t}{\cos t} \cdot \frac{1}{\cos t} = \tan t \, \sec t.$$

19. By the chain rule,

    $$f'(x) = \frac{d}{dx} 3\tan(\pi - x)$$

    $$= 3\sec^2(\pi - x) \cdot \frac{d}{dx}(\pi - x)$$

    $$= -3\sec^2(\pi - x).$$

25. By the product rule,

$$y' = \frac{d}{dx}(x \tan x) = x \cdot \frac{d}{dx}(\tan x) + (\tan x) \cdot \frac{d}{dx}x$$

$$= x \sec^2 x + \tan x.$$

31. Using the chain rule, and the solution to Exercise 13, we have

$$y' = \frac{d}{dt} \ln(\tan t + \sec t)$$

$$= \frac{1}{\tan t + \sec t} \frac{d}{dt}(\tan t + \sec t)$$

$$= \frac{1}{\tan t + \sec t}\left(\frac{d}{dt} \tan t + \frac{d}{dt} \sec t\right)$$

$$= \frac{1}{\tan t + \sec t}(\sec^2 t + \tan t \sec t)$$

$$= \frac{(\sec t + \tan t)\sec t}{\tan t + \sec t} = \sec t.$$

Chapter 8: Supplementary Exercises

Use the chapter checklist to review the main definitions and facts. You may also need to memorize some of the following facts: (1) the graphs of $\sin t$ and $\cos t$ (knowing the values of $\sin t$ and $\cos t$ when $t = 0$, $\pi/2$, π, $3\pi/2$, and 2π, for example); (2) selected trig identities from Section 8.2; and (3) the definitions of $\sec t$, $\cot t$, and $\csc t$. Check with your instructor.

1. The angle described is three quarter-revolutions of the circle or $3(\frac{\pi}{2}$ radians) $= \frac{3\pi}{2}$ radians.

7. First we find r.

$$r = \sqrt{x^2+y^2} = \sqrt{3^2+4^2} = \sqrt{25} = 5.$$

Therefore,

$$\sin t = \frac{y}{r} = \frac{4}{5} = .8, \quad \cos t = \frac{x}{r} = \frac{3}{5} = .6, \quad \tan t = \frac{y}{x} = \frac{4}{3}.$$

13. $\sin t = \cos t$ whenever the point on the unit circle defined by the angle t has identical x and y coordinates (i.e., the point lies on the line x = y). The points on the unit circle with this property are $(1/\sqrt{2}, 1/\sqrt{2})$ and $(-1/\sqrt{2},-1/\sqrt{2})$. The four angles between -2π and 2π that correspond to these points are $-\frac{3\pi}{4}$, $-\frac{7\pi}{4}$, $\frac{\pi}{4}$, $\frac{5\pi}{4}$.

19. $f'(t) = \frac{d}{dt} 3 \sin t = 3 \cos t.$

25. By the quotient rule,

$$f'(x) = \frac{d}{dx}\left(\frac{\cos 2x}{\sin 3x}\right)$$

$$= \frac{\sin(3x) \cdot \frac{d}{dx}\cos 2x - \cos(2x) \cdot \frac{d}{dx}\sin 3x}{(\sin 3x)^2}$$

$$= \frac{\sin(3x)(-2 \sin 2x) - 3\cos(2x)\cos(3x)}{\sin^2(3x)}$$

$$= -\frac{2\sin(3x)\sin(2x) + 3\cos(2x)\cos(3x)}{\sin^2(3x)}.$$

31. By the chain rule,

$$y' = \frac{d}{dx} \sin(\tan x) = \cos(\tan x)\frac{d}{dx} \tan x$$

$$= \cos(\tan x)\sec^2 x.$$

37. By the product and chain rules,

$$y' = \frac{d}{dx} e^{3x} \sin^4 x$$

$$= e^{3x}(4\sin^3 x)\frac{d}{dx} \sin x + (\sin^4 x)3e^{3x}$$

$$= 4e^{3x} \sin^3 x \cos x + 3e^{3x} \sin^4 x.$$

43. $f(t) = \sin^2 t.$

$$f'(t) = \frac{d}{dt}(\sin t)^2$$

$$= (2 \sin t)\cdot\frac{d}{dx} \sin t$$

$$= 2 \sin t \cdot \cos t.$$

$$f''(t) = \frac{d}{dt}(2 \sin t \cdot \cos t)$$

$$= 2\left[(\sin t)\cdot\frac{d}{dt} \cos t + (\cos t)\cdot\frac{d}{dt} \sin t\right]$$

$$= 2[(\sin t)(-\sin t) + \cos t \cdot \cos t]$$

$$= 2(\cos^2 t - \sin^2 t).$$

49. $y' = \dfrac{d}{dt} \tan t = \sec^2 t$.

The slope of tangent line when $t = \dfrac{\pi}{4}$ is

$$\sec^2\left(\dfrac{\pi}{4}\right) = \left(\dfrac{1}{\cos \dfrac{\pi}{4}}\right)^2 = \left(\dfrac{1}{\dfrac{\sqrt{2}}{2}}\right)^2 = 2.$$

At $t = \dfrac{\pi}{4}$, $y = \tan \dfrac{\pi}{4} = 1$, so $\left(\dfrac{\pi}{4}, 1\right)$ is a point on the line. Hence the equation of the line is

$$y - 1 = 2\left(t - \dfrac{\pi}{4}\right).$$

55. It is easy to check that the line $y = x$ is tangent to the graph of $y = \sin x$ at $x = 0$. From the graph of $y = \sin x$, it is clear that $y = \sin x$ lies below $y = x$ for $x \geq 0$. So the area between these two curves from $x = 0$ to $x = \pi$ is given by

$$[\text{Area}] = \int_0^{\pi} (x - \sin x)\, dx$$

$$= \left[\dfrac{x^2}{2} + \cos x\right]\Bigg|_0^{\pi} = \left[\dfrac{\pi^2}{2} + \cos \pi\right] - \left[0 + \cos 0\right]$$

$$= \dfrac{\pi^2}{2} + (-1) - [0 + 1] = \dfrac{\pi^2}{2} - 2.$$

Chapter 9

Techniques of Integration

9.1 Integration by Substitution

The technique of integration by substitution is best learned by trial and error. The more problems you work the fewer errors you will make in your first guess at a substitution. The basic strategy is to arrange the integrand in the form $f(g(x))g'(x)$. (This is possible for every problem in this section.) Look for the most complicated part of the integrand that may be expressed as a composite function, and let u be the "inside" function $g(x)$. Then proceed as discussed in the text.

Remember that you can check your answers to an antidifferentiation problem by differentiating your answer. (You ought to do this at least mentally for every indefinite integral you find.) We urge you to work *all* the problems (odd and even) in Section 9.1. Use the solutions in this guide to check your work, *not* to show you how to start a problem.

1. Let $u = x^2 + 4$. Then $du = \frac{d}{dx}(x^2+4)\, dx = 2x\, dx$. So

$$\int 2x(x^2+4)^5\, dx = \int u^5\, du$$

$$= \frac{1}{6}u^6 + c$$

$$= \frac{1}{6}(x^2+4)^6 + c.$$

7. Let $u = 4 - x^2$. Then $du = \frac{d}{dx}(4-x^2)\, dx = -2x\, dx$. So,

$$\int x\sqrt{4-x^2}\, dx = \int \left(-\frac{1}{2}\right)(-2)x\sqrt{4-x^2}\, dx$$

$$= -\frac{1}{2} \int \sqrt{4-x^2} \overbrace{(-2x)\,dx}^{du} = -\frac{1}{2} \int \sqrt{u}\,du$$

$$= -\frac{1}{2} \int u^{\frac{1}{2}}\,du = \frac{-\frac{1}{2}\,u^{\frac{3}{2}}}{\frac{3}{2}} + C = -\frac{1}{2}\cdot\frac{2}{3}\,u^{\frac{3}{2}} + C$$

$$= -\frac{1}{3}\,u^{\frac{3}{2}} + C = -\frac{1}{3}(4-x^2)^{\frac{3}{2}} + C.$$

13. Let $u = \ln(2x)$. Then $du = \frac{d}{dx}[\ln(2x)]\,dx = \frac{1}{2x}\cdot 2\,dx = \frac{dx}{x}$. Thus,

$$\int \frac{\ln 2x}{x}\,dx = \int \ln 2x\,\frac{dx}{x} = \int u\,du$$

$$= \frac{u^2}{2} + C = \frac{(\ln 2x)^2}{2} + C.$$

19. $\ln \sqrt{x} = \ln x^{1/2} = \frac{1}{2}\ln x$. This gives us the new form:

$$\int \frac{\ln \sqrt{x}}{x}\,dx = \int \frac{\frac{1}{2}\ln x}{x}\,dx = \frac{1}{2}\int \frac{\ln x}{x}\,dx.$$

So we first need to find $\int \frac{\ln x}{x}\,dx$.

Let $u = \ln x$. Then $du = \frac{d}{dx}\ln x\,dx = \frac{1}{x}\,dx$. Hence,

$$\int \frac{\ln x}{x}\,dx = \int u\,du = \frac{u^2}{2} + C = \frac{(\ln x)^2}{2} + C,$$

and this finally gives us

$$\int \frac{\ln \sqrt{x}}{x}\,dx = \frac{1}{2}\int \frac{\ln x}{x}\,dx = \frac{1}{2}\left[\frac{(\ln x)^2}{2} + C\right] = \frac{(\ln x)^2}{4} + C.$$

25. $\displaystyle\int \frac{1}{x \ln x^2}\,dx = \int \frac{dx}{2x \ln x} = \frac{1}{2}\int \frac{dx}{x \ln x}.$

Let $u = \ln x$. Therefore, $du = \frac{d}{dx}\ln x\,dx = \frac{dx}{x}$, and

$$\frac{1}{2}\int \frac{dx}{x \ln x} = \frac{1}{2}\int \frac{1}{u}\,du = \frac{1}{2}\ln|u| + C = \frac{1}{2}\ln|\ln x| + C.$$

31. If $f'(x) = \dfrac{x}{\sqrt{x^2+9}}$, then $f(x) = \displaystyle\int \dfrac{x}{\sqrt{x^2+9}}\,dx$. Let $u = x^2 + 9$.

Then $du = 2x\,dx$, so

$$\int \frac{x}{\sqrt{x^2+9}}\,dx = \int \frac{\left(\frac{1}{2}\right)2x}{\sqrt{x^2+9}}\,dx = \frac{1}{2}\int \frac{du}{\sqrt{u}} = \frac{1}{2}\int u^{-1/2}\,du$$

$$= \frac{1}{2}\,2u^{1/2} + C = u^{1/2} + C = \sqrt{x^2+9} + C.$$

But $f(4) = 8$, so $8 = \sqrt{4^2+9} + C$ which implies that $C = 3$.
Therefore, $f(x) = \sqrt{x^2+9} + 3$.

37. Let $u = \sin x$. Thus $du = \dfrac{d}{dx}(\sin x)\,dx = \cos x\,dx$. So

$$\int \sin x \cos x\,dx = \int u\,du$$

$$= \frac{u^2}{2} + C = \frac{(\sin x)^2}{2} + C.$$

Note: Another substitution is $u = \cos x$. Then
$du = -\sin x\,dx$, and

$$\int \sin x \cos x\,dx = \int -\cos x\,(-\sin x)\,dx = \int -u\,du$$

$$= -\frac{u^2}{2} + C = -\frac{(\cos x)^2}{2} + C.$$

How can the two functions $\dfrac{(\sin x)^2}{2}$ and $-\dfrac{(\cos x)^2}{2}$ both be antiderivatives of $\sin x \cos x$?

43. Let $u = 2 - \sin 3x$. Then,

$$du = \frac{d}{dx}(2 - \sin 3x)\,dx = -3\cos 3x\,dx.$$

So,

$$\int \frac{\cos 3x}{\sqrt{2 - \sin 3x}}\,dx = \int (2 - \sin 3x)^{-1/2}\left(-\frac{1}{3}\right)(-3\cos 3x)\,dx$$

$$= -\frac{1}{3}\int u^{-1/2}\,du = -\frac{1}{3}\left(2u^{1/2}\right) + C$$

$$= -\frac{2}{3}(2 - \sin 3x)^{1/2} + C.$$

9.2 Integration by Parts

Exercises 1-24 are all solved using integration by parts. This technique, like the method of substitution, is learned by working many problems. There is another method for integration by parts that some students may have seen elsewhere. It uses *u* in place of *f(x)* and *dv* in place of *g(x) dx*. Years ago we tried teaching both methods and we found that the one we now present in the text is easier to learn and use.

Once you have mastered integration by parts and by substitution, you are ready to try Exercises 25-36. These problems are harder because you have to decide which method to use!

a. Always consider the method of substitution first. This will work if the integrand is the product of two functions and one of the functions is the derivative of the "inside" of the other function (except maybe for a constant multiple).

b. If the integrand is the product of two unrelated functions, try integration by parts.

c. Some antiderivatives cannot be found by either of the methods we have discussed. We will never give you such a problem to solve, but you should be careful if you look in another text for more problems to work.

1.   Let $f(x) = x$, $g(x) = e^{5x}$,
   $f'(x) = 1$, $G(x) = \frac{1}{5}e^{5x}$.

   Then

   $$\int xe^{5x}\, dx = \frac{1}{5}xe^{5x} - \int \frac{1}{5}e^{5x}\, dx$$

   $$= \frac{1}{5}xe^{5x} - \frac{1}{5}\int e^{5x}\, dx$$

   $$= \frac{1}{5}xe^{5x} - \frac{1}{5}\cdot\frac{1}{5}e^{5x} + c$$

   $$= \frac{1}{5}xe^{5x} - \frac{1}{25}e^{5x} + c.$$

Helpful Hint: The various steps in your calculation of $\int xe^{5x}\, dx$ should be connected by equals signs, showing how you move from one step to the next. It requires a little more effort to rewrite the first term $\frac{1}{5}xe^{5x}$ on each line, but the solution is not correct otherwise. A careless student might write

$$\int xe^{5x}\,dx = \frac{1}{5}xe^{5x} - \int \frac{1}{5}e^{5x}\,dx$$

$$\boxed{=} \qquad - \frac{1}{5}\int e^{5x}\,dx$$

$$\boxed{\text{errors}} \to \boxed{=} \qquad - \frac{1}{5}\cdot\frac{1}{5}e^{5x} + C$$

$$\boxed{=} \qquad - \frac{1}{25}e^{5x} + C.$$

Avoid such "shortcuts" in your *homework* as well as on tests. Develop the habit of writing proper mathematical solutions on your homework. This will help to generate correct patterns of thought when you take an exam.

7. Let $f(x) = x$, $g(x) = \dfrac{1}{\sqrt{x+1}} = (x+1)^{-1/2}$,

$\qquad f'(x) = 1$, $G(x) = 2(x+1)^{1/2}$.

$\qquad$ Then $\displaystyle\int \frac{x}{\sqrt{x+1}}\,dx = 2x(x+1)^{1/2} - \int 2(x+1)^{1/2}\,dx$

$$= 2x(x+1)^{1/2} - 2\int (x+1)^{1/2}\,dx$$

$$= 2x(x+1)^{1/2} - 2\cdot\frac{2}{3}(x+1)^{3/2} + C$$

$$= 2x(x+1)^{1/2} - \frac{4}{3}(x+1)^{3/2} + C.$$

13. Let $f(x) = x$, $g(x) = \sqrt{x+1} = (x+1)^{1/2}$,

$\qquad f'(x) = 1$, $G(x) = \frac{2}{3}(x+1)^{3/2}$.

$\qquad$ Then $\displaystyle\int x\sqrt{x+1}\,dx = \frac{2}{3}x(x+1)^{3/2} - \int \frac{2}{3}(x+1)^{3/2}\,dx$

$$= \frac{2}{3}x(x+1)^{3/2} - \frac{2}{3}\int (x+1)^{3/2}\,dx$$

$$= \frac{2}{3}x(x+1)^{3/2} - \frac{2}{3}\cdot\frac{2}{5}(x+1)^{5/2} + C$$

$$= \frac{2}{3}x(x+1)^{3/2} - \frac{4}{15}(x+1)^{5/2} + C.$$

19. Let $f(x) = \ln 5x$, $g(x) = x$,

$\qquad f'(x) = \dfrac{5}{5x} = \dfrac{1}{x}$, $G(x) = \dfrac{x^2}{2}$.

Then $\displaystyle\int x \ln 5x\, dx = \frac{x^2}{2}\ln 5x - \int \frac{1}{x}\cdot\frac{x^2}{2}\, dx$

$$= \frac{x^2}{2}\ln 5x - \frac{1}{2}\int x\, dx$$

$$= \frac{x^2}{2}\ln 5x - \frac{1}{2}\cdot\frac{1}{2}x^2 + C$$

$$= \frac{x^2}{2}\ln 5x - \frac{1}{4}x^2 + C.$$

25. Since $x(x + 5)^4$ is the product of two functions, neither of which is a multiple of the derivative of the other, we use the technique of integration by parts.

Set $f(x) = x,\quad g(x) = (x + 5)^4,$
$\qquad f'(x) = 1,\quad G(x) = \frac{1}{5}(x + 5)^5.$

Then $\displaystyle\int x(x + 5)^4\, dx = \frac{1}{5}x(x + 5)^5 - \int \frac{1}{5}(x + 5)^5\, dx$

$$= \frac{1}{5}x(x + 5)^5 - \frac{1}{5}\cdot\frac{1}{6}(x + 5)^6 + C$$

$$= \frac{1}{5}x(x + 5)^5 - \frac{1}{30}(x + 5)^6 + C.$$

31. Since $x^2 + 1$ has $2x$ as a derivative, and $2x$ is a multiple of x, we use substitution to evaluate the integral. Let $u = x^2 + 1$. Then $du = 2x\, dx$. So,

$$\int x\sec^2(x^2 + 1)\, dx = \frac{1}{2}\int 2x\sec^2(x^2 + 1)\, dx = \frac{1}{2}\int \sec^2 u\, du$$

$$= \frac{1}{2}\tan u + C = \frac{1}{2}\tan(x^2 + 1) + C.$$

37. The slope is $\dfrac{x}{\sqrt{x+9}}$, so $f'(x) = \dfrac{x}{\sqrt{x+9}}$ and $f(x) = \displaystyle\int \frac{x}{\sqrt{x+9}}\, dx.$

We can integrate by parts. Since $f(x)$ already denotes a function, write $h(x)$ in place of the usual $f(x)$ in the formula for integration by parts. That is, let

$$h(x) = x,\quad g(x) = (x + 9)^{-1/2},$$
$$h'(x) = 1,\quad G(x) = 2(x + 9)^{1/2}.$$

Then

$$\int x(x + 9)^{-1/2}\, dx = x\cdot 2(x + 9)^{1/2} - \int 1\cdot 2(x + 9)^{1/2}\, dx$$

$$= 2x(x+9)^{1/2} - 2\int (x+9)^{1/2}\, dx$$

$$= 2x(x+9)^{1/2} - 2 \cdot \frac{2}{3}(x+9)^{3/2} + C.$$

Now, $(0,2)$ is on the graph of $f(x)$, so $2 = f(0)$. That is,

$$2 = 2(0)(0+9)^{1/2} - \frac{4}{3}(0+9)^{3/2} + C$$

$$= -\frac{4}{3}(9)^{3/2} + C = -\frac{4}{3}(27) + C = 36 + C.$$

Thus $C = 38$, and $f(x) = 2x(x+9)^{1/2} - \frac{4}{3}(x+9)^{3/2} + 38$.

9.3 Definite Integrals

One purpose of this section is to give you lots of practice choosing between integration by parts and by substitution. Another purpose is to show how these procedures may be simplified somewhat when working with definite integrals.

A common mistake in this section is to make a change of variable in a definite integral and *not* change the limits of integration. For example, here is an *incorrect* evaluation of the integral $\displaystyle\int_0^1 2x(x^2+1)^5\, dx$. Let $u = x^2 + 1$ and $du = 2x\, dx$. Then

$$\int_0^1 (x^2+1)^5 \cdot 2x\, dx \;\boxed{=}\; \int_0^1 u^5\, du \;=\; \frac{1}{6}u^6\Big|_0^1$$

$$\underset{\boxed{\text{error}}}{\nearrow}$$

$$= \frac{1}{6}(1)^6 - \frac{1}{6}(0)^6 = \frac{1}{6}.$$

The error in this calculation was made on the first line. The integral on the left equals $21/2$, not $1/6$. See Example 1.

Here is another incorrect solution whose final answer is correct. However the work contains two errors and therefore does not justify the final answer. As before, let $u = x^2 + 1$, $du = 2x\, dx$. Then

$$\int_0^1 (x^2+1)^5 \cdot 2x\, dx \;\boxed{=}\; \int_0^1 u^5\, du \;=\; \frac{1}{6}u^6\Big|_0^1$$

$$\underset{\boxed{\text{errors}}}{\Big\langle}$$

$$\boxed{=}\; \frac{1}{6}(x^2+1)^6\Big|_0^1 = \frac{1}{6}(2)^6 - \frac{1}{6}(1)^6$$

$$= \frac{63}{6} = \frac{21}{2}.$$

The symbol $\left.\frac{1}{6}u^6\right|_0^1$ represents the net change in $\frac{1}{6}u^6$ over the interval $0 \le u \le 1$. This number is not the same as the net change in $\frac{1}{6}(x^2 + 1)^6$ over the interval $0 \le x \le 1$.

The second incorrect solution above may be corrected by omitting the limits of integration at first, that is, by considering an antiderivative instead of a definite integral. Thus

$$\int (x^2 + 1)^5 \cdot 2x\, dx = \int u^5\, du = \frac{1}{6}u^6 + c = \frac{1}{6}(x^2 + 1)^6 + c$$

and hence

$$\int_0^1 (x^2 + 1)^5 2x\, dx = \left.\frac{1}{6}(x^2 + 1)^6\right|_0^1 = \frac{1}{6}(2)^6 - \frac{1}{6}(1)^6 = \frac{21}{2}.$$

This is the first solution method discussed in Example 1.

1. Let $u = 2x - 5$. Then $du = \frac{d}{dx}(2x - 5)\, dx = 2\, dx$.

    If $x = \frac{5}{2}$, then $u = 2\left(\frac{5}{2}\right) - 5 = 0$.

    If $x = 3$, then $u = 2(3) - 5 = 1$.

    Therefore $\displaystyle\int_{5/2}^3 2(2x-5)^{14}\, dx = \int_0^1 u^{14}\, du = \left.\frac{1}{15}u^{15}\right|_0^1$

    $$= \frac{1}{15}(1)^{15} - 0 = \frac{1}{15}.$$

7. Since $(x^2 - 9)$ has $2x$ as a derivative, and since this is a multiple of x, we use the substitution $u = x^2 - 9$. Then $du = 2x\, dx$. If $x = 3$, then $u = 3^2 - 9 = 0$; if $x = 5$, then $u = 5^2 - 9 = 16$.

    $$\int_3^5 x\sqrt{x^2 - 9}\, dx = \frac{1}{2}\int_3^5 2x\sqrt{x^2 - 9}\, dx = \frac{1}{2}\int_0^{16} \sqrt{u}\, du$$

    $$= \left.\frac{1}{2}\cdot\frac{2}{3}u^{3/2}\right|_0^{16} = \frac{1}{3}\cdot 16^{3/2} - 0 = \frac{64}{3}.$$

13. Since x^3 has $3x^2$ as a derivative, and since this is a multiple of x^2, we use the substitution $u = x^3$. Then $du = 3x^2\,dx$. If $x = 1$, then $u = 1^3 = 1$, and if $x = 3$, then $u = 3^3 = 27$.

$$\int_1^3 x^2 e^{x^3}\,dx = \frac{1}{3}\int_1^3 3x^2 e^{x^3}\,dx = \frac{1}{3}\int_1^{27} e^u\,du$$

$$= \frac{1}{3}e^u\Big|_1^{27} = \frac{1}{3}e^{27} - \frac{1}{3}e = \frac{1}{3}(e^{27} - e).$$

19. Since the integrand is the product of two unrelated functions, we use the technique of integration by parts. Let $f(x) = x$, and $g(x) = \sin \pi x$

$$f'(x) = 1, \quad G(x) = -\frac{1}{\pi}\cos \pi x.$$

Then $\displaystyle\int_0^1 x \sin \pi x\,dx = -\frac{1}{\pi}x \cos \pi x\Big|_0^1 - \int_0^1 -\frac{1}{\pi}\cos \pi x\,dx$

$$= \left[-\frac{1}{\pi}\cos \pi - 0\right] + \frac{1}{\pi}\int_0^1 \cos \pi x\,dx$$

$$= \frac{1}{\pi} + \frac{1}{\pi}\cdot\frac{1}{\pi}\sin \pi x\Big|_0^1$$

$$= \frac{1}{\pi} + \left[\frac{1}{\pi^2}\sin \pi - \frac{1}{\pi^2}\sin 0\right]$$

$$= \frac{1}{\pi} + 0 = \frac{1}{\pi}.$$

25. Find where $y = x\sqrt{4-x^2}$ cuts the x-axis $(y = 0)$, so

$$0 = x\sqrt{4-x^2},$$

$$x = 0, \text{ or } \sqrt{4-x^2} = 0 \Rightarrow 4 - x^2 = 0,$$

$$x^2 = 4, \text{ or } x = \pm 2.$$

The area of the portion from $x = 0$ to $x = 2$ is given by

$$\int_0^2 x\sqrt{4-x^2}\,dx.$$

To find $\displaystyle\int x\sqrt{4-x^2}\,dx$, let

$$u = 4 - x^2, \quad du = \frac{d}{dx}(4 - x^2)\,dx = -2x\,dx.$$

So,

$$\int x\sqrt{4-x^2}\,dx = \int\left(-\frac{1}{2}\right)(-2x)\sqrt{4-x^2}\,dx$$

$$= -\frac{1}{2}\int\sqrt{u}\,du = -\frac{1}{2}\int u^{1/2}\,du$$

$$= -\frac{1}{2}\frac{u^{3/2}}{3/2} = -\frac{1}{3}u^{3/2} + C$$

$$= -\frac{1}{3}\left(4-x^2\right)^{3/2} + C.$$

Therefore, the area from $x = 0$ to $x = 2$ is

$$\int_0^2 x\sqrt{4-x^2}\,dx = -\frac{1}{3}\left(4-x^2\right)^{3/2}\Bigg|_0^2$$

$$= -\frac{1}{3}(4-4)^{3/2} + \frac{1}{3}(4)^{3/2} = \frac{8}{3}.$$

By symmetry, the area from $x = -2$ to $x = 0$ is also $\frac{8}{3}$.

Total Area is $\frac{16}{3}$.

9.4 Approximation of Definite Integrals

It will be helpful for you to review Section 6.2 before you study Section 9.4. When you work the exercises in Section 9.4, do not be concerned if your answers differ slightly (in, say, the fourth or fifth significant figure) from the answers in the text. When numerical calculations are made that involve several steps, any decision (ours or yours) to "round off" intermediate answers can affect the final answer. Check with your instructor about how many significant figures you should retain in your calculations.

1. The interval has length $5 - 3 = 2$. If we divide this interval into 5 subintervals of equal length, then each subinterval will have length $\Delta x = \frac{2}{5} = .4$. Therefore the endpoints of the subintervals are:

$$a_0 = 3,$$
$$a_1 = 3 + .4 = 3.4,$$
$$a_2 = 3.4 + .4 = 3.8,$$
$$a_3 = 3.8 + .4 = 4.2,$$
$$a_4 = 4.2 + .4 = 4.6,$$
$$a_5 = 4.6 + .4 = 5.$$

7. If $n = 2$, then $\Delta x = (4 - 0)/2 = 2$. The first midpoint is $x_1 = a + \Delta x/2 = 0 + 2/2 = 1$. The second midpoint is $x_2 = 1 + \Delta x = 1 + 2 = 3$. Since $f(x) = x^2 + 5$, we have $f(1) = 6$, and $f(3) = 14$. Using the midpoint rule we have:

$$\int_0^4 (x^2 + 5)\,dx \approx [f(1) + f(3)] \cdot 2$$

$$= (6 + 14)2$$

$$= 40.$$

If $n = 4$, then $\Delta x = (4 - 0)/4 = 1$. The first midpoint is $x_1 = a + \Delta x/2 = 0 + 1/2 = .5$. Since the other midpoints are spaced 1 unit apart, we have $x_2 = 1.5$, $x_3 = 2.5$, and $x_4 = 3.5$. Hence

$$\int_0^4 (x^2 + 5)\,dx \approx [f(x_1) + f(x_2) + f(x_3) + f(x_4)]\,\Delta x$$

$$= \left\{ [(.5)^2 + 5] + [(1.5)^2 + 5] + [(2.5)^2 + 5] + [(3.5)^2 + 5] \right\}(1)$$

On an exam, some instructors may permit you to stop at this point, because the expression above shows that you know how to use the midpoint rule. (Check with your instructor.) Only arithmetic remains. For homework, of course, you should complete the calculation, and obtain

$$\int_0^4 (x^2 + 5)\,dx \approx \{5.25 + 7.25 + 11.25 + 17.25\}(1)$$

$$= 41.$$

Evaluating the integral directly, we have

$$\int_0^4 (x^2 + 5)\,dx = \left(\tfrac{1}{3}x^3 + 5x \right) \Big|_0^4 = \tfrac{64}{3} + 20 = 41\tfrac{1}{3}.$$

13. For $n = 3$, we have $\Delta x = (5 - 1)/3 = 4/3$. The endpoints of the three subintervals begin at $a_0 = 1$ and are spaced $\tfrac{4}{3}$ units apart. Thus $a_1 = 1 + \tfrac{4}{3} = \tfrac{7}{3}$, $a_2 = \tfrac{7}{3} + \tfrac{4}{3} = \tfrac{11}{3}$, and $a_3 = \tfrac{11}{3} + \tfrac{4}{3} = \tfrac{15}{3} = 5$. By the trapezoidal rule,

$$\int_1^5 \frac{1}{x^2}\,dx \approx \left[f(1) + 2f\left(\tfrac{7}{3}\right) + 2f\left(\tfrac{11}{3}\right) + f(5) \right] \left(\tfrac{4}{3}\right) \cdot \tfrac{1}{2}$$

$$= \left[1 + 2 \cdot \frac{1}{\left(\frac{7}{3}\right)^2} + 2 \cdot \frac{1}{\left(\frac{11}{3}\right)^2} + \frac{1}{5^2} \right] \left(\frac{4}{3}\right) \cdot \frac{1}{2}.$$

At this point, all substitutions into the trapezoidal rule are finished; only arithmetic remains. (Check to see if you can stop here on an exam.) The fractions above become quite messy, and it is best to use decimal approximations. We'll use five decimal places. (Check to see how many you should use on an exam.) We have

$$\int_1^5 \frac{1}{x^2} \, dx \approx [1 + .36735 + .14876 + .04](.66667)$$

$$= 1.03741.$$

Evaluating the integral directly produces

$$\int_1^5 \frac{1}{x^2} \, dx = \int_1^5 x^{-2} \, dx = -x^{-1} \Big|_1^5 = -\frac{1}{5} - (-1) = \frac{4}{5} = .8.$$

19. When $n = 5$, we recommend that you use decimals. In this exercise,

$$\Delta x = (5 - 2)/5 = 3/5 = .6.$$

It is often helpful to draw a picture. This is particularly true here because we need both the endpoints and midpoints of the subintervals, and the numbers involved are not as simple as in some exercises. Draw a line segment and, beginning at one end, mark off five equal subintervals. (This is easier than trying to divide one large interval into five equal parts.) Label the left endpoint $a_0 = 2$, and repeatedly add $\Delta x = .6$ to get the other endpoints.

The first midpoint is $2 + \Delta x/2 = 2 + .3 = 2.3$. Repeatedly add $\Delta x = .6$ to get the other midpoints.

Using the midpoint rule for $f(x) = xe^x$, we obtain

$$\int_2^5 xe^x \, dx$$

$$\approx \left[2.3e^{2.3} + 2.9e^{2.9} + 3.5e^{3.5} + 4.1e^{4.1} + 4.7e^{4.7} \right](.6)$$

$$\approx (955.69661)(.6) = 573.41797 = M.$$

For the trapezoidal rule, we have

$$\int_2^5 xe^x \, dx \approx \left[2e^2 + (2)2.6e^{2.6} + (2)3.2e^{3.2} + \right.$$

$$\left. + (2)3.8e^{3.8} + (2)4.4e^{4.4} + 5e^5 \right](.6) \cdot \frac{1}{2}$$

$$\approx (2040.36019)(.6)(.5) = 612.10806 = T.$$

We are now prepared to use Simpson's rule.

$$\int_2^5 xe^x \, dx \approx \frac{2M + T}{3} = \frac{2(573.41797) + 612.10806}{3}$$

$$= 586.31467 = S.$$

To evaluate the integral directly, we use the technique of integration by parts. Set

$$f(x) = x, \quad g(x) = e^x,$$

$$f'(x) = 1, \quad G(x) = e^x.$$

Then

$$\int_2^5 xe^x \, dx = xe^x \Big|_2^5 - \int_2^5 e^x \, dx$$

$$= (5e^5 - 2e^2) - e^x \Big|_2^5$$

$$= 5e^5 - 2e^2 - (e^5 - e^2)$$

$$= 4e^5 - e^2$$

$$\approx 586.26358.$$

25. We let f(x) represent the distance (in feet) from the shore to the property line as x runs from the top to the bottom of the diagram, and is measured in feet.

x = 0	f(0) = 100
x = 50	f(50) = 90
x = 100	f(100) = 125
x = 150	f(150) = 150
x = 200	f(200) = 200

So by the trapezoidal rule we have

$$[\text{Area of Property}] = \int_0^{200} f(x)\, dx$$

$$\approx \left[f(0) + 2f(50) + 2f(100) + 2f(150) + f(200) \right] \left(\frac{50}{2} \right)$$

$$= [100 + 180 + 250 + 300 + 200]25$$

$$= (1030)25$$

$$= 25,750 \text{ square feet.}$$

31. a. Note from Figure 12(a) in the text that the height of the triangle is $k - h$. The area of the triangle is $\frac{1}{2}(k - h)\ell$, and the area of the rectangle is $h\ell$. Therefore, the area of the trapezoid is given by

$$A = \frac{1}{2}(k - h)\ell + h\ell$$

$$= \left[\frac{1}{2}k - \frac{1}{2}h + h \right]\ell$$

$$= \left[\frac{1}{2}h + \frac{1}{2}k \right]\ell$$

$$= \frac{1}{2}(h + k)\ell.$$

b. We have $h = f(a_0)$, $k = f(a_1)$, and $\ell = \Delta x$. Therefore,

$$A = \frac{1}{2}[f(a_0) + f(a_1)]\Delta x.$$

c. We know the area of the first trapezoid is:

$$A = \frac{1}{2}[f(a_0) + f(a_1)]\Delta x = [f(a_0) + f(a_1)]\frac{\Delta x}{2}.$$

Similarly, the respective areas of the second, third, and fourth rectangles are

$$A_2 = [f(a_1) + f(a_2)]\frac{\Delta x}{2},$$

$$A_3 = [f(a_2) + f(a_3)]\frac{\Delta x}{2},$$

$$A_4 = [f(a_3) + f(a_4)]\frac{\Delta x}{2}.$$

So the sum of the areas is given by

$$A_1 + A_2 + A_3 + A_4 = \{[f(a_0) + f(a_1)] + [f(a_1) + f(a_2)]$$

$$+ [f(a_2) + f(a_3)] + [f(a_3) + f(a_4)]\}\frac{\Delta x}{2}$$

$$= \{f(a_0) + 2f(a_1) + 2f(a_2) + 2f(a_3) + f(a_4)\}\frac{\Delta x}{2}.$$

This quantity is the value of the trapozoidal rule with $n = 4$ for $\int_a^b f(x)\,dx$. The combined area of the trapezoids is approximately equal to the area under the graph of $f(x)$ from $x = a$ to $x = b$.

37. In this problem, $f(x) = 1/x$, $a = 1$, $b = 11$, $n = 10$, and $\Delta x = 1$. The formula for $f(x)$ is so simple, there is no need to use it to define Y_1. Just use it directly in the sum(seq(...)) command. When you compute the midpoint and trapezoidal estimates, store the results to variables, which you might as well call M and T.

Midpoint rule: $M = [1/1.5 + 1/2.5 + \cdots + 1/10.5] \cdot 1$.

    sum(seq(1/X,X,1.5,10.5,1)*1 = 2.361749156
    Ans→M

Trapezoidal rule: $T = [1/1 + 2(1/2) + \cdots + 2(1/10) + 1/11] \cdot \frac{1}{2}$.

    (1 + sum(seq(2/X,X,2,10,1)) + 1/11)/2 = 2.474422799
    Ans→T

Finally, $S = (2M + T)/3 = 2.399307037$. The exact answer is

$$\int_1^{11} \frac{1}{x}\,dx = \ln x \Big|_1^{11} = \ln 11 - \ln 1 = 2.397895273.$$

9.5 Some Applications of the Integral

The purpose of this section is to show how fairly difficult integration problems can arise easily in applications. The Riemann sum argument in Example 3 is well worth studying, but your instructor may not expect you to reproduce it every time you work an exercise. (Check with your instructor.)

1. Use the text's formula for present value, with $K(t) = 35,000$, $T_1 = 0$, $T_2 = 5$, and $r = .07$.

$$\text{P.V.} = \int_0^5 35000\, e^{-.07t}\, dt = \left. \frac{35000\, e^{-.07t}}{-.07} \right|_0^5$$

$$= -500,000 \left[e^{-.07(5)} - e^0 \right]$$

$$= -500,000 \left[e^{-.35} - 1 \right] \approx \$147,656.$$

7. a. [present value] $= \displaystyle\int_0^2 (30 + 5t)\, e^{-.1t}\, dt$.

b. First, find the appropriate antiderivative, using integration by parts:

$$\begin{array}{ll} f(t) = 30 + 5t & g(t) = e^{-.1t} \\ f'(t) = 5 & G(t) = -10e^{-.1t} \end{array}$$

$$\int (30 + 5t)\, e^{-.1t}\, dt$$

$$= (30 + 5t)(-10e^{-.1t}) - \int 5(-10e^{-.1t})\, dt$$

$$= (-300 - 50t)\, e^{-.1t} + 50 \int e^{-.1t}\, dt$$

$$= (-300 - 50t)\, e^{-.1t} + 50(-10e^{-.1t}) + c$$

$$= (-800 - 50t)\, e^{-.1t} + c.$$

Then use this to evaluate the definite integral.

$$\int_0^2 (30 + 5t)\, e^{-.1t}\, dt = \left. \left((-800 - 50t)\, e^{-.1t} \right) \right|_0^2$$

$$= -900e^{-.2} - (-800e^0) \approx 63.14.$$

The present value of the stream of earnings for the next two years is about 63.1 million dollars.

13. a. Area of ring is $2\pi t(\Delta t)$.

Population density of $40e^{-.5t}$ thousand per square mile. Thus the population living in the ring is:

$$2\pi t(\Delta t)\, 40e^{-.5t} = 80\pi t(\Delta t)\, e^{-.5t} \text{ thousand.}$$

b. $\dfrac{dP}{dt}$, or $P'(t)$.

c. It represents the number of people who live between $(5 + \Delta t)$ miles from the city center and 5 miles from the city center.

d. $P(t+\Delta t) - P(t) = 80\pi t(\Delta t)\, e^{-.5t}$ from (a), so

$$\frac{P(t+\Delta t) - P(t)}{\Delta t} \approx P'(t) = 80\pi t e^{-.5t}.$$

e. $\displaystyle\int_a^b P'(t)\, dt = P(b) - P(a)$, (by the Fundamental Theorem of Calculus)

$$= \int_a^b 80\pi t e^{-.5t}\, dt.$$

9.6 Improper Integrals

Although some instructors may disagree, we feel that the evaluation of an improper integral such as $\displaystyle\int_0^\infty e^{-x}\, dx$ should *not* use notation such as $\left. -e^{-x} \right|_0^\infty$ or $-e^{-\infty} + e^{-0}$. In the context of Section 9.6, the value of a function "at infinity" is not well-defined. The proper notation should involve a limit, such as $\lim_{b\to\infty} (1 - e^{-b})$. You should use two steps to evaluate an improper integral:

   i. Compute the net change in the antiderivative over a finite interval, such as from $x = 1$ to $x = b$.

  ii. Find the limit of the result in (i) as $b \to \infty$.

1. As b gets large, $\dfrac{5}{b}$ approaches zero. That is, $\displaystyle\lim_{b\to\infty} \frac{5}{b} = 0$.

7. As b gets large, $\sqrt{b+1}$ gets large, without bound. Hence $\dfrac{1}{\sqrt{b+1}} = (b+1)^{-1/2}$ approaches zero, and thus $2 - (b+1)^{-1/2}$ approaches 2.

13. The area is $\displaystyle\int_2^\infty x^{-2}\,dx$. First, compute

$$\int_2^b x^{-2}\,dx = -x^{-1}\Big|_2^b = -b^{-1} - (-2^{-1}) = \frac{1}{2} - \frac{1}{b}.$$

Then, take the limit as $b \to \infty$, namely,

$$\int_2^\infty x^{-2}\,dx = \lim_{b\to\infty}\left(\frac{1}{2} - \frac{1}{b}\right) = \frac{1}{2}.$$

19. $\displaystyle\int_1^b (14x + 18)^{-4/5}\,dx = \frac{1}{14}(5)(14x + 18)^{1/5}\Big|_1^b$

$$= \frac{5}{14}(14b + 18)^{1/5} - \frac{5}{14}(32)^{1/5}.$$

As $b \to \infty$, the quantity $\frac{5}{14}(14b + 18)^{1/5}$ grows without bound, so the region under the graph of $(14x + 18)^{-4/5}$ cannot be assigned any finite number as its area.

25. We take $b > 0$ and compute

$$\int_0^b e^{2x}\,dx = \frac{1}{2}e^{2x}\Big|_0^b = \frac{1}{2}e^{2b} - \frac{1}{2}.$$

Now consider the limit as $b \to \infty$. As $b \to \infty$, the number $\frac{1}{2}e^{2b} - \frac{1}{2}$ can be made larger than any specified number. Therefore, $\displaystyle\int_0^b e^{2x}\,dx$ has no limit as $b \to \infty$, so $\displaystyle\int_0^\infty e^{2x}\,dx$ is divergent.

31. $\displaystyle\int_0^b 6e^{1-3x}\,dx = \frac{6}{-3}e^{1-3x}\Big|_0^b = -2e^{1-3b} - (-2e^1) = 2e - 2e^{1-3b}.$

As $b \to \infty$, $1 - 3b$ becomes extremely negative, so $2e^{1-3b} \to 0$. Thus,

$$\int_0^\infty 6e^{1-3x}\,dx = \lim_{b\to\infty}(2e - 2e^{1-3b}) = 2e.$$

37. First consider the indefinite integral $\int 2x(x^2 + 1)^{-3/2} dx$ and let $u = x^2 + 1$, $du = 2x\,dx$. Thus

$$\int 2x(x^2 + 1)^{-3/2} dx = \int u^{-3/2}\,du = -2u^{-1/2} + C$$

$$= -2(x^2 + 1)^{-1/2} + C.$$

Using this antiderivative of $2x(x^2 + 1)^{-3/2}$, we compute

$$\int_0^b 2x(x^2 + 1)^{-3/2} dx = -2(x^2 + 1)^{-1/2}\Big|_0^b$$

$$= -2(b^2 + 1)^{-1/2} - (-2\cdot 1).$$

As $b \to \infty$, $(b^2 + 1)^{-1/2} \to 0$, so

$$\int_0^\infty 2x(x^2 + 1)^{-3/2} dx = \lim_{b\to\infty}\left(2 - 2(b^2 + 1)^{-1/2}\right) = 2.$$

43. Let $u = e^{-x} + 2$ and $du = -e^{-x} dx$, so that

$$\int \frac{e^{-x}}{(e^{-x} + 2)^2} dx = \int \frac{-1}{u^2}\,du = u^{-1} + C$$

$$= (e^{-x} + 2)^{-1} + C.$$

As $b \to \infty$, $e^{-b} \to 0$ and $\dfrac{1}{e^{-b} + 2} \to \dfrac{1}{2}$. Thus,

$$\int_0^\infty \frac{e^{-x}}{(e^{-x} + 2)^2} dx = \lim_{b\to\infty} (e^{-x} + 2)^{-1}\Big|_0^b$$

$$= \lim_{b\to\infty} [(e^{-b} + 2)^{-1} - 3^{-1}]$$

$$= \frac{1}{2} - \frac{1}{3} = \frac{1}{6}.$$

49. When the rate of income is a constant K dollars per year, the antiderivative of Ke^{-rt} is easy to find:

$$[\text{capital value}] = \lim_{b\to\infty} \int_0^b Ke^{-rt}\,dt = \lim_{b\to\infty} -\frac{1}{r}Ke^{-rt}\Big|_0^b$$

$$= \lim_{b \to \infty} \left(-\frac{K}{r} e^{-rb} + \frac{K}{r} e^0 \right)$$

$$= -\frac{K}{r} \left(\lim_{b \to \infty} e^{-rb} \right) + \frac{K}{r} = \frac{K}{r}.$$

Chapter 9: Supplementary Exercises

Sections 9.1-9.3 and 9.6 provide the tools for solving many of the problems in the next three chapters. It is essential that you master the techniques in Sections 9.1 and 9.2. Supplementary Exercises 19-36 will help you learn to recognize which technique to use.

1. Since $3x^2$ has $6x$ as a derivative, and this is a multiple of x, we use the technique of substitution. Let $u = 3x^2$; then $du = 6x\, dx$. We then have

$$\int x \sin 3x^2\, dx = \frac{1}{6} \int 6x \sin 3x^2\, dx$$

$$= \frac{1}{6} \int \sin u\, du$$

$$= -\frac{1}{6} \cos u + C$$

$$= -\frac{1}{6} \cos 3x^2 + C.$$

7. The derivative of $4 - x^2$ is a multiple of x (the factor next to the square root. So make the substitution

$$u = 4 - x^2, \quad du = -2x\, dx.$$
Then

$$\int x \sqrt{4-x^2}\, dx = -\frac{1}{2} \int (-2x) \sqrt{4-x^2}\, dx$$

$$= -\frac{1}{2} \int \sqrt{u}\, du$$

$$= -\frac{1}{2} \cdot \frac{2}{3} u^{3/2} + C$$

$$= -\frac{1}{3} (4 - x^2)^{3/2} + C.$$

13. First simplify the integrand, using the algebraic property $\ln x^2 = 2 \ln x$:

$$\int \ln x^2 \, dx = 2 \int \ln x \, dx$$

Then recall that $\int \ln x \, dx$ is easily found by integration by parts. Use $f(x) = \ln x$ and $g(x) = 1$. The details are in Example 7 of Section 9.2. Using the results of that example, we have

$$\int \ln x^2 \, dx = 2 \int \ln x \, dx = 2(x \ln x - x) + C.$$

Helpful Hint: Integrals of the form $\int x^k \ln x \, dx$ are found by integration by parts, with $f(x) = \ln x$ and $g(x) = x^k$.

19. Since the integrand is the product of two functions, x and e^{2x}, neither of which is a multiple of the derivative of the other, we use integration by parts. Set

$$f(x) = x, \quad g(x) = e^{2x}.$$

25. Since the integrand is the product of two functions, e^{-x} and $(3x - 1)^2$, and neither is a multiple of the derivative of the other, we use integration by parts. Set

$$f(x) = (3x - 1)^2, \quad g(x) = e^{-x}.$$

In order to complete the problem, we must integrate by parts a second time. Note that if we interchange $f(x)$ and $g(x)$ above, integration by parts will not yield a solution.

31. We observe that the derivative of $x^2 + 6x$ is $2x + 6$, which is a multiple of $x + 3$. Thus we use the technique of substitution, setting $u = x^2 + 6x$.

37. Since $x^2 + 1$ has $2x$ as a derivative, we use the technique of substitution. Let $u = x^2 + 1$. Then $du = 2x \, dx$. If $x = 0$, then $u = 1$, and if $x = 1$, then $u = 2$. So we have

$$\int_0^1 \frac{2x}{(x^2+1)^3}\,dx = \int_1^2 \frac{1}{u^3}\,du = \int_1^2 u^{-3}\,du$$

$$= -\frac{1}{2}u^{-2}\Big|_1^2 = -\frac{1}{2}\left(\frac{1}{4}\right) + \frac{1}{2} = \frac{3}{8}.$$

43. The interval has length 9 - 1 = 8, so with n = 4 we have $\Delta x = \frac{8}{4} = 2$. The subintervals have endpoints $a_0 = 1$, $a_1 = 3$, $a_2 = 5$, $a_3 = 7$, and $a_4 = 9$, and midpoints $x_1 = 2$, $x_2 = 4$, $x_3 = 6$, and $x_4 = 8$.

From the midpoint rule, with $f(x) = \frac{1}{\sqrt{x}} = x^{-1/2}$,

$$\int_1^9 f(x)\,dx \approx M = [f(2) + f(4) + f(6) + f(8)]\cdot 2$$

$$= [.70711 + .50000 + .40825 + .35355]\cdot 2$$

$$= 3.93782.$$

From the trapezoidal rule,

$$\int_2^9 f(x)\,dx \approx T = [f(1) + 2f(3) + 2f(5) + 2f(7) + f(9)]\cdot\frac{2}{2}$$

$$= [1 + 1.15470 + .89443 + .75593 + .33333]$$

$$= 4.13839.$$

By Simpson's rule,

$$\int_1^9 \frac{1}{\sqrt{x}}\,dx \approx \frac{2M + T}{3} = 4.00468.$$

49. Since the derivative of $x^2 + 4x - 2$ is $2x + 4$, which is a multiple of $x + 2$, we use the technique of substitution. Let $u = x^2 + 4x - 2$; then $du = 2x + 4\ dx$.

$$\int \frac{x+2}{x^2+4x-2}\,dx = \frac{1}{2}\int \frac{2x+4}{x^2+4x-2}\,dx = \frac{1}{2}\int \frac{1}{u}\,du$$

$$= \frac{1}{2} \ln|u| = \frac{1}{2} \ln|x^2+4x-2| + C.$$

Hence

$$\int_1^b \frac{x^2+2}{x^2+4x-2} \, dx = \frac{1}{2} \ln|x^2+4x-2| \Big|_1^b$$

$$= \frac{1}{2} \ln|b^2+4b-2| - \frac{1}{2} \ln 3.$$

As $b \to \infty$, the number $|b^2+4b-2|$ gets large, without bound, and so $\ln|b^2+4b-2|$ gets large, without bound. Therefore $\frac{1}{2} \ln|b^2+4b-2| - \frac{1}{2} \ln 3$ can be made larger than any specific number, $\int_1^b \frac{x+2}{x^2+4x-2} \, dx$ has no limit as $b \to \infty$, and $\int_1^\infty \frac{x+2}{x^2+4x-2} \, dx$ is divergent.

55. Use the text's formula for present value given in Section 9.5, with $K(t) = 50e^{-.08t}$, $r = .12$, $T_1 = 0$, and $T_2 = 4$.

$$[\text{present value}] = \int_0^4 50e^{-.08t} \cdot e^{-.12t} \, dt$$

Integration by parts is not necessary this time because the exponential functions can be combined:

$$[\text{present value}] = \int_0^4 50e^{-.20t} \, dt = -250e^{-.2t} \Big|_0^4$$

$$\approx -112.332 + 250 = 137.668.$$

The present value of the continuous stream of income over the next four years is \$137,668 (to the nearest dollar).

Chapter 10

Differential Equations

10.1 Solutions of Differential Equations

This section lays the foundation for the chapter. You should read the text and the examples several times. The high point of the chapter is Section 10.5, which presents a wide variety of applications. Our students find this material extremely interesting, and we know that they can master it if they are given adequate preparation. So each section includes a few problems that teach you how to read and understand a verbal problem about a differential equation. Be sure to try Exercise 19 or 20.

1. We replace y by $f(t) = \frac{3}{2}e^{t^2} - \frac{1}{2}$, and y' by $f'(t) = 3te^{t^2}$.

    Then $y' - 2ty = 3te^{t^2} - 2t\left[\frac{3}{2}e^{t^2} - \frac{1}{2}\right]$

    $$= 3te^{t^2} - [3te^{t^2} - t] = t.$$

    This is true for all t, so $f(t) = \frac{3}{2}e^{t^2} - \frac{1}{2}$ is a solution.

7. The derivative of the constant function $f(t) = 3$ is the constant function $f'(t) = 0$. If we replace y by $f(t) = 3$ and y' by $f'(t) = 0$, then

    $$y' = 6 - 2y,$$
    $$0 = 6 - 2(3).$$

    Both sides are zero for all t, so $f(t) = 3$ is a solution.

13. The differential equation $y' = .2(160 - y)$ describes a relationship between the acceleration (the derivative of the downward velocity) and the downward velocity, at each moment during the free fall. At a time when the velocity is 60 feet per second, the acceleration is

    $$y' = .2(160 - 60) = .2(100) = 20 \text{ feet per second}^2.$$

19. Let f(t) be the amount of capital invested. Then f'(t) is the rate of net investment. We are told that

$$\begin{bmatrix} \text{rate of net} \\ \text{investment} \end{bmatrix} [\text{is proportional to}]\left\{ C - \begin{bmatrix} \text{capital} \\ \text{investment} \end{bmatrix}\right\}.$$

So there is a constant of proportionality, k, such that

$$f'(t) = k\{C - f(t)\}.$$

To determine the sign of k, suppose that at some time f(t) is larger than C. Then C - f(t) is negative. Should f'(t) be positive or negative? That is, should f(t) be increasing or decreasing? Well, if the amount of f(t) is larger than the optimum level C, then it is reasonable to want f(t) to decrease down towards C. So when C - f(t) is negative, we want f'(t) to be negative, too. This means

that k must be positive.

$$f'(t) = k\{C - f(t)\},$$
$$[\text{neg}] = [\text{pos}] \cdot [\text{neg}].$$

You would arrive at the same conclusion that k is positive if you supposed that f(t) is less than C. The differential equation is simplified by writing y for f(t) and y' for f'(t), namely,

$$y' = k(C - y), \quad k > 0.$$

10.2 Separation of Variables

This is probably the most difficult section in Chapter 10 because it requires substantial integration and algebraic skills. Each example illustrates one or two situations you will encounter in the exercises. After you study Examples 1, 2, and 3, you may work on Exercises 1-6, 13-15, and 17, respectively.

Remember to use the examples properly. Study them carefully and then try to work the exercises *without referring to the examples*. If you really get stuck, take a peek at the appropriate example, but do not study the entire solution. As a last resort, peek at a solution in this study guide if a solution is available. You simply *must* train yourself to work independently. If you yield to the temptation to "copy" our solutions, you will not survive an examination on this material.

Exercises 33-38 are here to help you prepare for Section 10.5. You will be rewarded later if you spend some time on these exercises now.

1. Separating the variables, we have

$$y^2 \frac{dy}{dt} = 5 - t,$$

$$\int y^2 \frac{dy}{dt} \, dt = \int (5 - t) \, dt,$$

$$\int y^2 \, dy = \int (5 - t) \, dt.$$

One antiderivative of y^2 is $\frac{1}{3}y^3$. One antiderivative of $5 - t$ is $5t - \frac{1}{2}t^2$. Since antiderivatives of the same function differ by a constant, we have

$$\frac{1}{3}y^3 = 5t - \frac{1}{2}t^2 + c_1,$$

for some constant c_1. Then

$$y^3 = 3\left(5t - \frac{1}{2}t^2 + c_1\right).$$

Since c_1 is arbitrary, so is $3c_1$, and it is easier to write C in place of $3c_1$. Therefore

$$y^3 = 15t - \frac{3}{2}t^2 + C,$$

and

$$y = \left(15t - \frac{3}{2}t^2 + C\right)^{1/3}.$$

7. $\frac{dy}{dt} = \frac{t^2}{y^2}e^{t^3}$. By separating the variables,

$$y^2 \frac{dy}{dt} = t^2 e^{t^3}$$

$$\int y^2 \frac{dy}{dt} \, dt = \int t^2 e^{t^3} \, dt$$

$$\int y^2 \, dy = \int t^2 e^{t^3} \, dt.$$

One antiderivative of y^2 is $\frac{1}{3}y^3$, and similarly an antiderivative of $t^2 e^{t^3}$ is $\frac{1}{3}e^{t^3}$. (This is found by a substitution, $u = t^3$.) So

$$\frac{1}{3}y^3 = \frac{1}{3}e^{t^3} + C.$$

Hence,

$$y^3 = e^{t^3} + C \text{ (another constant C)},$$

and finally,

$$y = \left(e^{t^3} + C\right)^{1/3}.$$

13. $\frac{dy}{dt} = 2 - y.$

The constant function $y = 2$ is a solution because it makes both sides of the equation zero for all t. (The left-hand side is zero because the derivative of a constant function is zero.)

Now assuming $y \neq 2$, we may divide by 2-y:

$$\frac{1}{2-y}\frac{dy}{dt} = 1,$$

so,

$$-\frac{1}{y-2}\frac{dy}{dt} = 1, \text{ or } \frac{1}{y-2}\frac{dy}{dt} = -1,$$

$$\int \frac{1}{y-2}\frac{dy}{dt}\, dt = \int -1\, dt,$$

$$\ln|y-2| = -t + C,$$

$$|y-2| = e^{-t+C} = e^C \cdot e^{-t}.$$

In Section 10.4 we shall see that if $y \neq 2$, then $y - 2$ will be either positive for all t or negative for all t. Consequently

$$y - 2 = e^C \cdot e^{-t} \text{ or } y - 2 = -e^C \cdot e^{-t},$$

$$y = 2 + e^C \cdot e^{-t} \text{ or } y = 2 - e^C \cdot e^{-t}.$$

Since e^C is an arbitrary positive constant and $-e^C$ is an arbitrary negative constant, we may write these two types of solutions, together with the constant solution $y = 2 + 0 \cdot e^{-t}$, in the form

$$y = 2 + Ae^{-t}, \text{ A any constant.}$$

(The "C" in the answers in the text is the same as this "A".)

19. $y' = 2t\, e^{-2y} - e^{-2y}, \qquad y(0) = 3.$

The equation can be rewritten as

$$\frac{dy}{dt} = 2t\, e^{-2y} - e^{-2y} = e^{-2y}(2t - 1).$$

Thus applying the method of separation of variables,

$$\frac{1}{e^{-2y}}\frac{dy}{dt} = 2t - 1, \quad \left(\frac{1}{e^{-2y}} = e^{2y}\right),$$

$$\int e^{2y} \frac{dy}{dt} \, dt = \int (2t - 1) \, dt,$$

$$\int e^{2y} \, dy = \int (2t - 1) \, dt,$$

$$\frac{1}{2} e^{2y} = t^2 - t + C.$$

Hence, $e^{2y} = 2t^2 - 2t + C.$ (This C is actually 2 times the old C.)   Take the logarithm of both sides:

$$\ln e^{2y} = 2y \ln e = 2y = \ln(2t^2 - 2t + C).$$

Therefore,

$$y = \frac{1}{2} \ln (2t^2 - 2t + C).$$

Since $y(0) = 3$ we can find C: i.e., if $t = 0$, $y = 3$, giving,

$$3 = \frac{1}{2} \ln (2 \cdot 0^2 - 2(0) + C) = \frac{1}{2} \ln C,$$

$$6 = \ln C,$$

$$e^6 = C.$$

So finally,

$$y = \frac{1}{2} \ln(2t^2 - 2t + e^6).$$

25. $\frac{dy}{dt} = \frac{t+1}{ty}$, $t > 0$, $y(1) = -3$.

Separating the variables:

$$y \frac{dy}{dt} = \frac{t+1}{t} = 1 + \frac{1}{t},$$

$$\int y \frac{dy}{dt} \, dt = \int \left(1 + \frac{1}{t}\right) dt,$$

$$\int y \, dy = \int \left(1 + \frac{1}{t}\right) dt,$$

therefore,

$$\frac{y^2}{2} = t + \ln|t| + C.$$

Since $t > 0$ we can rewrite $\ln|t|$ as $\ln t$, so

$$\frac{y^2}{2} = t + \ln t + C,$$

$$y^2 = 2t + 2\ln t + C$$

(C is now 2 times the value of the old C).

$$y = \pm\sqrt{2t + 2\ln t + C}.$$

Since $y(1) = -3$, and since a square root cannot be negative, we use the "minus" form:

$$y = -\sqrt{2t + 2\ln t + C},$$

$$\text{i.e., } -3 = -\sqrt{2(1) + 2\ln(1) + C},$$

$$-3 = -\sqrt{2 + 0 + C}, \quad \text{(square both sides)}$$

$$9 = 2 + C, \text{ or } C = 7.$$

Therefore,

$$y = -\sqrt{2t + \ln t^2 + 7}.$$

31. Clearly $y = 0$ is a solution since this makes both sides of the equation equal zero. If $y \neq 0$ we may divide by y to obtain

$$\frac{1}{y}\frac{dy}{dp} = -\frac{1}{2}\cdot\frac{1}{p+3},$$

$$\int \frac{1}{y}\frac{dy}{dp}\,dp = \int -\frac{1}{2}\cdot\frac{1}{p+3}\,dp,$$

$$\int \frac{1}{y}\,dy = -\frac{1}{2}\int \frac{1}{p+3}\,dp,$$

$$\ln|y| = -\frac{1}{2}\ln|p+3| + C, \text{ C a constant}$$

$$\ln|y| = \ln|p+3|^{-1/2} + C,$$

$$|y| = e^{\ln|p+3|^{-1/2}+C} = |p+3|^{-1/2}\cdot e^C,$$

$$y = \pm e^C|p+3|^{-1/2}.$$

The general solution (including the constant solution) has the form

$$y = A|p+3|^{-1/2}, \text{ A any constant.}$$

Note, however, that both the price p and the sales volume y should be positive quantities. So the only solutions that make some sense economically have the form

$$y = A(p+3)^{-1/2}, \text{ A > 0.}$$

37. $\frac{dy}{dt} = -ay \ln\frac{y}{b}$. Note that y cannot be zero, because the logarithm would not be defined. However, $\ln\frac{y}{b}$ is zero when y = b. So the only constant solution is y = b. If y ≠ b, we may separate the variables:

$$\frac{1}{y \ln\frac{y}{b}} \cdot \frac{dy}{dt} = -a,$$

$$\int \frac{1}{y \ln\frac{y}{b}} \cdot \frac{dy}{dt} \, dt = \int -a \, dt,$$

$$\int \frac{1}{y \ln\frac{y}{b}} \frac{dy}{dt} = \int -a \, dt = -at + C.$$

To evaluate the left-hand side, let

$$u = \ln\frac{y}{b} \quad \Rightarrow \quad du = \frac{1}{\left(\frac{y}{b}\right)} \cdot \frac{1}{b} \, dy = \frac{1}{y} \, dy.$$

Then

$$\int \frac{1}{\ln\frac{y}{b}} \cdot \frac{1}{y} \, dy = \int \frac{1}{u} \, du = \ln|u| + C,$$

$$= \ln\left|\ln\frac{y}{b}\right| + C.$$

Therefore, setting the two sides equal,

$$\ln\left|\ln\frac{y}{b}\right| = -at + C \text{ (different C)}.$$

Next, take the exponential of both sides to produce:

$$\left|\ln\frac{y}{b}\right| = e^{-at+C} = e^{C} \cdot e^{-at} = Ce^{-at} \quad (C = e^{C}),$$

$$\text{(different C again)}$$

$$\left|\ln\frac{y}{b}\right| = Ce^{-at}, \text{ where C is positive,}$$

$$\ln\frac{y}{b} = \pm Ce^{-at}.$$

Let's write ±C as simply C, where now C can be positive or negative. The constant solution y = b corresponds to C = 0. So the general solution, with an arbitrary C, is

$$\frac{y}{b} = e^{Ce^{-at}}, \quad \text{and} \quad y = be^{Ce^{-at}}.$$

10.3 Numerical Solution of Differential Equations

Although this section is not essential for later work, it will focus your attention on ideas that will be of great help in Section 10.4. In particular, you should study Exercises 1-4, even if Section 10.3 is omitted. Likewise, Exercises 11(a) and 12(a) should be attempted as part of your ongoing program of preparation for Section 10.5.

1. If $f(t)$ is a solution of $y' = ty - 5$, then

$$f'(t) = tf(t) - 5,$$

for all t in the domain of $f(t)$. The graph of $f(t)$ passing through $(2,4)$ means that $f(2) = 4$. Setting $t = 2$ in the equation above, we find that

$$f'(2) = 2f(2) - 5,$$
$$= 2 \cdot 4 - 5 = 3.$$

So the slope of the graph is 3 at $t = 2$.

Helpful Hint: Make sure you understand the solutions to Exercises 1-4. They make good test questions and they prepare you for both Euler's method and the theory in Section 10.4.

7. Here $g(t,y) = 2t - y + 1$, $a = 0$, $b = 2$, $y(0) = 5$, and $h = (2-0)/4 = \frac{1}{2}$. Starting with $(t_0, y_0) = (0,5)$, we find $g(0,5) = 2(0) - 5 + 1 = -4$. Thus,

$$t_1 = \frac{1}{2}, \qquad y_1 = 5 + (-4) \cdot \frac{1}{2} = 3.$$

Next, $g(\frac{1}{2}, 3) = 2(\frac{1}{2}) - 3 + 1 = -1$, so

$$t_2 = 1, \qquad y_2 = 3 + (-1)\frac{1}{2} = \frac{5}{2}.$$

Next $g(1, \frac{5}{2}) = 2(1) - \frac{5}{2} + 1 = \frac{1}{2}$, so

$$t_3 = \frac{3}{2}, \qquad y_3 = \frac{5}{2} + (\frac{1}{2})\frac{1}{2} = \frac{11}{4}.$$

And finally, $g(\frac{3}{2}, \frac{11}{4}) = 2(\frac{3}{2}) - \frac{11}{4} + 1 = \frac{5}{4}$, so

$$t_4 = 2, \qquad y_4 = \frac{11}{4} + (\frac{5}{4})\frac{1}{2} = \frac{27}{8}.$$

Thus the approximation to the solution $f(t)$ is given by the polygonal path shown in the answer section of the text. The last point $(2, \frac{27}{8})$ is close to the graph of $f(t)$ at $t = 2$, so $f(2) \approx \frac{27}{8}$.

Helpful Hint: The fractions in Exercise 7 were rather simple. In many cases decimals are easier to use, particularly when h is smaller than $\frac{1}{4}$. Of course, a calculator becomes indispensable in such cases.

11. This problem is part of our program to prepare you for Section 10.5. You should definitely try part (a) even if the problem is not assigned. Before you look at the answer in your text, try to determine whether the constant of proportionality is positive or negative.

13. The graph is in the solutions at the end of the text.

19. The Appendix section **The Differential Equation y' = g(t,y)** has instructions for using a TI-calculator to construct an approximate solution to a differential equation. In this exercise, $a = 0$, $b = 4$, y_0 has a value described in (a)-(e). If you take $h = .1$, then the number of steps is $N = 40$. The main definition in sequence editor depends on which calculator you use:

TI-82: $U_n = U_{n-1} + .1$
           $V_n = V_{n-1} + .5(1 - V_{n-1})*(4 - V_{n-1})*.1$

TI-83: $u(n) = u(n-1) + .1$
        $v(n) = v(n-1) + .5*(1 - v(n-1))*(4 - v(n-1))*.1$

TI-85,86: $Q'1 = .5(1 - Q1)(4 - Q1)$

10.4 Qualitative Theory of Differential Equations

We hope you get to study this section! Some instructors omit it because they think it is too hard for first-year calculus students. (No other book at this level attempts to teach the material.) But we have found that our students do as well on the qualitative theory as on almost any material in the second half of the text. The secret is to spend about one week on this section.

One of the difficulties here is learning to sketch yz-graphs where the y-axis is horizontal. The difficulty is real though it is mainly psychological. To help you get used to yz-graphs, we have included them for Exercises 1-14. Study them there so you will be able to produce similar graphs in Exercises 15-31.

1. From $y' = 2y - 6$ we obtain the function $g(y) = 2y - 6$. The graph of $z = g(y)$ is shown in Fig. 1a. Setting $2y - 6 = 0$, we find $y = 3$. Thus $g(y)$ has a zero when $y = 3$. There-

fore the constant function y = 3 is a solution of the differential equation.   See Fig. 1b.

(a)   Figure 1   (b)

To sketch the solution corresponding to y(0) = 1, we locate this initial value on the y-axes in Fig. 2a and Fig.
2b, and we note that the z-coordinate in Fig. 2a is negative when y = 1.   That is, the derivative is negative when
y = 1.   So we place a downward arrow at the initial point
in Fig. 2b.

(a)   Figure 2   (b)

From Fig. 2b, the y-values will decrease as time passes,
so y will move to the left on the yz-graph.   See Fig. 3a.
As a result, the z-coordinate on the graph of z = 2y - 6
will become more negative.   That is, the slope of the solution curve will become more negative.   Thus the solution
curve is concave down, as in Fig. 3b.

(a)   Figure 3   (b)

To obtain the graph of the solution satisfying $y(0) = 4$, we make the following sketches. (The verbal description is omitted because it is too tedious to read.)

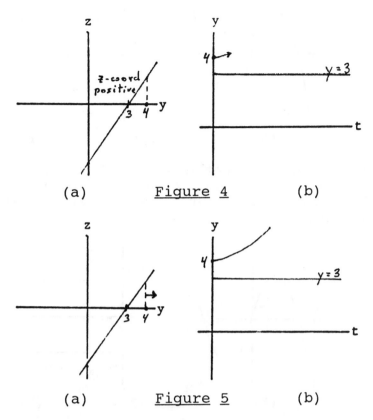

(a)   Figure 4   (b)

(a)   Figure 5   (b)

The z-coordinate becomes more positive in Fig. 5a, so the solution curve is concave up in Fig. 5b.

7. First we sketch the graph of $z = y^3 - 9y$. We find the zeros of $g(y) = y^3 - 9y$ by setting $g(y) = 0$ and solving for y.

$$y^3 - 9y = 0,$$
$$y(y^2 - 9) = 0,$$
$$y(y + 3)(y - 3) = 0.$$

The graph of $z = y^3 - 9y$ crosses the y-axis at $y = 0$, $y = \pm 3$. Next, to find where the graph has a relative maximum and relative minimum, we set $\dfrac{dz}{dy} = 0$ and solve for y.

$$\frac{d}{dy}(y^3 - 9y) = 3y^2 - 9 = 0.$$

Thus $3y^2 = 9$, $y^2 = 3$, and $y = \pm\sqrt{3}$. See Fig. 1a. The constant solutions are shown in Fig. 1b.

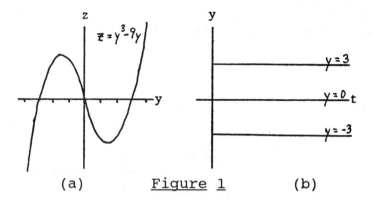

(a)   <u>Figure 1</u>   (b)

Figure 2 shows the sketches needed to obtain the graphs of
the solutions such that y(0) = -4, y(0) = -1, and y(0) =
4.   Note that the solution where y(0) = -1 cannot cross
the constant solution y = 0.

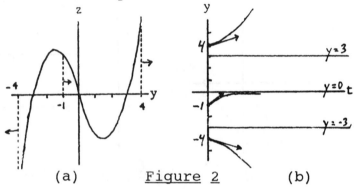

(a)   <u>Figure 2</u>   (b)

Figure 3 shows the work for the solution with y(0) = 2.
Since the initial z-coordinate in Fig. 3a is negative, the
y-values of the solution curve will decrease and y will
move to the left on the yz-graph.   At first, the z-coordinate will become more negative (i.e., the slope of the
solution curve will become more negative).   Then, as y
moves to the left past y = $\sqrt{3}$, the z-coordinates on the
yz-graph will become less negative (i.e., the slope of the
solution curve will become less negative).   Thus the solution curve will have an inflection point at y = $\sqrt{3}$, as in
Fig. 3b.

(a)   <u>Figure 3</u>   (b)

13. The graph of $z = g(y)$ shown in Fig. 1a has zeros at $y = 1$ and $y = 6$. So the constant solutions of $y' = g(y)$ are $y = 1$ and $y = 6$. The relative maximum of $g(y)$ occurs when $y = 4$, so a solution curve will have an inflection point whenever it crosses the dashed line shown in Fig. 1b. The inflection point at $y = 2$ on the graph of $g(y)$ has no influence on the general shape of solution curves, so we ignore it.

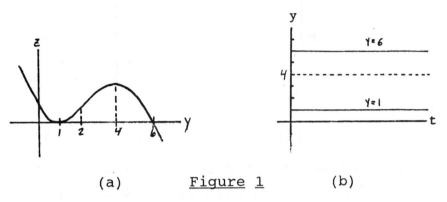

(a)   Figure 1   (b)

Figure 2 shows the work for the solution of $y' = g(y)$ such that $y(0) = 0$, $y(0) = 1.2$, $y(0) = 5$, and $y(0) = 7$.

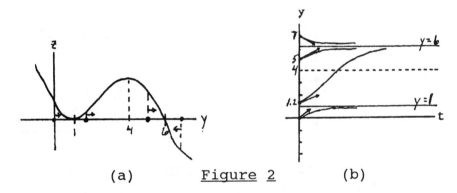

(a)   Figure 2   (b)

Warning: Although the function $g(y)$ in Exercise 13 has a minimum at $y = 1$, the minimum value is zero. Notice that rule 7 on page 518 applies only to <u>nonzero</u> relative maximum or minimum points.

19. The graph of $z = y^2 - 3y - 4$ is obviously a parabola. It opens upward because the coefficient of y^2 is positive. To find where the graph crosses the y-axis, we solve

$$y^2 - 3y - 4 = 0,$$
$$(y+1)(y-4) = 0,$$
$$y = -1, \text{ or } y = 4.$$

Setting $\dfrac{dz}{dy} = 0$, we find that $2y - 3 = 0$ and $y = \dfrac{3}{2} = 1.5$. Thus the parabola has a minimum at $y = 1.5$. This is

enough information to produce the graph in Fig. 1a and the
initial sketch in Fig. 1b.

(a)   **Figure 1**   (b)

Figure 2 shows the work for the solutions of the equation
$y' = y^2 - 3y - 4$ such that $y(0) = 0$ and $y(0) = 3$.

(a)   **Figure 2**   (b)

25. The graph of $z = \frac{1}{y}$ is shown in Fig. 1a.   The graph does
    not cross the y-axis, so there are no constant solutions
    of $y' = \frac{1}{y}$.   The solution satisfying $y(0) = 1$ is an in-
    creasing curve because the z-coordinate of the initial
    point on the yz-graph is positive.   However, as y increas-
    es on the yz-graph, the z-coordinates become less posi-
    tive; i.e., the slopes of the solution curve become less
    positive.   A similar solution holds for the solution sat-
    isfying $y(0) = -1$, where the slopes are negative and be-
    come less negative.   See Fig. 1b.

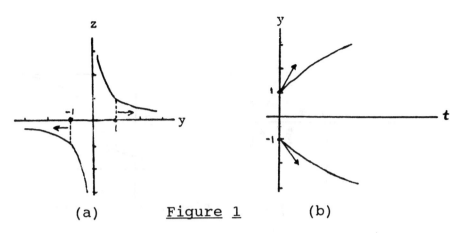

(a) <u>Figure 1</u> (b)

Warning: Exercise 27 has a feature similar to Exercise 13.

31. Let $f(t)$ be the height of the sunflower at time t. Then $f'(t)$ is the rate at which the sunflower is growing at time t. We are told that this rate is proportional to the product of its height and the difference between its height at maturity and its current height. If we let H be the sunflower's height at maturity, we have

$$f'(t) = kf(t)[H - f(t)] \qquad (1)$$

or equivalently,

$$y' = ky(H - y). \qquad (2)$$

Before we can sketch a solution, we must determine whether k is positive or negative. Clearly, $f(t)$ is increasing, so $f'(t)$ is positive. Also, $f(t)$ is less than H, so the factor $H - f(t)$ is positive. From this it follows that k must be positive.

From (2) we must sketch,

$$z = ky(H - y) = kHy - ky^2.$$

The graph of this equation is a parabola which opens down, with zeros at 0 and H, and maximum at H/2. See Fig. 1(a).

The initial height of the sunflower is $y(0)$, which is slightly greater than 0. Since z is positive here, this solution is increasing as it leaves the initial point. As y moves to the right, the z-coordinate becomes more positive until y reaches H/2. After than, the z-coordinate becomes less positive, and hence the curve has an inflection point at H/2, and is concave down after than point. Also, it is clear from equation (1) that the constant functions y = 0 and y = H are solutions. See Fig. 1b.

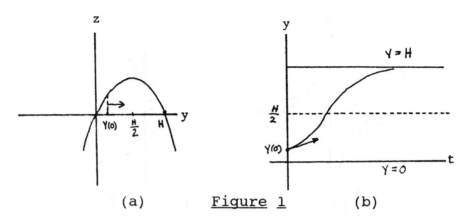

(a)   <u>Figure 1</u>   (b)

Helpful Hint: Exercise 31 is a key exercise. Work on it now!
You'll see more exercises like this in Section 10.5.

10.5 Applications of Differential Equations

Here we are! If you've been faithful in your work on the
"word problems" in Sections 10.1 to 10.4, you should be ready
for Section 10.5. The exercises fall into two categories: (1)
problems involving one constant of proportionality, and (2)
"one-compartment" problems. The first category is analyzed
carefully in the first two pages of the section. Most of
Section 5.4 concerned applications of the first category of
problems. One of the most important applications there involved logistic growth, and this subject is discussed again in
Section 10.5.

One-compartment problems are very common in applications.
Multi-compartment problems also arise. You can read about
them in *Mathematical Techniques for Physiology and Medicine*,
by William Simon (New York: Academic Press, 1972). This book
was at one time the text for a course at the Rochester School
of Medicine and Dentistry.

The material on population genetics was suggested to us by
one of our students. While in our class, she was taking a
course on population genetics where she saw a qualitative
analysis of certain differential equations. Only the yz-
graphs were shown in her textbook, *Population Genetics*, by C.
C. Li (Chicago: University of Chicago Press, 1955). Our student used her knowledge from our calculus course to provide
the ty-graphs of the solution curves. Now you, too, can have
a glimpse into this fascinating topic.

1. Let $y = f(t)$ be the percentage of the population having
    the information at time t. Then $0 \le f(t) \le 100$, and $100 -
    f(t)$ is the percentage that does not have the information.
    We are told that

$$\begin{bmatrix} \text{the rate of} \\ \text{spread of} \\ \text{information} \end{bmatrix} \begin{bmatrix} \text{is} \\ \text{proportional} \\ \text{to} \end{bmatrix} \begin{bmatrix} \text{percentage} \\ \text{not having} \\ \text{information} \end{bmatrix}.$$

Thus

$$f'(t) = k \cdot [100 - f(t)] \tag{1}$$

for some constant k. Equivalently,

$$y' = k(100 - y). \tag{2}$$

Before we can sketch a solution, we must determine whether k is positive or negative. Clearly, f(t) is increasing, so f'(t) is positive. Also, f(t) is not more than 100 percent, so 100 - f(t) is also positive. From this it follows that k is positive.

From (2) we must sketch

$$z = k(100 - y) = 100k - ky,$$

where k is positive. The graph of this equation is a straight line with negative slope. Also, when y = 100 we have z = 0. See Fig. 1(a) below. We are interested in the solution where y(0) = 1. Using the method of Section 10.4, we obtain the curve in Fig. 1(b).

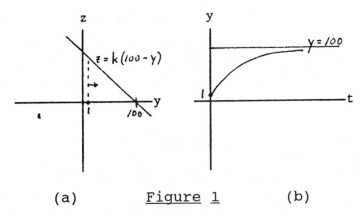

(a)   Figure 1   (b)

7.   Let y = f(t) be the amount of substance A at time t. Then f'(t) is the rate at which substance A is converted into substance B. We are told that this rate is proportional to the square of the amount of A. Thus we have

$$f'(t) = k[f(t)]^2 \tag{1}$$

where k is a constant of proportionality. Equivalently, we have

$$y' = ky^2. \tag{2}$$

Before we can sketch a solution, we must determine whether k is positive or negative. Clearly, f(t) is decreasing, so f'(t) is negative. Since f^2(t) is never negative, k must be negative.

From (2) we must sketch,

$$z = ky^2,$$

where k is negative, so we have a parabola that opens down. See Fig. 1(a) below. We are interested in a solution where y(0) is some positive number (representing the initial amount of substance A). Using the method of Section 10.4, we obtain the curve in Fig. 1(b).

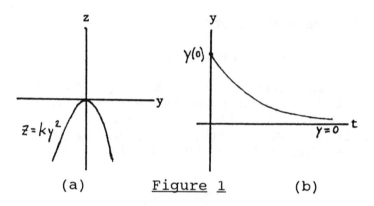

(a)   Figure 1   (b)

13. a. At first, let us ignore the deposits to the account. In Section 5.2 we showed that if no deposits or withdrawals are made, then f(t) satisfies the equation

$$y' = .05y.$$

That is, the account grows at a rate proportional to the amount in the account. We conclude that interest is being added to the account at a rate proportional to the amount in the account.

Now suppose that continuous deposits are being made to the same account at the rate of $10,000 per year. There are two influences on the way the amount of money in the account changes—the rate at which interest is added and the rate at which money is deposited. Let f(t) be the amount of money in the account at time t. Then the rate of change of f(t) is the net effect of these two influences. That is, f(t) satisfies the equation

$$f'(t) = .05f(t) + 10,000,$$

or equivalently,

$$y' = .05y + 10,000. \tag{1}$$

At time t = 0, we assume there is no money in the account. Hence y(0) = 0.

b. We note that $y = \dfrac{-10,000}{.05} = -200,000$ is a constant solution, since it makes both sides of equation (1) equal zero. Assuming that $y \neq -200,000$, we proceed using separation of variables. We have

$$y' = .05(y + 200,000),$$

$$\int \frac{y'}{(y+200,000)} \frac{dy}{dt} \, dt = \int .05 \, dt,$$

$$\int \frac{y'}{(y+200,000)} \, dy = \int .05 \, dt,$$

$$\ln|y+200,000| = .05t + C, \quad C \text{ a constant},$$

$$|y+200,000| = e^{.05t+C} = e^{C} \cdot e^{.05t}.$$

If $y \neq -200,000$, then $y + 200,000$ is either positive or negative for all t. Thus

$$y = \pm e^{C} \cdot e^{.05t} - 200,000.$$

The general solution (including the constant solution) has the form

$$y = Ae^{.05t} - 200,000, \quad A \text{ a constant}.$$

Since we have y(0) = 0, we see that A = 200,000. Hence

$$y = 200,000e^{.05t} - 200,000$$
$$= 200,000(e^{.05t} - 1).$$

The amount in the account after 5 years is given by

$$y(t) = 200,000(e^{.25} - 1)$$
$$\approx 56,806 \text{ dollars}.$$

19. We must first sketch

$$z = -.0001q^2(1 - q).$$

Clearly z = 0 when q = 0 or q = 1. Writing $z = .0001q^3 - .0001q^2$, we see that the graph is a cubic curve. To find relative extreme points we set $\frac{dz}{dq} = 0$.

$$.0003q^2 - .0002q = 0,$$
$$.0001q(3q - 2) = 0.$$

So q = 0, or 3q - 2 = 0 and q = 2/3. Since $\frac{d^2z}{dq^2} = .0006q$ - .0002 = .0002(3q-1), we see that $\frac{d^2z}{dq^2}$ is negative at q = 0 and positive at q = 2/3. Here is a rough sketch of the graph.

We are asked to find a solution when q(0) is close to but slightly less than 1, so we assume q(0) > 2/3. Using the method of Section 10.4, we obtain

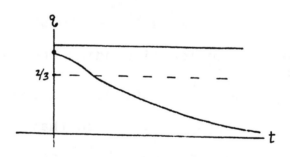

Review of Chapter 10

Except for one or two differential equations in Section 10.1, all of the equations have been *first-order* equations that involve only y′, y, and perhaps some functions of t. We have three methods for analyzing these equations: (1) separation of variables to find explicit solutions; (2) Euler's method to find an approximate solution; and (3) qualitative analysis of the equation. The chart below lists the methods that may be applied to first-order differential equations.

Form of the Equation	Methods of Solution
$y' = g(t,y)$	Euler's method
$y' = p(t)q(y)$	Euler's method, Separation of Variables
$y' = g(y)$	Euler's method, Separation of Variables, Qualitative Analysis

On an exam, your instructor might ask you to use more than one method on the same differential equation. This chart will help you anticipate what kinds of questions might be asked.

Chapter 10: Supplementary Exercises

1. We use separation of variables to obtain

$$\int y^2 \frac{dy}{dt}\, dt = \int (4t^3 - 3t^2 + 2)\, dt,$$

$$\int y^2\, dy = \int (4t^3 - 3t^2 + 2)\, dt,$$

$$\tfrac{1}{3}y^3 = t^4 - t^3 + 2t + C_1,$$

$$y^3 = 3(t^4 - t^3 + 2t + C_1),$$

$$y^3 = 3(t^4 - t^3 + 2t) + C, \text{ C a constant.}$$

Hence

$$y = \sqrt[3]{3t^4 - 3t^3 + 6t + C}.$$

7. We use separation of variables to obtain

$$yy' = 6t^2 - t,$$

$$\int y\frac{dy}{dt}\, dt = \int (6t^2 - t)\, dt,$$

$$\int y \, dy = \int (6t^2 - t) \, dt,$$

$$\tfrac{1}{2}y^2 = 2t^3 - \tfrac{1}{2}t^2 + C_1,$$

$$y^2 = 2(2t^3 - \tfrac{1}{2}t^2) + C, \ C \text{ a constant.}$$

Hence

$$y = \pm\sqrt{4t^3 - t^2 + C}.$$

Since $y(0) = 7$, we need the positive square root. (If $y(0)$ were negative here, we would use the negative square root.) Since $y(0) = \sqrt{C} = 7$, we have $C = 49$. Therefore,

$$y = \sqrt{4t^3 - t^2 + 49}.$$

13. Here $g(t,y) = .1y(20-y)$, $a = 0$, $b = 3$, $Y_0 = 2$, and $h = \dfrac{3-0}{6} = .5$. We have:

$$t_0 = 0, \quad Y_0 = 2, \ g(0,2) = .2(20-2) = 3.6,$$

$$t_1 = .5, \quad Y_1 = 2 + (3.6)(.5) = 3.8,$$
$$g(\tfrac{1}{2},3.8) = .38(20-3.8) = 6.16,$$

$$t_2 = 1, \quad Y_2 = 3.8 + (6.16)(.5) = 6.9,$$
$$g(1,6.9) = .69(20-6.9) = 9.04,$$

$$t_3 = 1.5, \quad Y_3 = 6.9 + (9.04)(.5) = 11.4,$$
$$g(3/2,11.4) = 1.14(20-11.4) = 9.8,$$

$$t_4 = 2, \quad Y_4 = 11.4 + (9.8)(.5) = 16.3,$$
$$g(2,16.3) = 1.63(20-16.3) = 6.03,$$

$$t_5 = 2.5, \quad Y_5 = 16.3 + (6.03)(.5) = 19.3,$$
$$g(5/2,19.3) = 1.93(20-19.3) = 1.35,$$

$$t_6 = 3, \quad Y_6 = 19.3 + (1.35)(.5) = 19.98.$$

The polygonal path connecting the points $(t_0,Y_0),\ldots,$ (t_6,Y_6) is shown in the answer section of the text.

19. From $y' = \ln y$ we obtain the function $z = \ln y$, whose graph is shown in Fig. 1a. Thus $g(y)$ has a zero at $y = 1$. Therefore, the constant function $y = 1$ is a solution of the differential equation.

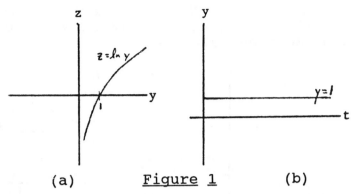

(a)   Figure 1   (b)

To sketch the solution corresponding to y(0) = 2, we observe that when y = 2, g(y) is positive. Hence the solution is increasing as it leaves the initial point. As y moves to the right, the z-coordinate gets more positive, and hence the solution is concave up, and will continue to increase without bound. See Figure 2.

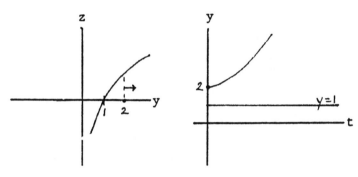

Figure 2

25. **a.** Let N = f(t) be the city's population at time t. Then f'(t) is the rate of change of the population of the city at time t. Since the birth rate is 3.5%, and the death rate is 2%, and 3000 people leave the city each year we have

$$f'(t) = .035f(t) - .02f(t) - 3000$$
$$= .015f(t) - 3000,$$

or equivalently,

$$N' = .015N - 3000.$$

b. We seek a constant function N which satisfies the differential equation N' = .015N - 3000 = .015(N - 200,000). Clearly the constant function N = 200,000 satisfies the equation since it makes both sides equal to zero. However, it is unlikely that a city could maintain this constant population in practice, for the graph indicates that the constant solution is unstable.

We note that z = .015N - 3000 is the graph of a line with positive slope, and with a zero at N = 200,000. Using the method of Section 10.4, we obtain

Chapter 11

Taylor Polyomials and Infinite Series

11.1 Taylor Polynomials

Taylor polynomials are often used in applications to approximate more complex functions, and they have an important connection with the Taylor series, to be discussed in Section 11.6.

The phrase "at x = 0" in "Taylor polynomial of f(x) at x = 0" indicates that the coefficients of the polynomial are computed by evaluating f(x) and its derivatives at x = 0. The phrase "at x = 0" does <u>not</u> mean that the x in the polynomial must be zero. However, in an application, the values of x are usually taken to be close to zero. In such cases, the remainder theorem is useful for estimating how close the values of a Taylor polynomial are to the values of the function f(x).

1. $\qquad f(x) = \sin x, \qquad\qquad\qquad f(0) = 0,$

$\qquad f'(x) = \cos x, \qquad\qquad\qquad f'(0) = 1,$

$\qquad f''(x) = -\sin x, \qquad\qquad\qquad f''(0) = 0,$

$\qquad f^{(3)}(x) = -\cos x, \qquad\qquad\qquad f^{(3)}(0) = -1.$

Therefore, the third Taylor polynomial at x = 0 is

$$p_3(x) = 0 + \frac{1}{1!}x + \frac{0}{2!}x^2 + \frac{-1}{3!}x^3$$
$$= x - \frac{1}{6}x^3.$$

7. $\qquad f(x) = xe^{3x}, \qquad\qquad\qquad\qquad f(0) = 0,$

$\qquad f'(x) = 3xe^{3x} + e^{3x}, \qquad\qquad\qquad f'(0) = 1,$

$\qquad f''(x) = 3e^{3x} + 3e^{3x} + 9xe^{3x}, \qquad f''(0) = 6,$

$\qquad f^{(3)}(x) = \underbrace{9e^{3x} + 9e^{3x} + 27xe^{3x} + 9e^{3x}}_{\text{from product rule}}, \quad f^{(3)}(0) = 27.$

Therefore,

$$p_3(x) = 0 + \frac{1}{1!}x + \frac{6}{2!}x^2 + \frac{27}{3!}x^3$$

$$= x + 3x^2 + \frac{9}{2}x^3.$$

13. Since $f(x) = f'(x) = f''(x) = \ldots = f^{(n)}(x) = e^x$, we have

$$f(0) = f'(0) = f''(0) = \ldots = f^{(n)}(0) = e^0 = 1.$$

Therefore, the nth Taylor polynomial for $f(x) = e^x$ at $x = 0$ is:

$$p_n(x) = 1 + \frac{1}{1!}x + \frac{1}{2!}x^2 + \frac{1}{3!}x^3 + \ldots + \frac{1}{n!}x^n$$

$$= 1 + x + \frac{1}{2}x^2 + \frac{1}{3!}x^3 + \ldots + \frac{1}{n!}x^n.$$

Helpful Hint: If your class plans to cover Section 11.5, then you should memorize now the formulas for the Taylor polynomials of e^x and $1/(1 - x)$, as described in Examples 2 and 3.

19. $\quad\quad\quad f(x) = \cos x, \quad\quad\quad\quad f(\pi) = -1,$
$\quad\quad\quad\quad\; f'(x) = -\sin x, \quad\quad\quad\quad f'(\pi) = 0,$
$\quad\quad\quad\quad\; f''(x) = -\cos x, \quad\quad\quad\quad f''(\pi) = 1,$
$\quad\quad\quad\; f^{(3)}(x) = \sin x, \quad\quad\quad\quad f^{(3)}(\pi) = 0,$
$\quad\quad\quad\; f^{(4)}(x) = \cos x, \quad\quad\quad\quad f^{(4)}(\pi) = -1.$

Thus the third Taylor polynomial at $x = \pi$ is

$$p_3(x) = -1 + \frac{0}{1!}(x-\pi) + \frac{1}{2!}(x-\pi)^2 + \frac{0}{3!}(x-\pi)^3$$

$$= -1 + \frac{1}{2}(x-\pi)^2,$$

and the fourth Taylor polynomial is

$$p_4(x) = -1 + \frac{0}{1!}(x-\pi) + \frac{1}{2!}(x-\pi)^2 + \frac{0}{3!}(x-\pi)^3 + \frac{-1}{4!}(x-\pi)^4$$

$$= -1 + \frac{1}{2}(x-\pi)^2 - \frac{1}{24}(x-\pi)^4.$$

Notice that $p_3(x)$ is a polynomial of degree 2, not degree 3, because $f^{(3)}(\pi) = 0$. See Practice Problem 1.

25. Be sure to try the Practice Problems before you attempt
this problem. You should realize from Practice Problem 2
that if f(x) is a polynomial of degree 3, then the third
Taylor polynomial of f(x) at x = 0 is f(x) itself. This
is true because f(x) is a polynomial that agrees with f(x)
and all of its derivatives at x = 3.

Now write the abstract *formula* for the 3rd Taylor polynomial of f(x), set that equal to f(x), and equate corresponding coefficients. From this you should be able to
discover what the values of f"(0) and f‴(0) must be. Try
to do this. (The rest of the solution appears after the
solution of Exercise 31.)

31. From Example 3, you should know that the fourth Taylor
polynomial of $Y_1 = 1/(1 - X)$ is the polynomial given by

$$Y_2 = 1 + X + X^2 + X^3 + X^4.$$

When you graph Y_1 and Y_2 in the window $[-1,1]$ *by* $[-1,5]$,
you'll probably find that their graphs appear identical
for x between about -.66 and .51, or perhaps .53. So b is
about .53.

You can use TRACE to display the y-values of points on
the two curves with the same x-coordinates. At x =
.5106383, for instance, $Y_1 - Y_2 \approx 2.04348 - 1.97253 =$
.07095. Another method for comparing values of Y_1 and Y_2
is shown in Fig. 5, just before the Practice Problems.

25. (continued) The 3rd Taylor polynomial of f(x) is

$$p_3(x) = f(0) + \frac{f'(0)}{1}x + \frac{f''(0)}{2!}x^2 + \frac{f'''(0)}{3!}x^3$$

and

$$f(x) = 3 + 4x + -\frac{5}{2!}x^2 + \frac{7}{3!}x^3.$$

Since $p_3(x)$ equals f(x) for all x, the polynomials must
have the same coefficients. That is, f(0) = 3, f'(0) = 4,
f"(0)/2! = -5/2! and f‴(0)/3! = 7/3!. Accordingly, f"(0) =
-5 and f‴(0) = 7.

11.2 The Newton-Raphson Algorithm

A calculator is indispensable for this section. In order to
memorize the Newton-Raphson algorithm, it is important to work
several problems by hand using a calculator. If you have ac-
cess to an IBM-compatible computer, you should experiment with
Visual Calculus, which will show you geometrically how the
algorithm works.

1. $\sqrt{5}$ is a zero of the function $x^2 - 5$. Note that $\sqrt{5}$ lies between 2 and 3 because $2^2 < 5 < 3^2$. For an initial approximation, take $x_0 = 2$. (The value $x_0 = 3$ would probably work just as well.) Since $f'(x) = 2x$, we have:

$$x_1 = x_0 - \frac{x_0^2 - 5}{2x_0} = 2 - \frac{(2)^2 - 5}{2(2)}$$

$$= 2 - \frac{-1}{4} = \frac{9}{4} = 2.25,$$

$$x_2 = 2.25 - \frac{(2.25)^2 - 5}{2(2.25)}$$

$$= 2.25 - \frac{.0625}{4.5} = 2.2361,$$

$$x_3 = 2.2361 - \frac{(2.2361)^2 - 5}{2(2.2361)}$$

$$= 2.2361 - \frac{.00014}{4.4722} = 2.23607.$$

7. Here $f(x) = \sin x + x^2 - 1$ and $x_0 = 0$. First, compute $f'(x) = \cos x + 2x$, and then use the N-R algorithm:

$$x_1 = x_0 - \frac{\sin x_0 + x_0^2 - 1}{\cos x_0 + 2x_0} = 0 - \frac{\sin 0 + 0^2 - 1}{\cos 0 + 2(0)}$$

$$= 0 - \frac{-1}{1} = 1,$$

$$x_2 = 1 - \frac{\sin 1 + 1^2 - 1}{\cos(1) + 2(1)} = 1 - \frac{.84147}{2.54030} = .66875,$$

$$x_3 = .66875 - \frac{.62001 + .44723 - 1}{.78460 + 1.3375}$$

$$= .66875 - .03168 = .63707.$$

13. Let i be the monthly rate of interest. The present value of an amount A to be received in k months is $A(1+i)^{-k}$. Therefore, we must solve the following equation for i:

$$\begin{bmatrix} \text{amount of initial} \\ \text{investment} \end{bmatrix} = \begin{bmatrix} \text{sum of present} \\ \text{values of returns} \end{bmatrix}$$

$$500 = 100(1+i)^{-1} + 200(1+i)^{-2} + 300(1+i)^{-3}.$$

Multiply both sides by $(1+i)^3$, take all terms to the left, and obtain

$$500(1+i)^3 - 100(1+i)^2 - 200(1+i) - 300 = 0.$$

Let $x = 1+i$, and solve the resulting equation by the Newton-Raphson algorithm with $x_0 = 1.1$.

$$f(x) = 500x^3 - 100x^2 - 200x - 300 = 0,$$
$$f'(x) = 1500x^2 - 200x - 200.$$
$$x_1 = 1.1 - \frac{500(1.1)^3 - 100(1.1)^2 - 200(1.1) - 300}{1500(1.1)^2 - 200(1.1) - 200}$$
$$\approx 1.1 - .018$$
$$= 1.082,$$
$$x_2 = 1.082 - \frac{500(1.082)^3 - 100(1.082)^2 - 200(1.082) - 300}{1500(1.082)^2 - 200(1.082) - 200}$$
$$\approx 1.082 - (-.00008)$$
$$\approx 1.082.$$

Therefore, the solution is $x = 1.082$. Hence $i = .082$ and the investment had an internal rate of return of 8.2% per month.

19. The slope of the tangent line is 4, so $f'(3) = 4$. Also, $f(3) = 4(3) + 5 = 17$. If the initial guess is 3, then the N-R algorithm produces:

$$x_1 = 3 - \frac{f(3)}{f'(3)} = 3 - \frac{17}{4} = \frac{-5}{4}.$$

25. When $f(x) = x^{1/3}$, and $f'(x) = \frac{1}{3}x^{-2/3}$, the Newton-Raphson formula is

$$x_1 = x_0 - \frac{f(x_0)}{f'(x_0)} = x_0 - \frac{x_0^{1/3}}{(1/3)x_0^{-2/3}} = x_0 - 3x_0 = -2x_0.$$

Similarly, $x_2 = -2x_1$, $x_3 = -2x_2$, ..., and $x_{n+1} = -2x_n$. If $x_0 = 1$, then the Newton-Raphson algorithm produces the sequence 1, -2, 4, -8, and so on. This sequence does *not* converge to the actual root, $r = 0$. Can you draw a picture, based on Figure 10(a) in the text, to show what is happening?

11.3 Infinite Series

Most students who take this calculus course will see an application of infinite series in some other course. More often than not, the application will involve a geometric series.

Make sure you completely master the material in this section. It will really help you to understand the concepts in the sections to follow.

1. $1 + \frac{1}{6} + \frac{1}{6^2} + \frac{1}{6^3} + \frac{1}{6^4} + \ldots = (\frac{1}{6})^0 + (\frac{1}{6})^1 + (\frac{1}{6})^2 + (\frac{1}{6})^3 + (\frac{1}{6})^4 + \ldots$

Thus $a = 1$, $r = \frac{1}{6}$, and the series converges to

$$\frac{a}{1-r} = \frac{1}{1-\frac{1}{6}} = \frac{1}{\frac{5}{6}} = \frac{6}{5}.$$

7. We find r by dividing any term by the preceding term. So

$$r = \frac{\frac{1}{5^4}}{\frac{1}{5}} = \frac{5}{5^4} = \frac{1}{5^3} = \frac{1}{125}.$$

The first term of the series is $a = \frac{1}{5}$, so the sum of the series is

$$\frac{\frac{1}{5}}{1 - \frac{1}{125}} = \frac{1}{5} \cdot \frac{125}{124} = \frac{25}{124}.$$

13. We find r by dividing any term by the preceding term. So,

$$r = \frac{4}{5}.$$

The first term of the series is $a = 5$, so the sum of the series is

$$\frac{5}{1 - \frac{4}{5}} = 5 \cdot 5 = 25.$$

19. The technique here is to find a rational number that represents .011011, and then to add 4 to this number. We have

$$.011\underline{011} = .011 + .000011 + .000000011 + \ldots$$

$$= \frac{11}{1000} + \frac{11}{1000^2} + \frac{11}{1000^3} + \ldots,$$

which is a geometric series with $a = \frac{11}{1000}$ and $r = \frac{1}{1000}$.

The sum of the series is: $\dfrac{\frac{11}{1000}}{1 - \frac{1}{1000}} = \dfrac{11}{1000} \cdot \dfrac{1000}{999} = \dfrac{11}{999}$. So

$$4.011\underline{011} = 4 + \frac{11}{999} = \frac{3996}{999} + \frac{11}{999} = \frac{4007}{999}.$$

25. **a.** We construct a sum of the present value of all future payments. That is, we express capital value as

$$100 + 100(1.01)^{-1} + 100(1.01)^{-2} + \ldots = \sum_{k=0}^{\infty} 100(1.01)^{-k}.$$

b. This is a geometric series. We have $a = 100$ and $r = (1.01)^{-1} = \frac{1}{1.01}$, (so $|r| < 1$). So the sum of the series is $\dfrac{100}{1 - \frac{1}{1.01}} = 100\,\dfrac{1.01}{.01} = 10{,}100$. Thus the

capital value of the perpetuity is \$10,100.

31. At the end of the first "day" (a 24-hour period), 25% of the original dose of M mg has been eliminated, and only .75M remains. Immediately after the next dose, the body contains M + .75M mg of the drug. At the end of the second day, only 75% of that M + .75M remains, which may be written as .75(M + .75M), or .75M + $(.75)^2$M. When a dose of M mg is given again, the new amount in the body is

$$M + .75M + (.75)^2M \quad \text{(after the third dose)}.$$

After n full days, just after then next dose is given, the amount in the body is

$$M + .75M + (.75)^2M + \cdots + (.75)^nM \quad \text{milligrams}.$$

This is a partial sum of a geometric series whose initial term is M and whose ratio is $r = .75$. When n is large, the value of this partial sum will be very close to the sum of the infinite series

$$\sum_{k=0}^{\infty} M(.75)^k = \frac{M}{1 - .75} = \frac{M}{.25} = 4M.$$

To make this amount equal to 20 mg, M must be 5 mg. This is the "maintenance dose."

37. $\displaystyle\sum_{j=1}^{\infty} 5^{-2j} = \dfrac{1}{5^2} + \dfrac{1}{5^4} + \dfrac{1}{5^6} + \dfrac{1}{5^8} + \cdots.$

This is a geometric series with $a = 1/5^2$ and $r = 1/5^2$. So the sum of the series is

$$\dfrac{\dfrac{1}{25}}{1 - \dfrac{1}{25}} = \dfrac{1}{25} \cdot \dfrac{25}{24} = \dfrac{1}{24}.$$

43. The first entry in the sum(seq(...)) command displays the general term, 6(.5)^X, from which you can see that a = 6 and the ratio is r = .5. The remaining entries in the sum(seq(...X,0,10,1)) command show that the "counter" X, begins at 0 and ends at 10, with increment (step size) 1. (On the TI-83 and TI-86, the value for the increment may be omitted.) Thus the calculator is computing the partial sum

$$6 + 6(.5) + 6(.5)^2 + \cdots + 6(.5)^{10}.$$

The exact sum of the corresponding geometric series is a/(1 - r) = 6/(1 - .5) = 6/.5 = 12.

49. Unfortunately, the TI-82 sum(seq(...)) command is limited to 99 terms, so let's begin there. You should find that

$$\text{sum(seq(X\^-2,X,1,99,1)} \approx 1.634884$$

(to six decimal places). Also, $\pi^2/6 = 1.644934$, which is a difference of about .01. With 99 replaced by 999, the computation is much slower, but the result 1.6439934 differs from $\pi^2/6$ only by about .001.

11.4 Series with Positive Terms

The integral test provides a nice link between infinite series and improper integrals. Your understanding of both topics should be strengthened by studying them together. It may be helpful to review Section 9.6 before you begin the exercises in Section 11.4.

Problems involving the comparison test can be very hard. Knowing what series to use for comparison is a skill that requires a lot of experience—more than we expect you to obtain in this course. We have made Exercises 21-26 more reasonable by suggesting one or two series for comparison.

1. To apply the integral test, compute

$$\int_1^\infty \frac{3}{\sqrt{x}}\, dx = \int_1^\infty 3x^{-1/2}\, dx = \lim_{b\to\infty} \int_1^b 3x^{-1/2}\, dx$$

$$= \lim_{b\to\infty} \left(6x^{1/2}\Big|_1^b \right) = \lim_{b\to\infty} (6b^{1/2} - 6) = \infty.$$

The series $\displaystyle\sum_{k=1}^\infty \frac{3}{\sqrt{k}}$ is divergent, because the corresponding improper integral is divergent.

7. Study the improper integral $\displaystyle\int_1^\infty \frac{x}{(x^2+1)^{3/2}}\, dx.$ Begin by finding an antiderivative of $x(x^2 + 1)^{-3/2}$, using the method of substitution. Set $u = x^2 + 1$ and $du = 2x\, dx$. Then

$$\int \frac{x}{(x^2+1)^{3/2}}\, dx = \frac{1}{2}\int (x^2+1)^{-3/2}\cdot 2x\, dx = \frac{1}{2}\int u^{-3/2}\, du$$

$$= \frac{1}{2}\left(-2u^{-1/2} \right) = -(x^2+1)^{-1/2} + C.$$

Next,

$$\int_1^b \frac{x}{(x^2+1)^{3/2}}\, dx = -(x^2+1)^{-1/2}\Big|_1^b$$

$$= -\frac{1}{\sqrt{b^2+1}} - \left(-\frac{1}{\sqrt{1^2+1}} \right).$$

Thus,

$$\int_1^\infty \frac{x}{(x^2+1)^{3/2}}\,dx = \lim_{b\to\infty}\left(\frac{1}{\sqrt{2}} - \frac{1}{\sqrt{b^2+1}}\right) = \frac{1}{\sqrt{2}}.$$

Since the improper integral is convergent, the corresponding infinite series also is convergent.

Warning: The sum of the series in Exercise 7 is _not_ $1/\sqrt{2}$. The integral test only shows that the series converges.

13. Evaluate $\int_1^\infty xe^{-x^2}\,dx$. To find an antiderivative for xe^{-x^2}, either guess e^{-x^2} and adjust the guess to obtain $-\frac{1}{2}e^{-x^2}$, or use substitution with $u = -x^2$, $du = -2x\,dx$, and compute

$$\int xe^{-x^2}\,dx = -\frac{1}{2}\int -2xe^{-x^2}\,dx = -\frac{1}{2}\int e^u\,du$$

$$= -\frac{1}{2}e^u + C = -\frac{1}{2}e^{-x^2} + C.$$

Next, compute

$$\int_1^\infty xe^{-x^2}\,dx = \lim_{b\to\infty}\int_1^b xe^{-x^2}\,dx = \lim_{b\to\infty}\left(-\frac{1}{2}e^{-x^2}\Big|_1^b\right)$$

$$= \lim_{b\to\infty}\left(-\frac{1}{2}e^{-b^2} - (-\frac{1}{2}e^{-1})\right)$$

$$= \lim_{b\to\infty}\left(-\frac{1}{2}e^{-b^2} + \frac{1}{2}e^{-1}\right) = \frac{1}{2}e^{-1}.$$

Since the improper integral is convergent, so is the infinite series $\sum_{k=1}^\infty ke^{-k^2}$.

19. Evaluate the integral $\int_1^\infty \frac{x}{e^x}\,dx = \int_1^\infty xe^{-x}\,dx$, using integration by parts. Set

$$f(x) = x, \quad g(x) = e^{-x},$$
$$f'(x) = 1, \quad G(x) = -e^{-x}.$$

Then

$$\int \frac{x}{e^x} \, dx = -xe^{-x} - \int -e^{-x} \, dx = -xe^{-x} + \int e^{-x} \, dx$$

$$= -xe^{-x} - e^{-x} + C$$

and

$$\int_1^b \frac{x}{e^x} \, dx = \left(-xe^{-x} - e^{-x} \right) \Big|_1^b$$

$$= \left(-be^{-b} - e^{-b} \right) - \left(-e^{-1} - e^{-1} \right)$$

$$= 2e^{-1} - be^{-b} - e^{-b}.$$

For the next step, we need the fact that $\lim\limits_{b \to \infty} be^{-b} = 0$.

$$\int_1^\infty \frac{x}{e^x} \, dx = \lim_{b \to \infty} \left(2e^{-1} - be^{-b} - e^{-b} \right) = 2e^{-1} - 0 - 0.$$

Since the improper integral is convergent, so is the infinite series $\sum\limits_{k=1}^\infty \frac{k}{e^k}$.

25. First compare

$$\sum_{k=1}^\infty \frac{1}{5^k} \cos^2\left(\frac{k\pi}{4}\right) = \frac{1}{5} \cos^2\left(\frac{\pi}{4}\right) + \frac{1}{25} \cos^2\left(\frac{\pi}{2}\right) + \frac{1}{125} \cos^2\left(\frac{3\pi}{4}\right) + \dots$$

with

$$\sum_{k=1}^\infty \cos^2\left(\frac{k\pi}{4}\right) = \cos^2\left(\frac{\pi}{4}\right) + \cos^2\left(\frac{\pi}{2}\right) + \cos^2\frac{3\pi}{4} + \dots.$$

Note that each term of the first series is less than the corresponding term of the second series. Since $|\cos(k\pi/4)| = 1/\sqrt{2}$ when k is odd, and $|\cos(k\pi/4)| = 1$ when k is even, the second series has the form

$$\frac{1}{2} + 0 + \frac{1}{2} + 1 + \frac{1}{2} + 0 + \frac{1}{2} + 1 + \dots.$$

Since these terms keep repeating the series diverges. We

have learned nothing about the convergence of the first series. Next, compare the first series with

$$\sum_{k=1}^{\infty} \frac{1}{5^k} = \frac{1}{5} + \frac{1}{5^2} + \frac{1}{5^3} + \frac{1}{5^4} + \dots ,$$

which is a convergent geometric series because $|r| = \frac{1}{5} < 1$. Now, since

$$\frac{1}{5^k} \cos^2 \left(\frac{k\pi}{4}\right) \le \frac{1}{5^k} \quad \text{for all values of k,}$$

each term of $\sum 5^{-k}$ is greater than the corresponding term of the first series shown above. Since $\sum 5^{-k}$ converges, so does the first series.

31.

$$\sum_{k=0}^{\infty} \frac{8^k + 9^k}{10^k} = \frac{8^0 + 9^0}{10^0} + \frac{8^1 + 9^1}{10^1} + \frac{8^2 + 9^2}{10^2} + \dots$$

$$= \left(\frac{8^0}{10^0} + \frac{9^0}{10^0}\right) + \left(\frac{8^1}{10^1} + \frac{9^1}{10^1}\right) + \left(\frac{8^2}{10^2} + \frac{9^2}{10^2}\right) + \dots .$$

$$= \sum_{k=0}^{\infty} \left(\frac{8^k}{10^k} + \frac{9^k}{10^k}\right)$$

$$= \sum_{k=0}^{\infty} \frac{8^k}{10^k} + \sum_{k=0}^{\infty} \frac{9^k}{10^k} \quad \text{by Exercise 29,}$$

$$= \sum_{k=0}^{\infty} \left(\frac{8}{10}\right)^k + \sum_{k=0}^{\infty} \left(\frac{9}{10}\right)^k$$

Each term in this sum is a convergent geometric series. The first has a = 1 and r = .8, and its sum is a/(1 - r) = 1/(1 - .8) = 5. The second has a = 1 and r = .9, and its sum is 1/(1 - .9) = 10. By Exercise 29, the original series is convergent, and its sum is 5 + 10 = 15.

11.5 Taylor Series

One of the main ideas in this section is that a Taylor series is a function. Be sure to read the text on pages 571-72 and 574-75.

   You need to know the general formula for a Taylor series at x = 0 and the specific formulas for e^x and 1/(1-x). Check with your instructor to see if you also need to memorize the Taylor series at x = 0 for cos x and sin x. Study Examples 3, 5, and 6 carefully to get ideas for the solutions of Exercises 5-27.

1. Compute:

$$f(x) = \frac{1}{2x+3} = (2x+3)^{-1}, \qquad f(0) = \frac{1}{3},$$

$$f'(x) = -2(2x+3)^{-2}, \qquad f'(0) = \frac{-2}{9} = -\frac{2}{9},$$

$$f''(x) = 8(2x+3)^{-3}, \qquad f''(0) = \frac{8}{27},$$

$$f^{(3)}(x) = -48(2x+3)^{-4}, \qquad f^{(3)}(0) = \frac{-48}{81} = -\frac{16}{27},$$

$$f^{(4)}(x) = 384(2x+3)^{-5}, \qquad f^{(4)}(0) = \frac{384}{243} = \frac{128}{81}.$$

Then write

$$f(x) = \frac{1}{3} + \frac{-\frac{2}{9}}{1!}x + \frac{\frac{8}{27}}{2!}x^2 + \frac{-\frac{16}{27}}{3!}x^3 + \frac{\frac{128}{81}}{4!}x^4 + \dots$$

$$= \frac{1}{3} - \frac{2}{9}x + \frac{4}{27}x^2 - \frac{8}{81}x^3 + \frac{16}{243}x^4 + \dots$$

$$= \frac{1}{3} - \frac{2}{9}x + \frac{2^2}{3^3}x^2 - \frac{2^3}{3^4}x^3 + \frac{2^4}{3^5}x^4 + \dots.$$

7. In the Taylor series at x = 0 for $\frac{1}{1-x}$, replace x by $-x^2$ to obtain

$$\frac{1}{1-(-x^2)} = \frac{1}{1+x^2} = 1 - x^2 + x^4 - x^6 + \dots.$$

13. In the Taylor series at x = 0 for $\frac{1}{1-x}$, replace x by $-x$ to obtain

$$e^{-x} = 1 + (-x) + \frac{1}{2!}(-x)^2 + \frac{1}{3!}(-x)^3 + \frac{1}{4!}(-x)^4 - \dots.$$

Hence

$$1 - e^{-x} = 1 - (1 - x + \frac{1}{2!}x^2 - \frac{1}{3!}x^3 + \frac{1}{4!}x^4 - \dots)$$

$$= x - \frac{1}{2!}x^2 + \frac{1}{3!}x^3 - \frac{1}{4!}x^4 + \dots.$$

19. In the Taylor series at $x = 0$ for $\cos x$, replace x by $3x$ to obtain

$$\cos 3x = 1 - \frac{9}{2!}x^2 + \frac{81}{4!}x^4 - \frac{729}{6!}x^6 + \ldots$$

Now differentiate both sides and divide by -3 to obtain

$$-3 \sin 3x = -\frac{18}{2!}x + \frac{4(81)}{4!}x^3 - \frac{6(729)}{6!}x^5 + \ldots$$

$$\sin 3x = \frac{6}{2!}x - \frac{4(27)}{4!}x^3 + \frac{6(243)}{6!}x^5 - \ldots$$

$$= 3x - \frac{27}{3!}x^3 + \frac{243}{5!}x^5 - \ldots$$

$$= 3x - \frac{3^3}{3!}x^3 + \frac{3^5}{5!}x^5 - \ldots$$

25. In the Taylor series expansion at $x = 0$ for $\dfrac{1}{\sqrt{1+x}}$, replace x by $-x$ to obtain

$$\frac{1}{\sqrt{1-x}} = 1 + \frac{1}{2}x + \frac{1 \cdot 3}{2 \cdot 4}x^2 + \frac{1 \cdot 3 \cdot 5}{2 \cdot 4 \cdot 6}x^3 .$$

31. If you are reading this before you work the exercise, stop and study Practice Problem 4. Then try the exercise again before reading on with the solution. We observe that the term in the series containing x^5 is $\dfrac{f^{(5)}(0)}{5!}x^5 = \dfrac{2}{5}x^5$. So $\dfrac{f^{(5)}(0)}{5!} = \dfrac{2}{5}$, and

$$f^{(5)}(0) = (5!)\frac{2}{5} = (4!)2 = 24 \cdot 2 = 48.$$

37. In the Taylor expansion at $x = 0$ for $\dfrac{1}{1-x}$, replace x by $-x^3$ to obtain

$$\frac{1}{1+x^3} = 1 - x^3 + x^6 - x^9 + \ldots$$

Then integrate both sides, term by term:

$$\int \frac{1}{1+x^3}\,dx = \int (1 - x^3 + x^6 - x^9 + \ldots)\,dx$$

$$= [x - \frac{1}{4}x^4 + \frac{1}{7}x^7 - \frac{1}{10}x^{10} + \ldots] + C.$$

43. Since $e^x = 1 + x + \frac{1}{2}x^2 + \frac{1}{6}x^3 + \ldots$, for all x, we have $e^x > \frac{1}{6}x^3$ when $x > 0$. The idea now is to find a function

which approaches 0 as $x \to \infty$, with the property that for every value of x greater than 0, this function is greater than the function $x^2 e^{-x}$. From the inequality above, we have

$$\frac{1}{e^x} < \frac{6}{x^3}$$

and so

$$x^2 e^{-x} < x^2 \cdot \frac{6}{x^3} = \frac{6}{x}.$$

As $x \to \infty$, $\frac{6}{x}$ approaches 0. Since $\frac{6}{x} > x^2 e^{-x}$ for all $x > 0$, we conclude that $x^2 e^{-x}$ must approach 0 as $x \to \infty$.

Chapter 11: Supplementary Exercises

1. $f(x) = x(x+1)^{3/2}$, $f(0) = 0$,

         $f'(x) = \frac{3}{2}x(x+1)^{1/2} + (x+1)^{3/2}$, $f'(0) = 1$,

         $f''(x) = \frac{3}{4}x(x+1)^{-1/2} + \frac{3}{2}(x+1)^{1/2} + \frac{3}{2}(x+1)^{1/2}$

               $= \frac{3}{4}x(x+1)^{-1/2} + 3(x+1)^{1/2}$, $f''(0) = 3$.

Hence

$$p_2(x) = 0 + \frac{1}{1!}x + \frac{3}{2!}x^2$$
$$= x + \frac{3}{2}x^2.$$

7. $f(t) = -\ln(\cos 2t)$, $f(0) = -\ln(1) = 0$,

         $f'(t) = \frac{2 \sin 2t}{\cos 2t}$, $f'(0) = 0$,

         $f''(t) = \frac{\cos 2t(4 \cos 2t) + 2 \sin 2t(2 \sin 2t)}{\cos^2 2t}$

            $= \frac{4 \cos^2 2t + 4 \sin^2 2t}{\cos^2 2t}$

            $= 4 + \frac{4 \sin^2 2t}{\cos^2 2t}$, $f''(0) = 4$.

Hence $p_2(t) = 0 + \frac{0}{1!}t + \frac{4}{2!}t^2 = 2t^2$.

The area under the graph of $y = f(t)$ is approximately equal to the area under the graph of $y = p_2(t)$. Thus

$$[\text{Area}] \approx \int_0^{1/2} 2t^2 \, dt = \left.\frac{2}{3}t^3\right|_0^{1/2} = \frac{2}{3}\cdot\frac{1}{8} = \frac{1}{12}.$$

13. The series is a geometric series with $a = 1$ and $r = -\frac{3}{4}$. Since $\left|-\frac{3}{4}\right| < 1$, the series is convergent and converges to

$$\frac{1}{1+\frac{3}{4}} = \frac{4}{7}.$$

19. We observe that

$$e^x = 1 + \frac{1}{1!}x + \frac{1}{2!}x^2 + \frac{1}{3!}x^3 + \frac{1}{4!}x^4 + \cdots$$

Therefore

$$1 + 2 + \frac{2^2}{2!} + \frac{2^3}{3!} + \frac{2^4}{4!} + \cdots$$

$$= 1 + \frac{1}{1!}(2) + \frac{1}{2!}(2)^2 + \frac{1}{3!}(2)^3 + \frac{1}{4!}(2)^4$$

$$= e^2.$$

25. Use the integral test, and consider $\int_1^\infty \frac{\ln x}{x} \, dx$. First, let $u = \ln x$ and $du = (1/x) \, dx$. Then

$$\int \frac{\ln x}{x} \, dx = \int u \, du = \frac{1}{2}u^2 + C = \frac{1}{2}(\ln x)^2 + C.$$

Next,

$$\int_1^b \frac{\ln x}{x} \, dx = \left.\frac{1}{2}(\ln x)^2\right|_1^b = \frac{1}{2}(\ln b)^2 - 0.$$

This quantity grows arbitrarily large as $b \to \infty$, so the improper integral above is divergent. By the integral test, the infinite series $\displaystyle\sum_{k=1}^\infty \frac{\ln k}{k}$ also is divergent.

31. $\dfrac{1}{(1-3x)^2} = \dfrac{1}{3}\dfrac{d}{dx}\left[\dfrac{1}{1-3x}\right] = \dfrac{1}{3}\dfrac{d}{dx}\left[1 + 3x + 3^2x^2 + 3^3x^3 + \cdots\right]$

$$= 1 + 6x + 7x^2 + 4\cdot3^3x^3 + \cdots$$

37. a. The fifth Taylor polynomial consists of all terms in the sixth Taylor polynomial with degree ≤ 5. Therefore, $p_5(x) = x^2$.

b. Since the coefficient of x^3 in $p_6(x)$ is zero, $\dfrac{f^{(3)}(0)}{3!} = 0$. Therefore, $f^{(3)}(0) = 0$.

c. $\displaystyle\int_0^1 \sin x^2 \, dx \approx \int_0^1 \left(x^2 - \frac{1}{6}x^6 \right) dx = \frac{x^3}{3} - \frac{1}{42}x^7 \bigg|_0^1 = \frac{1}{3} - \frac{1}{42}$

$$\approx .3095 \quad \text{(exact value: .3103)}.$$

43. $\displaystyle\sum_{k=1}^{\infty} 10{,}000 \, e^{-.08k} = \sum_{k=1}^{\infty} 10{,}000 (e^{-.08})^k = \frac{10{,}000(e^{-.08})}{1 - e^{-.08}}$

$$\approx \$120{,}066.70.$$

Chapter 12

Probability and Calculus

12.1 Discrete Random Variables

Although this section is provided mainly as a background for the sections that follow, there are interesting and important problems here. The main concepts are: relative frequency table, probability, expected value, variance, and (discrete) random variable. The probability density histogram on page 586 will be used in Section 12.2 to motivate the definition of a probability density function.

1. There are two possible outcomes, 0 and 1, with probabilities $\frac{1}{5}$ and $\frac{4}{5}$, respectively. Thus we have

$$E(X) = 0 \cdot \frac{1}{5} + 1 \cdot \frac{4}{5} = \frac{4}{5}.$$

$$\text{Var}(X) = \left(0 - \frac{4}{5}\right)^2 \cdot \frac{1}{5} + \left(1 - \frac{4}{5}\right)^2 \cdot \frac{4}{5} = .128 + .032 = .16.$$

Standard deviation of $X = \sqrt{.16} = .4$.

7. a. Recall that the area of a circle of radius r is given by $[\text{Area}] = \pi r^2$. Thus the area of a circle of radius 1 is π, and the area of a circle of radius $\frac{1}{2}$ is $\pi\left(\frac{1}{2}\right)^2 = \frac{1}{4}\pi$. To find the percentage of points lying in the circle of radius $\frac{1}{2}$, we set up the ratio

$$\frac{\left[\text{Area of circle of radius } \frac{1}{2}\right]}{[\text{Area of circle of radius } 1]} = \frac{\frac{1}{4}\pi}{\pi} = \frac{1}{4} = .25 = 25\%.$$

Thus 25% of the points lie within $\frac{1}{2}$ unit of the center.

b. The area of a circle of radius c is: [Area] = πc^2. To find the percentage of points lying within this circle we set up the ratio

$$\frac{[\text{Area of circle of radius c}]}{[\text{Area of circle of radius 1}]} = \frac{\pi c^2}{\pi} = c^2 = 100c^2\%.$$

12.2 Continuous Random Variables

We recommend that you study the theoretical parts of Sections 6.1 and 6.3 (particularly the fundamental theorem of calculus) as background for the discussion here of the cumulative distribution function F(x) and the probability density function f(x). Given either function, you should be able to find the other with no difficulty. Observe that F'(x) = f(x) and that F(x) is the unique antiderivative of f(x) for which F(A) = 0, when X is a random variable on A ≤ x ≤ B. You should also be able to use either F(x) or f(x) to compute various probabilities of the form Pr(a ≤ X ≤ b).

Pay attention to Example 6 because it provides a nice connection with earlier material on improper integrals and it introduces ideas that are needed in Section 12.4. For these reasons, questions similar to Example 6 often appear on exams.

1. Clearly f(x) ≥ 0, since $\frac{1}{18}x$ ≥ 0 when 0 ≤ x ≤ 6. Thus Property I is satisfied. For Property II we check that

$$\int_0^6 f(x)\,dx = \int_0^6 \frac{1}{18}x\,dx = \frac{1}{36}x^2\Big|_0^6 = \frac{1}{36}(6)^2 - 0 = 1.$$

Thus Property II is also satisfied, and f(x) is indeed a probability density function.

7. In order to satisfy Property I, we require that k ≥ 0, for if k < 0 and 1 ≤ x ≤ 3, then f(x) = kx < 0. For Property II we set $\int_1^3 kx\,dx = 1$, and solve for k.

$$\int_1^3 kx\,dx = \frac{k}{2}x^2\Big|_1^3 = \frac{k}{2}(9) - \frac{k}{2} = 4k = 1.$$

Therefore the value k = $\frac{1}{4}$ satisfies both Properties I and II, and f(x) = $\frac{1}{4}x$, 1 ≤ x ≤ 3, is a probability density function.

13. The set of possible values of X is determined by the domain of the density function f(x). In this problem the
domain is 0 ≤ x ≤ 4, so the values of X range between 0
and 4. Since X can't be less than 0, the probability that
X is less than or equal to 1 is the same as the probability that X is between 0 and 1. Thus Pr(X ≤ 1) is an abbreviation for Pr(0 ≤ X ≤ 1). Similarly, since X cannot be
larger than 4, Pr(3.5 ≤ X) is an abbreviation for Pr(3.5
≤ X ≤ 4).

a. Pr(X ≤ 1) is represented by the area under the graph of
f(x) = $\frac{1}{8}$x where 0 ≤ x ≤ 1.

b. Pr(2 ≤ X ≤ 2.5) is represented by the area under the
graph of f(x) = $\frac{1}{8}$x where 2 ≤ x ≤ 2.5.

c. Pr(3.5 ≤ X) is represented by the area under the graph
of f(x) = $\frac{1}{8}$x where 3.5 ≤ x ≤ 4.

19. The probability that the lifetime X of a battery is *at
least* 35 hours is given by Pr(35 ≤ X). However, we are
told in this problem that the values of X range between 30
and 50. So Pr(35 ≤ X) = Pr(35 ≤ X ≤ 50), and

$$Pr(35 \le X) = \int_{35}^{50} \frac{1}{20}\, dx = \frac{1}{20}x \Big|_{35}^{50} = \frac{50}{20} - \frac{35}{20} = \frac{15}{20} = \frac{3}{4}.$$

Thus the probability is $\frac{3}{4}$ that the battery will last
longer than 35 hours.

25. a. $\Pr(2 \le X \le 3) = \int_2^3 \frac{1}{21}x^2 \, dx = \frac{1}{63}x^3 \Big|_2^3 = \frac{27}{63} - \frac{8}{63} = \frac{19}{63}.$

b. Since $F(x)$ is an antiderivative of $f(x) = \frac{1}{21}x^2$, we have

$$F(x) = \int \frac{1}{21}x^2 \, dx = \frac{1}{63}x^3 + C.$$

Since X has values greater than or equal to 1, we have $F(1) = 0$. Setting $F(1) = \frac{1}{63} + C = 0$, we find that $C = -\frac{1}{63}$, so

$$F(x) = \frac{1}{63}x^3 - \frac{1}{63} = \frac{1}{63}(x^3 - 1).$$

c. $\Pr(2 \le X \le 3) = F(3) - F(2)$

$$= \frac{1}{63}(3^3 - 1) - \frac{1}{63}(2^3 - 1) = \frac{26}{63} - \frac{7}{63}$$

$$= \frac{19}{63}.$$

31. $\Pr(0 \le X \le 5) = \int_0^5 2k e^{-kx} \, dx = \frac{2k}{-k} e^{-kx} \Big|_0^5 = -2e^{-kx} \Big|_0^5.$

Since $k = (\ln 2)/10 \approx .0693$, we have

$$\Pr(0 \le X \le 5) = -2e^{-.0693x} \Big|_0^5 = -2e^{(-.0693)(5)} - [-2e^0]$$

$$\approx -1.4142 + 2$$

$$= .5858.$$

Alternate calculation:

$$-2e^{-kx} \Big|_0^5 = -2e^{-k(5)} - (-2e^0) = -2e^{-5(\ln 2)/10} + 2.$$

Observe that

$$-2e^{-5(\ln 2)/10} = -2e^{-(1/2)\ln 2} = -2e^{\ln 2^{-1/2}}$$

$$= -2 \cdot 2^{-1/2} = -2^{1/2} = -\sqrt{2}.$$

Thus

$$\Pr(0 \le X \le 5) = -\sqrt{2} + 2 \approx -1.4142 + 2 = .5858.$$

37. a. Clearly $f(x) = 4x^{-5} \geq 0$ for all values of x greater than or equal to 1, so Property I is satisfied. For Property II we check that $\int_1^\infty 4x^{-5}\,dx = 1$. If $b \geq 1$, then

$$\int_1^b 4x^{-5}\,dx = -x^{-4}\Big|_1^b = -(b)^{-4} - [-(1)^{-4}] = 1 - \frac{1}{b^4}.$$

Since as $b \rightarrow \infty$, the number b^4 gets arbitrarily large, $\dfrac{1}{b^4}$ approaches zero. Thus

$$\int_1^\infty 4x^{-5}\,dx = \lim_{b\to\infty} \int_1^b 4x^{-5}\,dx = \lim_{b\to\infty}\left(1 - \frac{1}{b^4}\right) = 1.$$

b. Since $F(x)$ is an antiderivative of $f(x) = 4x^{-5}$, we have

$$F(x) = \int 4x^{-5}\,dx = -x^{-4} + C.$$

Since X has values greater than or equal to 1, we have $F(1) = 0$. Setting $F(1) = -1 + C = 0$, we find that $C = 1$, so

$$F(x) = -x^{-4} + 1 = 1 - x^{-4}.$$

c. $\Pr(1 \leq X \leq 2) = F(2) - F(1) = \dfrac{15}{16} - 0 = \dfrac{15}{16}.$ Observe that $\Pr(1 \leq X \leq 2) + \Pr(2 \leq X) = 1$, since <u>all</u> values of X are greater than or equal to 1. Hence

$$\Pr(2 \leq X) = 1 - \Pr(1 \leq X \leq 2) = 1 - \frac{15}{16} = \frac{1}{16}.$$

Helpful Hint: Decide now what you would do on an exam if you were given Exercise 37 with no mention of parts (a), (b), and $\Pr(1 \leq x \leq 2)$. Certainly there would be no need to find the cumulative distribution function. Would you want to compute $\Pr(1 \leq X \leq 2)$? Compute (a) and (b) below, and decide which approach is easier for you.

(a) $\Pr(2 \leq X) = 1 - \Pr(1 \leq X \leq 2) = 1 - \displaystyle\int_1^2 4x^{-5}\,dx.$

(b) $\Pr(2 \leq X) = \displaystyle\int_2^\infty 4x^{-5}\,dx.$

12.3 Expected Value and Variance

The expected value of a random variable X is easier to understand and compute than the variance. However, both concepts are important in statistics. An explanation of how E(X) and Var(X) are related to the graph of the probability density function for X will be given in Section 12.4, in the discussion of normal random variables. Check with your instructor to see if you need to know the definition of Var(X), or if the alternate formula for Var(X) will suffice. The alternate formula is easier to compute.

Calculations of E(X) and Var(X) sometimes seem to require integration by parts, but this can be avoided when the probability density function is a polynomial. Observe how the integrals $\int_0^1 xf(x)\,dx$ and $\int_0^1 x^2 f(x)\,dx$ in Practice Problem 2 are simplified by expanding f(x) so that xf(x) and $x^2 f(x)$ are simple polynomials that are easily integrated.

1. We have

$$E(X) = \int_0^6 x \cdot \frac{1}{18}x\,dx = \int_0^6 \frac{1}{18}x^2\,dx = \frac{1}{54}x^3 \Big|_0^6 = 4.$$

To compute the alternate formula for Var(X), we compute

$$\int_0^6 x^2 \cdot \frac{1}{18}x\,dx = \int_0^6 \frac{1}{18}x^3\,dx = \frac{1}{72}x^4 \Big|_0^6 = \frac{1296}{72} = 18.$$

Therefore

$$Var(X) = \int_0^6 x^2 \cdot \frac{1}{18}x\,dx - E(X)^2 = 18 - (4)^2 = 2.$$

7. We have

$$E(X) = \int_0^1 x \cdot 12x(1-x)^2\,dx = \int_0^1 12x^2(1-2x+x^2)\,dx$$

$$= \int_0^1 (12x^2 - 24x^3 + 12x^4)\,dx$$

$$= (4x^3 - 6x^4 + \frac{12}{5}x^5) \Big|_0^1 = \frac{2}{5}.$$

$$\text{Var}(X) = \int_0^1 x^2 \cdot 12x(1-x)^2 \, dx - E(X)^2$$

$$= \int_0^1 (12x^3 - 24x^4 + 12x^5) \, dx - \left(\frac{2}{5}\right)^2$$

$$= (3x^4 - \frac{24}{5}x^5 + 2x^6)\Big|_0^1 - \frac{4}{25}$$

$$= \frac{1}{5} - \frac{4}{25} = \frac{1}{25}.$$

13. The average time is the expected value of X.

$$E(X) = \int_0^{12} \frac{1}{72}x^2 \, dx = \frac{1}{216}x^3 \Big|_0^{12} = \frac{1728}{216} = 8.$$

Therefore, the average time spent reading the editorial page is 8 minutes.

19. We set $\int_0^M \frac{1}{18}x \, dx = \frac{1}{2}$ and solve for M.

$$\int_0^M \frac{1}{18}x \, dx = \frac{1}{36}x^2 \Big|_0^M = \frac{1}{36}M^2 = \frac{1}{2}.$$

So $M^2 = 18$, and $M = \sqrt{18} = 3\sqrt{2}$. We note that $-3\sqrt{2}$ is not a solution since $0 \le M \le 6$.

25. We have $E(X) = \int_A^B xf(x) \, dx$, so we integrate by parts, setting

$$h(x) = x, \quad f(x) \quad [= g(x) \text{ in integ. by parts formula}]$$

$$h'(x) = 1, \quad F(x) \quad [= \text{antiderivative of } f(x)]$$

where $f(x)$ is any probability density function on $A \le x \le B$ and $F(x)$ is the cumulative distribution function corresponding to $f(x)$. So we have

$$E(X) = \int_A^B xf(x) \, dx = xF(x)\Big|_A^B - \int_A^B F(x) \, dx$$

$$= BF(B) - AF(A) - \int_A^B F(x) \, dx$$

$$= B - \int_A^B F(x) \, dx,$$

since $F(B) = 1$ and $F(A) = 0$.

12.4 Exponential and Normal Random Variables

This section deserves your attention because exponential and normal random variables arise so often in applications. In a situation when an exponential density function ke^{-kx} is appropriate for a random variable X, the value of $E(X)$ is often estimated from experimental data, and then the constant k is obtained from the relation

$$E(X) = \frac{1}{k}, \quad \text{or equivalently,} \quad k = \frac{1}{E(X)}.$$

You need to know this relation in order work Exercises 5—14.

The text's discussion of arbitrary normal random variables provides an opportunity to review changes of variable in a definite integral. Check with your instructor about how much detail you should show when you make a substitution $z = (x - \mu)/\sigma$.

1. Here $k = 3$, so we have

$$E(X) = \frac{1}{3}, \quad \text{and Var}(X) = \frac{1}{9}.$$

7. The mean is given by $E(X) = \frac{1}{k} = 3$. Hence $k = \frac{1}{3}$, and the probability density function is $f(x) = \frac{1}{3}e^{-(1/3)x}$. The probability that a customer is served in less than 2 minutes is given by

$$Pr(0 \le X \le 2) = \int_0^2 \frac{1}{3}e^{-(1/3)x} \, dx = -e^{-(1/3)x}\Big|_0^2$$

$$= -e^{-2/3} - (-e^0)$$

$$= 1 - e^{-2/3}.$$

13. The average life span (or mean) is given by $E(X) = \frac{1}{k} = 72$. Hence $k = \frac{1}{72}$, and the probability density function is $f(x) = \frac{1}{72}e^{-(1/72)x}$. The probability that a component lasts for more than 24 months is given by

$$Pr(24 \leq X) = \int_{24}^{\infty} \frac{1}{72}e^{-(1/72)x}\,dx$$

$$= \lim_{b\to\infty} \int_{24}^{b} \frac{1}{72}e^{-(1/72)x}\,dx$$

$$= \lim_{b\to\infty} \left[-e^{-(1/72)x} \Big|_{24}^{b} \right]$$

$$= \lim_{b\to\infty} \left[e^{-1/3} - e^{-b/72} \right].$$

We note that as $b \to \infty$, the number $-\frac{b}{72}$ approaches $-\infty$, so $e^{-b/72}$ approaches zero. Therefore

$$Pr(24 \leq X) = \lim_{b\to\infty} \left[e^{-1/3} - e^{-b/72} \right] = e^{-1/3}.$$

19. To find a relative maximum, we first set $f'(x) = 0$ and solve for x.

$$f'(x) = -xe^{-x^2/2} = 0.$$

Since $e^{-x^2/2}$ is strictly positive for all values of x, we see that $f'(x) = 0$ if and only if $x = 0$. To check that $f(x)$ has a maximum at $x = 0$, we check $f''(0)$.

$$f''(x) = x^2 e^{-x^2/2} - e^{-x^2/2}$$

$$f''(0) = 0 - 1 = -1 < 0.$$

Thus $f(x)$ is indeed concave down at $x = 0$. Therefore $f(x)$ has a relative maximum at $x = 0$.

25. a. We have $\mu = 6$ and $\sigma = \frac{1}{2}$. Note that $\frac{x-\mu}{\sigma} = \frac{x-6}{1/2} = 2x - 12$ and $\frac{1}{\sigma\sqrt{2\pi}} = \frac{1}{(1/2)\sqrt{2\pi}} = \frac{2}{\sqrt{2\pi}}$. Thus the normal density function for X, the gestation period, is $f(x) = \frac{2}{\sqrt{2\pi}}e^{-(1/2)(2x-12)^2}$. So we have

$$\Pr(6 \le X \le 7) = \int_6^7 \frac{2}{\sqrt{2\pi}}e^{-(1/2)(2x-12)^2}\,dx.$$

Using the substitution $z = 2x - 12$, $dz = 2\,dx$, we see that if $x = 6$, then $z = 0$, and if $x = 7$, then $z = 2$. So

$$\int_6^7 \frac{2}{\sqrt{2\pi}}e^{-(1/2)(2x-12)^2}\,dx = \int_0^2 \frac{1}{\sqrt{2\pi}}e^{-(1/2)z^2}\,dz.$$

The value of this integral is the area under the standard normal curve from 0 to 2. Thus

$$\Pr(6 \le X \le 7) = A(2) = .4772.$$

Therefore, about 47.72% of births occur after a gestation period of between 6 and 7 months.

b. Proceeding as in part (a), we use the same substitution to evaluate $\int_5^6 \frac{2}{\sqrt{2\pi}}e^{-(1/2)(2x-12)^2}\,dx$, noting that if $x = 5$, then $z = 2x - 12 = -2$, and if $x = 6$, then $z = 0$. Therefore,

$$\Pr(5 \le X \le 6) = \int_{-2}^0 \frac{2}{\sqrt{2\pi}}e^{-(1/2)z^2}\,dz$$

$$= A(-2) = A(2) = .4772.$$

Therefore, about 47.72% of births occur after a gestation period of between 5 and 6 months.

31. We have the normal density function

$$f(x) = \frac{1}{(.8)\sqrt{2\pi}}e^{-(1/2)[(x-18.2)/.8]^2}.$$

Let X be the diameter of a bolt selected at random from the supply of bolts. We have

$$Pr(20 \leq X) = \int_{20}^{\infty} \frac{1}{(.8)\sqrt{2\pi}} e^{-(1/2)[(x-18.2)/.8]^2} dx.$$

Using the substitution $z = (x - 18.2)/.8$, $dz = (1/.8)\,dx$, we note that if $x \rightarrow \infty$, then $z \rightarrow \infty$ too, and if $x = 20$, then $z = 1.8/.8 = 2.25$. Hence

$$Pr(20 \leq X) = \int_{2.25}^{\infty} \frac{1}{\sqrt{2\pi}} e^{-(1/2)z^2} dz.$$

The value of this integral is the area under the standard normal curve from 2.25 to ∞. If we consider areas under the standard normal curve, we see that

$$\begin{bmatrix} \text{area to} \\ \text{right of } 2.25 \end{bmatrix} = \begin{bmatrix} \text{area to} \\ \text{right of } 0 \end{bmatrix} - \begin{bmatrix} \text{area between} \\ 0 \text{ and } 2.25 \end{bmatrix}.$$

That is,

$$\begin{aligned} Pr(20 \leq X) &= .5 \quad\quad\quad\quad - \quad A(2.25) \\ &= .5 - .4878 \\ &= .0122. \end{aligned}$$

Therefore, about 1.22% of the bolts will be discarded.

37. Set $Y_1 = e^{\wedge}(-X^2/2)/\sqrt{}(2\pi)$. To graph Y_1, use the window $[-5,5]$ *by* $[-.2,.5]$, with Yscl $= .1$. For the definite integral of $x^2 f(x)$, use

$$\text{fnInt}(X^2 * Y_1, X, -4, 4).$$

The **fnInt** command is on the MATH menu for the TI-82 and TI-83, and on the CALC menu for the TI-85 and TI-86. Repeat the command (use the [2nd] ENTRY key to save time), with ±4 replaced by ±N, for N = 6 and 8. Report your calculations, which should suggest that the improper integral of $x^2 f(x)$ from $-\infty$ to ∞ is 1. Since $E(Z) = 0$, this calculation shows that $Var(Z) = 1$ and hence the standard deviation of Z is 1, too.

Section 12.5 Poisson and Geometric Random Variables

This last section of the text combines the probability theory in this chapter with the Taylor series for e^x (from Section 11.5) and the geometric series (Section 11.3). For convenience, state all probabilities to four decimal places.

1. From Example 1, $p_5 = .1008$. Since $p_n = (\lambda/n)p_{n-1}$,

$$p_6 = (3/6)p_5 = 3*.1008/6 = .0504$$
$$p_7 = (3/7)p_6 = 3*.0504/7 = .0216$$
$$p_8 = (3/8)p_7 = 3*.0216/8 = .0081.$$

7. Since the average of a Poisson random variable equals the parameter for the variable, $\lambda = 1.5$ for this problem.

   a. $\Pr(X = 0) = p_0 = e^{-\lambda} = e^{-1.5} = .2231.$

   b. First, compute $p_1 = (1.5/1)p_0 = .3347$, $p_2 = (1.5/2)p_3 = .2510$, and $p_3 = (1.5/3)p_2 = .1255$. Then

   $$p_2 + p_3 = .2510 + .1255 = .3765.$$

   c. $\Pr(X \geq 4) = 1 - \Pr(X < 4)$
   $$= 1 - (p_0 + p_1 + p_2 + p_3)$$
   $$= 1 - (.2231 + .3347 + .2510 + .1255)$$
   $$= 1 - .9343$$
   $$= .0657.$$

13. The number of X of Red taxis that appear before the first Blue taxi appears is a geometric random variable, with "success" corresponding to the arrival of a Red taxi. At any given time, the probability of success is $p = 3/4$, because three out of every four cabs are Red.

   a. For $n \geq 1$, the probability of n successes (Red taxis) before the first failure (a Blue taxi) is

   $$p_n = p^n(1 - p) = (\tfrac{3}{4})^n(\tfrac{1}{4})$$

   b. The probability of observing at least three Red taxis in a row is 1 minus the probability of observing less than three Red taxis, namely, $1 - (p_0 + p_1 + p_2)$. This probability is

   $$1 - \left[\tfrac{1}{4} + (\tfrac{3}{4})(\tfrac{1}{4}) + (\tfrac{3}{4})^2(\tfrac{1}{4}) \right]$$

   $$= 1 - (.25 + .046875 + .03516) \approx .6680.$$

c. The average number of Red taxis observed in a row is given by $E(X) = p/(1-p) = \frac{3}{4} \div \frac{1}{4} = 3$.

19. It can be shown that the number of defective fuses found in a box selected at random is a Poisson random variable. Let $f(\lambda) = (\lambda^2/2)e^{-\lambda}$, the probability of selecting a box with two defective fuses. Then

$$f'(\lambda) = (\lambda^2/2)(-e^{-\lambda}) + \lambda e^{\lambda} \quad \text{(by the product rule)}$$
$$= (\lambda - \lambda^2/2)e^{-\lambda}$$
$$f''(\lambda) = (\lambda - \lambda^2/2)(-e^{-\lambda}) + (1 - \lambda)e^{\lambda}$$

A possible maximum occurs when

$$(\lambda - \lambda^2/2)e^{-\lambda} = 0, \quad \text{or} \quad \lambda(1 - \lambda/2)e^{-\lambda} = 0$$

Since $e^{-\lambda} \neq 0$ and $\lambda \neq 0$ (because there are some defective fuses in the box sampled), we conclude that $\lambda = 2$. Checking $f''(2) = 0 + (1 - 2)e^{-2}$, we see that $f''(2)$ is negative, so $f(\lambda)$ has a maximum at $\lambda = 2$. Thus, given one sample which has two defective fuses, the maximum likelihood estimate of the Poisson parameter is $\lambda = 2$.

25. a. Since $p_n = (\lambda/n)p_{n-1}$, we have $p_7 = (6.9/7)p_6 < p_6$. So the answer is "no," seven babies are less likely to be born than six babies."

b. The answer requires computing $p_0 + \cdots + p_{15}$. Use the basic formula for p_n and the sum(seq(...)) command, (discussed in the Appendix section, **Riemann sums**):

sum(seq(λ^n/n!*p_0,n,0,15,1))

Here $\lambda = 6.9$ and $p_0 = e^{-6.9}$. Note: X is more convenient to use than n. The sum is

sum(seq(6.9^X/X!*e^-6.9,X,0,15,1)) $\approx$ .997906.

For the TI-83, you can use the command **poissonpdf**, which is entry "B" in the DISTR menu. Place this inside the sum(seq(...)) command, as follows:

sum(seq(poissonpdf(6.9,X),X,0,15,1)).

Review of Chapter 12

Work through the *Review of the Fundamental Concepts* at the end of the chapter and determine which concepts you must know and which terms and formulas you must memorize. Summarized below are the main skills you should have, listed by the various types of random variables.

    a. *Discrete random variable.* Compute $E(X)$, $Var(X)$, and the standard deviation of X.

    b. *Continuous random variable on a finite interval.* Compute $E(X)$, $Var(X)$; test if $f(x)$ is a probability density function; given one of $f(x)$ and $F(x)$, find the other; use $f(x)$ or $F(x)$ to compute probabilities. Remember that $Pr(X \le b)$ stands for $Pr(A \le X \le b)$, etc. Harder questions are found in Exercises 32—36.

    c. *Continuous random variable on an infinite interval.* A typical probability density function is $f(x) = kx^{-(k+1)}$ for $x \ge 1$. Same skills as for (b), plus use the formula $Pr(X \ge b) = 1 - Pr(X \le b)$ to simplify calculations.

    d. *Exponential random variable.* The probability density function is $f(x) = ke^{-kx}$ for $x \ge 0$. Show that $f(x)$ *is a* probability density function. Compute various probabilities and the cumulative distribution function. You probably will not have to compute $E(X)$ and $Var(X)$, unless your instructor gives you the following limits to learn:

$$\lim_{b \to \infty} be^{-kb} = 0 \quad \text{and} \quad \lim_{b \to \infty} b^2 e^{-kb} = 0 \quad \text{for } k > 0.$$

However, you should know that $E(X) = 1/k$ and $Var(X) = 1/k^2$.

    e. *Normal random variable.* Use a table to compute probabilities for a standard normal random variable, and make a change of variable to compute probabilties for an arbitrary normal random variable.

    f. *Poisson random variable.* If X is a Poisson random variable with parameter λ, then you should know that $p_0 = e^{-\lambda}$,

$$p_n = \frac{\lambda^n}{n!} e^{-\lambda} \quad (n = 1, 2, \ldots), \quad \text{and } E(X) = \lambda.$$

    g. *Geometric random variable.* If X is a geometric random varfiable and the probability of success on one trial is p, then you should know that

$$p_n = p^n (1 - p) \quad (n = 0, 1, 2, \ldots), \quad \text{and } E(X) = p/(1 - p).$$

Chapter 12: Supplementary Exercises

1. **a.** $\Pr(X \le 1) = \int_0^1 \frac{3}{8}x^2 \, dx = \frac{1}{8}x^3 \Big|_0^1 = \frac{1}{8} - = .125.$

   b. $\Pr(1 \le X \le 1.5) = \int_1^{1.5} \frac{3}{8}x^2 \, dx = \frac{1}{8}x^3 \Big|_1^{1.5}$

   $$= .4219 - .125 = .2969.$$

7. **a.** From the definition of expected value, we have

   $$E(X) = 1(.599) + 11(.401) = 5.01.$$

   This can be interpreted as saying that if a large number of samples are tested in batches of ten samples per batch, then the average number of tests per batch will be close to 5.01.

   b. The 200 samples will be divided into 20 batches of ten samples. In part (a) we found that, on the average, 5.01 tests must be run on each batch. So the laboratory should expect to run about $(20)(5.01) \approx 100$ tests altogether.

13. **a.** We must find the value of k that satisfies the equation

    $$\int_5^{25} kx \, dx = 1.$$

    We compute

    $$\int_5^{25} kx \, dx = \frac{k}{2}x^2 \Big|_5^{25} = \frac{k}{2}625 - \frac{k}{2}25 = 300k = 1.$$

    Therefore $k = \frac{1}{300}$.

    b. $\Pr(20 \le X \le 25) = \int_{20}^{25} \frac{1}{300}x \, dx = \frac{1}{600}x^2 \Big|_{20}^{25}$

    $$= \frac{1}{600}625 - \frac{1}{600}400 = \frac{1}{600}(625 - 400) = .375.$$

    c. $E(X) = \int_5^{25} \frac{1}{300}x^2 \, dx = \frac{1}{900}x^3 \Big|_5^{25} = \frac{1}{900}(15,625 - 125)$

= 17.222.

Therefore, the mean annual income is $17,222.

19. We first show that $Pr(X \le 4) = 1 - e^{-4k}$. We have

$$Pr(X \le 4) = \int_0^4 ke^{-kx}\, dx = -e^{-kx}\Big|_0^4 = 1 - e^{-4k}.$$

To make $Pr(X \le 4) = .75$, the parameter k must satisfy

$$1 - e^{-4k} = .75$$

$$e^{-4k} = .25$$

$$-4k = \ln .25 \approx -1.386$$

Thus

$$k = \frac{-1.386}{-4} \approx .35.$$

25. We know that $Pr(a \le Z)$ is the area under the standard normal curve to the right of a. Since $Pr(a \le Z) = .4$, and $Pr(0 \le Z) = .5$, we conclude that a lies to the right of zero. That is, a is positive. Thus

$$\begin{bmatrix} \text{area to} \\ \text{right of a} \end{bmatrix} = \begin{bmatrix} \text{area to} \\ \text{right of 0} \end{bmatrix} - \begin{bmatrix} \text{area between} \\ \text{0 and a} \end{bmatrix}$$

$$Pr(a \le Z) = Pr(0 \le Z) - Pr(0 \le Z \le a)$$

$$.4 = .5 - Pr(0 \le Z \le a).$$

So we have $Pr(0 \le Z \le a) = A(a) = .1$. From the A(z) table, we look for the z that makes A(z) as close to .1 as possible. Since $A(.25) = .0987 \approx .1000$, we conclude that $a \approx .25$.

31. For $\lambda = 4$, $p_4 = \lambda^4 e^{-4}/4! = (4)^4 e^{-4}/24 \approx .1954$.

Visual Calculus

The Visual Calculus software enhances the visualization and therefore the understanding of the *ideas* behind the calculus. Visual Calculus can be run on *any* IBM compatible computer. Visual Calculus can be used with or without a mouse.

To Invoke Visual Calculus from Windows 95 (or later version):

1. Place the Visual Calculus diskette in a drive, say drive A.
2. Click the Start button, point to Programs, and click MS-DOS Prompt.
3. If the DOS window does not fill the screen, hold down the Alt key and press the Enter key to enlarge the window.
4. Type A: and press the Enter key.
5. Type VC and press the Enter key.

To Invoke Visual Calculus from Windows 3.1:

1. Place the diskette in a drive, say drive A.
2. From Program Manager, double-click on the DOS icon in the Main program group. Or, exit Windows.
3. Type A: and press the Enter key.
4. Type VC and press the Enter key.

To Invoke Visual Calculus from a computer not containing Windows:

1. Place the diskette in a drive, say drive A.
2. Type A: and press the Enter key.
3. Type VC and press the Enter key.

Note: If you are using a slow computer, first copy the files from the diskette into a subdirectory of your hard drive and run VC from that subdirectory. Otherwise, there will be some noticeable delays in the execution of the program.

To select a routine from a menu, do one of the following:

(a) Press the first letter of the routine.

(b) Press the down-arrow and up-arrow keys to highlight the routine, and press Enter.

(c) Double-click the routine with a mouse.

To manage a screen used to display functions:

(a) Use the right- and left-arrow keys to move the crosshairs around the graph – or click on a new point with the mouse. (Notice information about the point at the crosshairs is displayed in the upper-left part of the screen.) Use the down- and up-arrow keys to decrease or increase the distance that the crosshairs moves.

(b) To invoke a bracketed command found in the left column, either press the key surrounded by <>, or click on the command with the mouse.

To manage a screen used to input functions:

(a) Use Tab (or Shift+Tab) to move forward (or backwards) from region to region.

(b) Buttons are activated by pressing Alt+*highlighted letter* or by moving to the button and pressing the Enter key.

(c) With a mouse, you can move to a box (or activate a button) by clicking on the box (or button).

(d) Whenever a function is requested, the user can either type in a function or press F4 to select from lists of functions in the textbook. To select an item from a list, highlight the item by either cursoring down to it, clicking on it, or pressing the first digit of the item one or more times, and then press Enter. (Alternatively, double-click on the item.) To remove the lists without making a selection, press F4 again.

(e) A caret (^) must be used for exponentiation. (For example, $x^5 \sin x$ is written x^5sin x.) The following functions can appear in expressions: log (common log), ln (natural log), sin, cos, tan, cot, csc, sec, arcsin, arccos, arctan, arcsec, arccsc, arccot, exp (same as e^x, but more efficient), sqr (square root), fact (factorial), int, sgn. In the routine "Graphs of Functions", the expression for g(x) can involve f(x), e.g. f(x–2), and the expression for h(x) can involve f(x) and/or g(x), e.g. f(g(x)).

(f) Press P to display π and press I to display ∞. In a numeric input box, press S to display $\sqrt{\ }$.

To print the graph of a function

The graphing routines have a "Print graph(s)" command that works with most dot-matrix or laser printers and prints a smooth curve. If the command does not work with your printer, you can produce a printout of the screen with one of the following two methods.

Method A: (*For computers that have Windows*)

Note: This method assumes that you have invoked DOS from the Windows environment; that is, Windows is running.

1. Press the Print Screen key.
2. Return to Windows and invoke Paint from the Accessories program group.
3. Press Ctrl+V to place a copy of the graphics screen in the window.
4. Press Ctrl+ I to invert the colors on the screen. (Otherwise, your printout will appear as white-on-black.)
5. Make sure your printer is turned on and ready to print.
6. Press Ctrl+P to print the contents of the Paint window.

Method B: (Requires DOS only or Windows 3.1)

1. To prepare for graphics screen dumps, you must enter the command GRAPHICS from DOS before invoking Visual Calculus.
2. In Visual Calculus, press Shift+PrintScreen at any time to produce a printout of the screen.

To enter functions:

Mathematical Expression	Computer Expression	Mathematical Expression	Computer Expression
x^2	x^2	$\frac{1}{2x}$	1/(2x)
$\frac{1}{x+1}$	1/(x+1)	$\frac{1}{x}+1$	1/x + 1
$\sqrt{x}$	sqr(x) or x^(1/2)	$x^{1/3}$	cbr(x)
$\log_e x$	ln x or ln(x)	$\log_{10} x$	log x or log(x)
$\ln 3x$	ln(3x)	$x^2 \ln x$	x^2ln x
$x!$	fact(x)	$[x]$	int(x)

Summary of Operation for Input Screen

<Tab>	move around input screen
Shift+<Tab>	move around input screen in reverse order
Alt+*highlighted letter*	push button marked with the letter
Click Mouse	move to input box or activate button
F4	obtain list of appropriate functions from textbook (must be used in a function input box)
P	obtain π
S	obtain $\sqrt{}$ (cannot be used in input box for a function)
I	obtain ∞ (used only in Limits and Series)

To copy a function from one input box to another:

1. Place the cursor at the beginning of the function.
2. Hold down a shift key and press <End>. (The function is now highlighted.)
3. Press Ctrl+Ins or Ctrl+C. (The function is now saved in the clipboard.)
4. Move to another function input box either in the same routine or in another routine.
5. Press Shift+Ins or Ctrl+V.

Invocation options

When Visual Calculus invoked with the command VC, bw and/or cga can be added to affect the operation of the program. For instance, to obtain the bw option, enter VC bw.

Option	Effect
bw	All graphics will appear in blue and white. This option should be invoked if you are doing screen dumps. (It isn't needed when using the Print command.) This option might be helpful when projecting images onto a large screen or when using a monochrome monitor.
cga	Emulates Color Graphics Adapter. In graphics mode, graphs and text will be thicker. This option might be helpful in a classroom when projecting images onto a large screen.

Main Routines

Analyze a Function and its Derivatives displays the graphs of one or more of f, f', f'' and displays the values of these functions at any point. A Solve command finds zeros, relative extreme points, and inflection points. A Tangent Line command draws a tangent line to $f(x)$ or $f'(x)$ at the crosshairs.

Examine Solutions of Differential Equations graphs the solution of a differential equation of the form $y' = g(t, y)$ with an initial value and determines the coordinates of points on the graph. Graphs with different initial values can be superimposed. Successive Euler approximations may be displayed.

Function Evaluator (1 and 2 variables) displays the value of a function and its derivatives. [1 variable: $f(x)$, $f'(x)$, and $f''(x)$ are displayed. 2 variables: $f(x, y)$, $\partial f/\partial x$, and $\partial f/\partial y$ are displayed.] A single push of a button increases the value of x (and/or y) by an amount input by the user and recomputes the function values.

Graphs of Functions sketches the graphs of 1, 2, or 3 functions. The coordinates of points can be found by moving crosshairs with the arrow keys or clicking on the point with a mouse. A Solve command finds the zeros of a function or the intersection points of two functions. A Zoom command enlarges a rectangular region.

Integrals, Definite calculates the definite integral of a function. Also, illustrates five numerical methods.

Least Squares calculates the line of best fit and also allows the user to move a line around the screen to find the best fit.

Observe Limit of f(x) as x → a evaluates $f(a + h)$ and $f(a - h)$ for $h = .1, .01, .001,$ ... and guesses the limit. Can have a = ∞.

Series and Partial Sums evaluates finite and infinite sums.

Demonstration Routines

Ball Thrown Straight Up shows the connection between the motion of a ball and the graph of its height function.

Car in Motion moves a car across the screen with its position, and hence velocity, determined by a function input by the user.

Garden Fencing Problem shows the connection between a function to be optimized and the corresponding physical problem.

Plot Cosine and Sine Functions traces out the graphs of the sine and cosine functions as a point moves around the unit circle.

Secant Line Approaching Tangent Line moves a secant line closer and closer to a tangent line.

Tangent Line Approaching Curve illustrates the fact that locally a curve looks like its tangent line.

Copyright

This SOFTWARE is owned by David I. Schneider and is protected by United States copyright laws and international treaty provisions. Therefore, you must treat the SOFTWARE like any other copyrighted material (e.g., a Book or musical recording) except that you may either (a) make one copy of the SOFTWARE solely for backup or archival purposes, or (b) transfer the SOFTWARE to a single hard disk provided that you keep the original solely for backup or archival purposes.

Disclaimer of Warranty and Limitation of Liability

The programs on this diskette is provided "as is" without warranty of any kind. We make no warranties, expressed or implied, that the programs are free of error, or are consistent with any particular standard of merchantability, or that they will meet your requirements for any particular application. They should not be relied on for solving a problem whose incorrect solution could result in injury to a person or loss of property. If you do use the programs or procedures in such a manner, it is at your own risk. The author and publisher of this diskette (or diskettes) disclaim liability for direct, incidental, or consequential damages resulting from the use of the programs or procedures in this diskette (or diskettes).